A NOTE

FROM THE PUBLISHER OF

The Heritage Reprints

This series of books has been made necessary by the government's wartime regulation that, whenever a book is reprinted, *less* paper must be used in the reprint. Originally, this edition of this great work was prepared for private distribution to the subscribing members of The Heritage Club: and only a limited number of copies was sold to the general public. A continued demand for a reprint, from the general public, has brought *this* reprint into existence; and this reprint is different from the original edition in compliance with the government's desire to conserve paper and other materials. *The Heritage Club is a division of, and The Heritage Reprints are issued by,* THE HERITAGE PRESS: GEORGE MACY, DIRECTOR: 595 MADISON AVENUE, NEW YORK (22).

R. v. *R*.

THE LIFE OF REMBRANDT VAN RIJN

is. an account of the last years and the death of one

REMBRANDT HARMENSZOON VAN RIJN

a painter and etcher of some renown, who lived and worked (which in his case was the same) in the town of Amsterdam (which is in Holland) and died of general neglect and divers other unfortunate circumstances on the fourth of October of the year of Grace 1669 (*God have mercy upon his soul*) and who was attended in his afflictions by one

JOANNIS VAN LOON

doctor medicinae and chirurgeon in extraordinary to a vast number of humble citizens whose enduring gratitude has erected him a monument less perishable than granite and more enduring than porphyry and who during a most busy life yet found time to write down these personal recollections of the greatest of his fellow-citizens and which are now for the first time presented (provided with as few notes, emendations and critical observations as possible) by his great-great-grandson, nine times removed

HENDRIK WILLEM VAN LOON

in the year of grace 1930
and in the town of Veere, which is in Zeeland

SELF-PORTRAIT (PAINTING)

THE BOARD OF THE CLOTH-MAKERS' GUILD OF AMSTERDAM (PAINTING)

R. v. R.

THE LIFE OF
REMBRANDT VAN RIJN

BY HENDRIK WILLEM VAN LOON

Revised especially for this edition by the author

and illustrated with 150 reproductions

of the drawings, etchings and paintings of Rembrandt

selected and arranged by J. B. NEUMANN

NEW YORK : THE HERITAGE REPRINTS

List of Chapters

vii

LIST OF CHAPTERS

viii

LIST OF CHAPTERS

Pictures

PICTURES

PICTURES

PICTURES

xiii

PICTURES

PICTURES

PICTURES

PICTURES

xvii

PICTURES

PICTURES

Foreword

EXPLAINING HOW I CAME TO WRITE THIS BOOK

CHRIST CARRIED TO THE TOMB
(ETCHING)

Amsterdam, October 9, 1669
In the house called De Houttuyn

WE buried him yesterday and I shall never forget that terrible morning. The rain, which had been pouring down ever since the beginning of the month, had ceased. A cold and gloomy fog had thrown a dark and chilling pall over the whole city. The empty streets seemed filled with a vague sense of futile uselessness. The small group of mourners stood silently by the side of the church-door, waiting for the coffin to arrive.

Last Friday, a few hours before he died and during a moment of semi-consciousness, he had whispered to me that he wanted to rest next to Saskia. He must have forgotten that he had sold her grave long ago, when Hendrickje passed away and when he was caught without a penny and had been forced to sell the family lot in the Old Church to buy a grave for his second wife. I promised him that I would do my best, but of course the thing was out of the question. I am glad I told him this lie, for he went to his last sleep fully convinced that soon all would be well and that his dust would mingle with that of the woman he had loved in the days of his youth.

And then three days ago Magdalena van Loo called. I had never cared for her. I had found her mean and jealous and apt to whine, but I had tried to like her on account of her father-in-law and of the poor boy she had married.

She told me a long rambling story about some gold pieces which apparently had belonged to Cornelia and to her. Over and over again she repeated the same sentences: "I am sure father took some of that money before he died. And now what shall we do? We can't even buy milk for the baby. I am sure father took it," and so on and so forth.

Then followed a long and circumstantial account of her being sick and being unable to nurse the baby herself. I tried to reassure her. The money undoubtedly would be found. Had she looked for it carefully? No, she had not, but she felt convinced that the old man had appropriated some of it. For weeks and weeks he had sold nothing. He had just sat and stared or he had scratched meaningless lines on the back of some old copper plates. He had been without a cent when Titus died, for uncle Uylenburgh had paid for the funeral. That she knew for a fact. All the same, the old man had been able to buy himself food and drink, especially drink. He must have stolen some of Cornelia's gold, and "half of it was to come to me!" It was impossible to get her mind off the subject and so I asked her whether the sexton had been around to see her about the funeral.

Then she broke into tears once more. She felt so ashamed that she could not possibly hope to survive this last humiliation. The sexton had not come himself. He had merely sent one of the grave-diggers. The man had been drunk and quite rude. He had asked her how much she could pay and she had answered that she wanted things done very simply and could not afford more than five guilders. He had laughed out loud. People from the poor-house were given a better burial than that, but then, of course, what could one expect of those fine gentlemen who never did a stroke of work, who merely sat before an easel all day long and gave themselves airs! Finally he had got her into such a state of vapors that she had cried out for the shoe-maker who lived on the ground floor to come and help her. He had taken the unruly ruffian by the scruff of the neck and had thrown him out into the street and that, at least, had made her happy.

I then asked her whether that was where matters stood and she answered yes and at once went off on another tirade, telling me that no woman had ever been treated as she had been treated ever since she had married into that irresponsible family of painter people, and much more to the same effect, until in sheer despair I had ordered a hackney-coach and had driven her to the Roozengracht to see the sexton of the West Church (a man I cordially detested, but what will you? The corpse could not remain above ground forever) and had asked him what he meant by such conduct. At once the miserable creature became most obsequious. He apologized for the behavior of his grave-digger, and then annoyed me with his confidences. "If only you knew, Doctor," he said, "how hard it is to get good workmen these days! The job does no longer pay so very well and what is found in the old graves nowadays is not worth the digging. Ever since it has become the custom to bury people merely in their shrouds, the money has gone out of the grave-digging business."

I bade him hold his tongue and after some preliminaries we settled on a "full funeral"—that is to say, sixteen men to carry the coffin and the usual length of broadcloth to cover the remains. I paid him fifteen guilders and gave him some extra stivers for beer-money for the men, and he promised in advance that everything would be done in a first-class manner, very quietly and with great dignity.

But when I got to the church yesterday morning, the men were there, but they gave every evidence of having visited the alehouse before they went to work and I felt so strongly upon the subject that I mentioned it to Abraham Francen, one of the master's old friends, who was leaning against a tree in the yard.

"This is an outrage," I said.

But one drunken scoundrel heard me and scowled at me and gave me an evil look and—

"And why not?" he leered. "Our friend here didn't mind a drop himself at the right time, did he?"

When I called the sexton to task, he merely repeated what he had told me the day before—that it was terribly difficult to get respectable men for his sort of work. For now that the war with England had come to an end, everybody had plenty of money and nobody wanted to be a grave-digger any more.

Finally we came to the spot that had been chosen and without any further ceremony the coffin was lowered into the grave. I had meant to say a few words to bid my old friend a last farewell, but I was not given the chance, for as soon as the ropes had been pulled out from underneath the coffin the sexton said quite loudly: "Come now, my men, don't stand there doing nothing and just looking sheepish. Get busy! We have four other customers this morning." Whereupon we all turned around (there were, as I said, only a handful of us) and I walked to the part of the church reserved for divine service and I knelt down (something I had not done a single time these last five and thirty years) and I prayed whatever God might hear my supplication that he might deal mercifully with the soul of this poor, suffering mortal, who had given so much to this world and had received so little in return.

Then I slowly walked home, but while crossing the Dam, I ran across old Vondel, the poet. He had changed so greatly since I last saw him that I hardly recognized him. He seemed sick and he was shivering beneath his shabby, threadbare coat. It hurt me to see such a person in such a condition. The town these last few months has been full of a strange new affliction of the lungs, and those who were weakest were of course the first to be attacked. I asked him whether he had breakfasted and he said "No," but then he rarely took anything before noon. I suggested that we have a cup of coffee in one of those new taverns that make a specialty of this beverage, and he accepted my offer with pathetic eagerness. He even mentioned that there was a new coffee shop a few doors away where the coffee was very good and the prices were not exorbitant. I must have looked surprised, for he added, "You see, these places are often patronized by sailors and there is always a chance that one of them may bring me news of my son."

The human heart is a strange thing. Small loss when young Vondel was packed off to the Indies, these many years ago. The boy was an utter misfit. He drank. He gambled. He ran after women, and what sort of women! He was directly responsible for his father's financial failure. And here the old man was wasting his few hard-earned pennies, drinking coffee in mean taverns because some day one of the sailors might perhaps bring him some news of "his darling child."

We sat down and I pretended to be hungry and ordered some bread and cheese. "You might keep me company," I suggested to Vondel, and he consented. But a moment later he jumped to his feet. "Pardon me," he said, "but there is Captain Jan Floriszoon of the *Dolphin*. He got in yesterday from Malacca. He may have news for me from my boy."

"Bring him over here," I called out, and a moment later the captain appeared. He was a sailor of the old school, hard as nails and thrifty as the Bank, but not unkind. Yes, he would take something. He would take something with much pleasure. It was a cold and wet day. A gin and bitters would not be amiss. He had had a most prosperous voyage, only a year and a half for the round trip and less than forty percent of his crew had died. Ever hear of a certain Jan van den Vondel? No, never! Could not remember that he had ever run across him. But that of course meant nothing. There were so many ships and India was a big country, hundreds and thousands of islands. Some day the boy would undoubtedly show up and come back.

The captain was more considerate than I had expected a man of his caliber to be and I asked the poet how he himself was getting along. Vondel, with an eager face, hastened to inform me that things could not be better. Poor devil! He reminded me of a patient I had visited the day before in the poor-house and who had asked me not to let him die because he had been allowed to raise a crocus in his little room and he was afraid the poor little plant would not be able to survive if he were not there to take care of it.

Here I was, sitting face to face with the greatest genius that ever handled our language—a shabby, broken-down clerk—and he was explaining that he really had every reason to feel deeply grateful for the way in which fate had treated him.

"Their Lordships have been most kind to me," he explained. "Of course, the pawn-shop can't afford to pay me very much, but my needs are small and besides, I have a lot of time for myself. With the exception of Saturdays, when we stay open till midnight, I rarely work more than ten hours a day and quite often they allow me to come a little later in the morning, that I may make the rounds of the harbor and ask for news of my son. Within another year I hope to get my pension. I want to finish my last play, 'Noah,' and I must get at it before I am too old to handle a pen."

And so on and so forth. Until the honest captain interrupted him and turned to me and remarked with a polite bow that he was pleased to have made my acquaintance, for he had often heard of me from his sister, Anneke Floriszoon, the wife of Anthony Blauw, whom I remembered as one of my patients a number of years ago, and then he ordered another gin at my expense and drank to my health and said that he was glad to see that the Amsterdam chirurgeons took their work seriously and were going about at such an early hour of the morning. But I told him that I rarely visited this part of Amsterdam at that hour, but that I had happened to cross the Dam on my way home from the funeral of a friend.

"And who might that be?" the old poet asked, "for I am not aware that any one of importance has died."

"No," I answered, "I suppose not. He died quite suddenly. Yet you knew the man. It was Rembrandt van Rijn."

He looked at me with slight embarrassment.

"Of course I knew him," he said. "A very great artist. Of course, I could not always follow him and he thought very differently from me upon many subjects. For one thing, I don't believe that he was ever truly a Christian. But a great painter, nevertheless. Only tell me, Doctor, are you sure it was not an impostor? For Rembrandt, if I recollect rightly, died five years ago, yes, more than five years ago. He died in Hull in England. He had gone there to escape from his creditors. That is, if I remember correctly."

"Hull?" interrupted the captain. "Hull nothing! I know all about that fellow. He did a piece once of Joris de Caullery with whom I served as second mate in the battle of Dover in '52 when we licked Blake. Yes, I know all about him. It was he who had that quarrel with the dominies about his servant girl. But he went to Sweden some six or seven years ago. I have a friend who sails to Danzig, and he took him to Gothenburg in '61 or '62. He told me so himself and so I know it to be true."

"Nevertheless, my good friends," I answered, "Rembrandt died last Friday and we buried him this morning."

"Strange, very strange!" Vondel murmured. "Died right here in this town, and I did not even know he was still alive!"

"Well," said the good-natured captain, willing to make all the world feel as merry as he did himself and signaling to the waiter to bring him a third gin and bitters, "well, that is too bad. But we all have to die sooner or later and I am sure there are plenty of painters left. So here is to you, gentlemen! Happy years and many of them!"

* * *

Hofwyck, Voorburg, October 23, 1669.

Two weeks have gone by and a great many things have happened. The evening of the funeral I dropped in at the house on the

Roozengracht to prescribe a sedative for poor Magdalena who was still worrying about that little bag of gold that had belonged to Cornelia and her and that had disappeared. A few days later, Cornelia was to find it behind a pile of clean sheets, but just then Rembrandt was still suspected of having stolen his daughter's money and so Magdalena wept and whined until at last she dropped off to sleep and I went back to the hospital and composed a letter to My Lord Constantin Huygens who had had some dealings with the dead painter in the days of the late Prince Henry and who had been ever full of admiration for his genius, and late that same night I carried it to the skipper of the boat to The Hague, who promised me as a personal favor that he would deliver it to His Lordship the next morning together with some official-looking documents which had been entrusted to him by the Burgomasters and had to do with a vacancy in the Board of Aldermen.

Three days later I received an answer from the famous old diplomat, who by this time must have been well past seventy.

"I have to thank you, my dear Doctor," so he wrote in his precise Latin (for he never got over the feeling that a letter in the vernacular was a breach of good form, almost as inexcusable as paying an official call without a ruff or finishing a dinner without wiping off one's mouth), "I have to thank you for your favor of October the ninth and I was deeply shocked to hear your most unfortunate news. I knew him well, this extraordinary miller's son, upon whom the gods had bestowed such exceeding gifts. What a sad—a most sad ending! But such seems to be the fate of those among us who dare to storm the tops of high Olympus. In any other country he would have been deemed worthy of a national funeral; kings would have felt honored to march behind his bier. But did not the Athenians banish Pheidias? And what reward but a sentence of death did Florence ever bestow upon the greatest of her many gifted sons?

"I am an old man now, my learned friend, and I live far away from the vapid noise of the turbulent world. I have had another (and serious) attack of the gout and writing does not come easily to me these days. You must be in need of a change of scene after these most distressing events. Why not visit me here in my quiet retreat for a few days? I have little to offer you but a most cordial welcome and some of that noble vintage from the ancient city of Avignon, which almost persuades an old heretic like myself that there must have been some good in the institution of a Supreme Pontiff. For truly, the men who grew that wine must have been past-masters in the art of living.

"Farewell for the nonce and send me your reply by messenger. Tell me the hour of your arrival and a carriage will await you at Veur and it is only a short ride to the humble roof of your most faithful and obedient servant,

"C. H."

I had no reason to refuse. Young Willem was away at his studies in Leyden. The excellent Jantje could look after the household and my cousin Fijbo (one of the Frisian van Loons, come to settle in Amsterdam three years ago) could take care of my practice. I answered that I would accept with pleasure and three days later I took the boat for the south.

An uneventful trip, except for an acrimonious debate between a short, fat man who looked like a clergyman (and proved to be a shoe-maker) and a tall, lean fellow who looked like a shoe-maker (and proved to be a clergyman) who for some obscure reason revived the ancient quarrel about "homoousian" and "homoiousian" and got so excited about the "unbegotten begotten son" as opposed to the "ever begotten son" that they would surely have come to blows if the skipper had not threatened to throw them both overboard unless they moderated their language.

Except for this unfortunate incident, unavoidable in a country like ours where everybody is certain that he alone possesses a key to the right kind of Truth, the voyage was pleasant and dull (as a pleasant voyage should be) and at Veur I found Pieter, the old coachman, waiting for me and an hour later I was sitting in front of a bright open fire in that corner room that I knew so well and that looked across the fields all the way to the leaning tower of Delft.

I can't say that I ever enjoyed a holiday quite so much. For a holiday it has been so far, in the best and truest sense of the word. A holiday enlivened by good talk, good fare and the constant consideration of a courteous host. Indeed, if this strange new land of ours had done naught but produce this one man, I would not consider the experiment to have been a failure. He has been everywhere. He has known every one. Yet he has remained as simple as the gardener who delighted him yesterday with a few fresh radishes. He writes Latin like his native tongue, but handles our obstinate language as if it were the pliable vernacular of Ariosto. He is well versed in music and has fair skill in the art of drawing and painting. His mathematical ability has come to glorious fruition in his son Christiaan, who is now in Paris making further experiments with his pendulum clock. He seems to have suffered some financial reverses during the recent war with England, but the simplicity of the household is so perfect in all its details that life at the court of the Grand Monarch himself could be no more agreeable than existence here at Hofwyck.

I spend the morning in my own room which overlooks the old marshes of Schieland, now turned into fertile pastures. There is an excellent library on the ground floor and I am urged to take as many books to my own quarters as suit my fancy.

Old Pieter, who has been with his master for almost forty years, brings me my breakfast and informs me about the state of the weather which has been fairly good since I arrived last Thursday.

At one o'clock I take a short walk in the garden which has been laid out according to the French taste (and which the French for some unaccountable reason call a "Dutch garden"). At two o'clock we take a short drive and the afternoon and evening we spend together. And of course the conversation almost invariably turns to the loss of our friend of the Roozengracht.

I am a physician and familiar with death. I am not much of a churchman and cannot for the life of me understand the gruesome delight with which Christians, ever since the days of the Catacombs, have been pleased to enlarge upon the horrors of the charnel-house. The people of ancient times were much more rational in their attitude toward that sublime sleep that is bestowed upon us as a pleasant sample of eternity. They knew that the world only exists through contrasts. That there is no light unless there be darkness, no joy unless there be sorrow, no life unless there be death. I accept their wisdom and it is not so much the fact that Rembrandt has ceased to exist that worries me (God knows, life held little of pleasure for him) as the realization of the utter futility of all effort.

I sometimes am afraid of the conclusions to which this sort of reasoning may lead us and yesterday My Lord Huygens read me a serious lecture upon the dangers of this sort of speculation.

"Have a care," he said, "or I shall have to send your doubts to my neighbor, the learned Jew, and he will wash them in a mixture of Cartesian and Baconian philosophies and then he will bleach them in the light of his own merciless logic and when they are returned to you, they will have shrunk to the three letters Q.E.D. neatly embroidered on the remnants of something that only a short while before was still a fairly useful garment that might have kept people from freezing in the realm of doubt."

"No," I answered, "that would not solve the difficulty. I have little love for that strange celestial potentate whom our Calvinists call their righteous Jehovah, but neither do I want the Almighty to be reduced to a mathematical formula. And my worries are not of the theological variety.

"I knew Spinoza in the old days, before his own people so kindly tried to murder him. A charming man. A learned man. An honest man. But I am a little wary of those philosophers who try to weave their spiritual garments out of their own inner consciousness. I am not enough of a mystic and prefer the 'Praise of Folly' to all the metaphysical cogitations in the world. No, what worries me is not the fate of poor old Rembrandt. He is either entirely out of it or he is trying so hard to solve the problem of reducing the Light Everlasting to a few smears of chrome-yellow and flake-white that he will forget everything else. No, it is something else that is on my mind."

"The living, rather than the dead?"

"Exactly. Here we are. Since we got our freedom, our land has been blessed beyond anything that has ever been seen before. Our dominies, with their usual sense of modesty, take all the credit upon themselves and see in these riches an expression of approval of the Lord Almighty and an endorsement of the policies of the House of Orange. They may be right, but it seems to me that our fortunate geographic location may have as much to do with our favorable rate of exchange as the approbation of an ancient Jewish deity who had tantrums and liked the smell of burning entrails. I hope I am not offending you?"

My Lord Constantin shook his head. "These are hardly the expressions I would have used when I dined with King James (of blessed memory) and dozed my way through the endless sessions of the Great Synod. But here we are alone and old Pieter is deaf and, to tell you the truth, I too prefer one page of Erasmus to all the homilies of the sour-faced doctor from Geneva. So go ahead and tell me your troubles."

"Well, as I was saying, here we are part of a strange new experiment in statecraft. We have turned a swamp into another Rome. We rule black people and yellow people and red people—millions of them in every part of the world. Until a short time ago we kept a larger standing army than any one had ever dreamed possible and we paid for it and it did not ruin us. We probably have a larger navy than any other country and, somehow or other, we seem to have enough funds to keep the ships going without an unusual number of riots.

"We juggle with slices of territory larger than the Holy Roman Empire as if we were children playing with marbles, and one day we take a few hundred thousand square miles of forests in North America and say that they belong to us and half a century later, we trade them off for a couple of hundred thousand square miles of sugar lands in South America and nobody knows and nobody cares and it really makes no difference either one way or another.

"We supply the whole world with grain and with fish and whale-bone and linen and hides and our store-houses fairly burst with the bales of nutmeg and pepper that are dumped into them twice or three times a year and in between we fight a couple of wars and the people at home go to church and pray for victory and then go back to business and make a little more money and speculate in Indian shares and in tulips and in Spitzbergen sperm-oil and in Amsterdam real estate and lose fortunes and gain fortunes as if they never had been doing anything else all their lives and as if we had not known their fathers and grandfathers when they were perfectly respectable butchers and bakers and candle-stick makers who had to work dev-ilishly hard for every stiver they made and were contented if once every fifteen years they could afford a new suit of Sunday clothes.

"But that is not so much what fills me with such anxiety for the future. We have all of us got to begin sometime. When the Emperor of Austria tried to raise funds on the Amsterdam exchange to de-velop his mercury mines, he had a prospectus printed to prove that he was descended in a straight line from Julius Caesar, but in the days of my grandfather, whenever old Charles of Habsburg got full

on Louvain beer and French cognac, and was told by my grandpapa
that no human stomach on earth could stand such atrocious mix-
tures, he used to weep and ask him what one could expect of a fellow who was half Spanish peasant and half Flemish bastard and
whose earliest ancestor had driven a Swiss ox-cart as a sutler in the
army of Charlemagne.

"Perhaps he exaggerated a bit, but when the great French Queen
visited Amsterdam and the Burgomasters forced her to listen to endless speeches about 'Your Majesty's illustrious forebears, the enlightened rulers of Tuscany,' or wherever it was, I remember that when
it was my turn to be presented and she was told that I was the con-
sultant physician of the Hospital of St. Catherine, and silly old Witsen, who knew my aversion to drugs, said, 'Yes, Your Majesty, and
he has prescribed more pills in his day than any other man now
alive,' the old Queen smiled rather sourly and said, 'Monseigneur, I
know all about pills. I have got three of them in my coat-of-arms.'

"No, it isn't that we are rich that worries me. It is rather pleasant
to see every one well fed and decently clothed and it never did any
harm to a man's self-respect to have an extra change of linen. But
what are we going to do with all our wealth? The envoy of His late
Majesty James of England (the tactful one who is said to have given
a party the day they killed old John of Barneveldt) in his usual
charming way wrote to his royal master and asked what one could
expect of a country that was merely 'a counting-house defended by
a navy.'

"But that Puritan boor was right. At least in part. As long as our
merchants are able to make one hundred percent on their money, by
buying something for a guilder and selling it for two, and as long as
the common people are fairly obedient to Their Lordships, and go
to church three times on Sunday, we ask no questions and we are
contented to be rich and smug and not any too finicky in our pastimes, but when it comes to something not of this earth earthy, we
let our greatest poet handle a goose-quill in a dirty pawn-shop ten
hours a day to keep himself from starving; we drag the greatest
painter of our time through every court in the whole bailiwick and
a couple of rice-peddlers who have just spent thousands of guilders
for an escutcheon with sixteen quarterings swindle him out of his

last pennies and even your fine old Prince has to be dunned eight or nine times before he will pay him.

"And what happens to Rembrandt and Vondel has happened to all the others. The King of Spain and the King of Denmark and the Emperor and the King of England and even that wild potentate of Muscovy (wherever that is) keep agents in Amsterdam to supply them with the work of our great men. And we quietly let them die in the poor-house as if they were so many tramps."

I talked in that vein most of the afternoon and My Lord Constantin listened with great patience, but I do not think that he answered me very fully. Perhaps he did, but I am a bit hazy about it.

*　　*　　*

I am tired and have a pain at the back of my head. I shall go to bed and finish this to-morrow.

Hofwyck, December 20, 1669.

For a while, it looked as if there were to be no "to-morrow" at all.

I must have caught a cold on the day of Rembrandt's funeral, for I remember that I had one or two chills on board the canal-boat when I traveled to Voorburg, and that my teeth were chattering when I reached Hofwyck. I hear that my kind old host consulted with no less than three doctors from The Hague and that when they were unable to break the fever he sent to Leyden for a young professor who was experimenting with the cinchona bark and who gave me of his tincture with apparent success, for from that day on I am told that I began to improve.

And whether my affliction was "march poison," as the ague fits and the dry heat seemed to indicate, or an attack of the "English sweat" which had been so common during the last century, or some entirely new disease come to us from America or Asia, upon that point my learned professional brethren do not seem to have been able to make a decision. But the cinchona bark was apparently quite effective (I shall try it on my own patients as soon as I return to practice) or perhaps it was the excellent care which I received at the hands of my good host which kept me from joining the Great Majority.

FOREWORD

Most important of all, I do not appear to be suffering from anemia or any of the other after effects which are so common and so disastrous in cases of this sort. But as soon as I was allowed to sit up and as soon as I once more began to take an interest in my surroundings, I noticed (what had so often worried me with my own patients) that I seemed mentally exhausted and could not rid myself of a few simple thoughts which kept repeating themselves in my mind and kept repeating and repeating themselves until I was ready to shriek and had to be restrained from doing myself bodily harm.

After a few days there was a slight improvement, but then it began to look as if something in my mind had congealed at the moment I was taken ill and that it refused, no matter how hard I tried, to let itself be thawed out. The death of Rembrandt, I am willing to confess it, had made more of an impression upon me than almost anything else that had ever happened to me. I had come to Hofwyck full of his sad fate and until I was taken ill, I had thought and talked of practically nothing else.

All during the fever, whenever I wandered in my delirium (so My Lord Constantin told me last week) I had been fighting Rembrandt's battles. No doubt he had deserved a better fate and no doubt most of our people are hopelessly indifferent about the really great men who bring honor to our nation. But I used to be possessed of a certain philosophic calm and I used to accept the iniquities of this world with great and satisfying equanimity of soul.

Whenever as children we got greatly excited about some particularly stupid piece of business on the part of our neighbors, our grandfather used to warn us to remember the safe advice of our famous cousin Erasmus that "since the world loved to be swindled, we might just as well let it be swindled." He admonished us to keep strictly to honest practices in our own dealings with mankind, but not let ourselves be upset every time we came in contact with some particular phase of human folly.

"For once you begin to take the human race too seriously," he warned us, "you will either lose your sense of humor or turn pious, and in either case, you had much better be dead."

In a general way I had always been able to stick to this wise and tolerant rule of conduct. I had never wasted much time pitying my fellow men nor had I indulged in too great expressions of merriment when for the millionth time in history I watched how they hoisted themselves with the petard of their own willful ignorance. I had simply accepted them as I found them and had not tried to improve too much upon God's unfortunate handiwork.

But now something had happened. Try however I might, I could not rid myself of the obsession that in one way or another I was responsible for the death of my friend and no matter how hard my host and my doctor friend from Leyden tried (he knew something beyond mere powders and pills, which I can't say for most of my colleagues) I could not purge my poor, tired brain of the vision of that last terrible morning in the West Church, with the grinning pall-bearers and the drinking, cursing grave-diggers who handled that sacred coffin as if it had held the carcase of some indifferent lout, killed in a drunken street-brawl.

And yet, if life, if my life at least, had to go on, I must first of all purge my mind of these all-too-persistent depressions and I knew it and at the same time I could not do it and then the consciousness that I knew it and could not do it added itself to my other tribulations, and thereupon Hell itself held no such terrors as I experienced during those weeks I was trying to regain my physical health and to establish some sort of mental equilibrium.

And I know not what the end would have been, had not My Lord Constantin, trying to divert me and so get me away from my own depressing thoughts, one day called on me in the company of the learned Jew of whom we had been talking a short time before I was taken ill.

I had met Spinoza several times before in the olden days in Amsterdam and I had once visited him in Rijnsburg, but so many things had happened since then, that I had almost forgotten what a charming and simple-minded fellow he was. Of his ideas, as I have said before, I have never understood a great deal and anyway, theological and philosophical speculations have never been very much to my taste. But Spinoza proved a veritable godsend to a man recovering from a long illness and I bade him (with my host's gracious permission) to come again and to come as often as he could.

He was living in very modest quarters in the village of Voorburg, which was only a few minutes away, and quite frequently, after he got through with his day's work, he used to drop in for a short talk.

FOREWORD

I admired the liberality of mind of my host, for soon the people of The Hague must have heard that Hofwyck was being patronized by the most dangerous heretic then alive and five days after his first visit (which took place on a Tuesday) not fewer than three clergymen in that gossipy village (God forbid that it should ever acquire the dignity of a town) made veiled allusions in their sermons to "the influence which certain people of libertine principles were said to be gaining once more upon those in close connection with the House of Orange."

But as My Lord Constantin merely shrugged his shoulders when he heard of it, I did not let it worry me and continued to enjoy the visits of this keen-eyed young Jew with the soft Portuguese accent, who actually seemed to believe that all the eternal verities could be reduced to mathematical equations.

Now whether my host had mentioned my strange mental affliction to this amiable and kindly prophet (great Heavens! what an improvement that boy was upon the average ranting and maundering rabbi of his quarrelsome tribe!), but in the most tactful way he one day brought the conversation upon the subject of Rembrandt and how shocked he had been to hear of his untimely death and how much he had admired his work—especially his etchings which were more in keeping with his own mathematical turn of mind, and then he asked me to tell him about the last days of the great master and about his funeral and of course, I was only too delighted and he repeated this performance three days in succession, and then quite suddenly one day he said:

"You know, Doctor, you are bound for the lunatic asylum, and they tell me it is not pleasant in there."

To which, with unusual calm and clearness of vision, I answered: "Yes, my friend, I know that, but what can I do about it?"

To which he gave me the totally unexpected answer: "Write it all down and get rid of it that way, before you go insane. That is what I am doing myself."

Amsterdam, April 3, 1670.

The cure has worked.

And I, in my old age, discover that I have most unexpectedly become the father of a book.

XXXV

FOREWORD

I did not mean to write one, for I am a physician and not an author, but what of it? These pages will be carefully packed away among my other belongings. They have no literary value. My son is not interested in such things and they will never be published, no matter what happens.

And Rembrandt, if he knows, will understand.

My task is finished. And now I must go back to the business of living, for I have loafed long enough and there is work to be done, a great deal of work.

Two weeks from next Monday I shall be seventy years old. That is not as old as my good host of Hofwyck, who is well in the seventies, but neither is it an age to take lightly. Ten more good years at the very most. After that—whatever follows.

And so I bid farewell to this labor of love which has well served me during my days of convalescence.

From now on, my hand shall only touch the scalpel. May it be as true and honest in all things as the brush that lies on my desk, the only tangible memory of the dearest of my friends and the greatest of my race.

JAN VAN LOON.

SUPPER AT EMMAUS (PAINTING)

SASKIA WITH A PINK (PAINTING)

R. v. R.

THE LIFE OF REMBRANDT VAN RIJN

Illustrated by himself

Chapter I

I MEET SASKIA FOR THE FIRST TIME AND FIND HER
A VERY SICK WOMAN

THE ARTIST'S MOTHER (ETCHING)

THE fall of the year '41 was a period of endless rainstorms and the month of November was by far the worst. There were floods, and a great many head of cattle were drowned and the cities lay drenched by the endless dampness and the walls were covered with mildew, for as it had begun to rain before the peat had been shipped to town, the available fuel was all water-logged and either refused to burn at all, or filled the room with such vast clouds of smoke that most people preferred to shiver rather than choke.

There was a great deal of sickness and when Jantje, the second maid (for I could afford two servants by now and have ever held that the highest form of thinking goes best with the most comfortable mode of living, and I firmly believe that Thomas à Kempis would have been a more enjoyable and more useful philosopher if he had spent his days in the pleasant tower of the Sieur de Montaigne rather than among the sandy hills of Overijsel)—when Jantje entered and told me that there was a girl who had come to ask me to visit a sick woman, I thought: "Oh, well, another case of a bad cold! I wish that they would leave me in peace."

For by this time I had practically discontinued my general practice. I still went to the hospital every day because I wanted to learn

3

as much of surgery as I possibly could, but I took no further private patients and spent all my days in a small workshop or laboratory which I had fixed up in the basement of my house where I had a large fire-place (which I heated with coal) and could experiment without the danger of setting the house on fire.

I went into the hall and found not a girl but a middle-aged woman, whose face did not in the least appeal to me, and I was about to send her away and bid her go and find some one else, when she interrupted me in a scolding tone of voice and said: "If it were not a matter of great urgency, my master would have sent for some well-known physician, but my mistress seems to be dying and they told me to get the nearest leech I could find—any one would do."

Somehow or other, the utter lack of graciousness, the painful directness of this person who had come to ask a favor and found the opportunity to offer an insult, appealed to my sense of humor. The good Doctor François Rabelais, who cured more people by his laughter than by his pills and poultices, would have been delighted with this sharp-tongued shrew. He probably would have given her in marriage to Pantagruel and his life thereafter would have been about as merry as that of Socrates during his more domestic periods. And so I did not answer her as I should have done, but took my cloak and followed her.

We did not have far to go. We went down the Houtkoopers Gracht and turned to the left past the Anthonie Sluys and into the Anthonie Breestraat, where we stopped before a two-story brick house which looked as if it were the house of some well-to-do merchant.

The door was opened almost before we had knocked and an anxious voice asked: "Is that the doctor?" To which my unpleasant companion sharply answered: "Well, it is some sort of a leech. He was the nearest one I could find. I hope he will do." To which the voice replied: "Keep a civil tongue in your head, my good woman, and ask the Master to step in while I get a candle."

For indeed the hall was very dark and it was filled with the sharp odor of some acid which made me think for a moment that I had come to the house of a person who occupied himself in his spare time with experiments in alchemy. But when the candle was lit, I saw at once that this was not a laboratory, for the small table in the center and the chairs were all of them covered with drawings

SELF-PORTRAIT (PAINTING)

SASKIA (PAINTING)

and sketches, and against the walls (though I could only see them dimly) there stood a number of canvases, but they were painted in such somber colors that I could not make out the subjects they represented.

Nor could I place the man who had apparently made them. He was a stockily built fellow with the shoulders and arms of a mason or carpenter. Indeed, the first impression I got when he opened the door was that of some better-class working-man, some one accustomed to heavy physical exercise but at the same time trained to read charts and architectural plans—perhaps the foreman of a building company. Such a fellow, however, would hardly have lived in a house of his own on one of the best streets in town, but in that strange city of ours, with new blocks of houses going up like mushrooms and new fortunes being made overnight (especially by those who were in some way connected with the board of aldermen) all things were possible and some of the best houses on the Heerengracht belonged to people who only a few years before had never seen a fork or known the use of a napkin. And so I quietly accepted the situation and asked: "Where is the patient?"

"In the Big Room," he answered, and his voice struck me, for it was very gentle and not in the least in keeping with his somewhat rough and plebeian exterior. Wherefore, while I removed my coat (which was wet, for of course outside the rain was pouring) and now suspecting that I had to deal with a member of my own class, I introduced myself and said:

"I am Doctor van Loon."

And he extended his hand (he had put the candle down on a chair to help me with my cloak) and gave me a slight bow and said: "I am glad you came, Doctor. My name is van Rijn and it is my wife who needs your services," and he picked up the candle once more and led me across the hall into the room situated in the rear part of the house. Here a small oil lamp was burning and there was a fire and as a result it was not quite dark and I got a general impression of the apartment, and it increased the feeling of discomfort which had come over me when I first entered the house.

It is always very difficult to define such emotions and a doctor is at a disadvantage, for he lives so closely with his patients that he often loses track of the sequence of events, and because this particular patient eventually died, it would be easy to argue that those presentiments of doom which had struck me so forcibly when I first entered that house had been invented by me long after the final disaster; indeed, that my unconscious self had invented them as a consolation for the complete failure of my ministrations.

But in this instance at least that was not true. As I have already taken the opportunity to explain, I am not a religious man in the usual, conventional sense of the word. I am, alas, a true descendant of my gloriously blasphemous grandfather, who having had his ears cut off by one brand of religion and his livelihood destroyed by another variety, decided that he would compose himself a new faith of his own which he did by rejecting everything except that famous law of Christ which bids us be pleasantly spoken and amiable to our neighbors—that rule of Kung-fu-Tze, the great Chinese philosopher, which states that the truly wise man minds his own business, and one single line borrowed from a famous Latin poet, who fifteen hundred years before had discovered that there really was no reason in the world why we should not speak the truth with a smile.

To this mixture compositum I had added a liberal supply of the writings of a Frenchman by the name of Michel de Montaigne, who was just then beginning to be known in our country and who (in my opinion) gave us the most honest book that has ever been written by the pen of mortal man.

In this home-made system of theology (which my grandfather bestowed upon me much as my grandmother revealed unto me with profound injunctions of secrecy the family recipe for the making of a perfect omelette, an art almost as simple yet as complicated as that of saving souls)—in this concise but exceedingly handy "Guide to Every-Day Happiness" there was no room for spooks, miracles and ectoplastic manifestations of a premonitory nature. It was then the habit in our city (a habit not restricted by any means to the more ignorant classes) never to undertake a single action without first consulting a soothsayer. Some patronized crystal-gazers and others went to the descendants of the ancient Haruspices who explained the future from the bowels of some unfortunate cat that was slaughtered for the occasion. Many took great stock in the stars and not a few tried to read the divine mysteries by a study of names or numbers or a handful of grass, plucked at random from some near-by churchyard.

I never fell a victim to any of these absurd superstitions. Sometimes I wished that I had been able to become a confirmed pyromancist or rhabdomancist or psephomancist (or whatever these strange cults call themselves), for if once I could have convinced myself that red-hot irons or fountains or pebbles were able to reveal the intentions of the Almighty, I might have been able to believe (as the vast majority of my neighbors did) that all the wisdom of the ages lay buried between the covers of a single book, writ two or three thousand years before by a tribe of wandering shepherds and peddlers whose ignorance was only surpassed by their love for bloodthirsty detail and their conviction that they and they alone held the true key to salvation.

And so, with the possible exception of a slight leaning toward predicting the weather by means of a game of lansquenet (a harmless enough trick which I had learned from the captain of a Swiss regiment of foot, and which failed as often as it came true), I never took any interest in the supernatural and let myself be guided exclusively by the dictates of my conscience as revealed unto me by the wisdom of Socrates, and by the sum total of those scientific conclusions which had been left unto us by the great sages of the ancient world.

Therefore when I speak of certain chill premonitions which gripped me when I entered this house, I do not refer to anything supernatural. But I hold with Pythagoras of Samos that there is neither life nor death—that all creation is but the tangible expression of one Primeval Force, just as all clouds and rivers and glaciers and snowstorms, yea, even wells and subterranean sources, are manifestations in somewhat different forms and shapes of one vast body of water which encircles and covers the greater part of our globe.

I further believe with him that nothing can ever be added to this original mass of what the Greeks called Energy nor that anything can ever be taken away from it. As a result of this profound conviction, I am able to anticipate Death (that hideous bugaboo of all my Christian friends) without the slightest qualm of fear. For I know that there is neither beginning nor end, but that all life is merely the

7

visible manifestation of that Eternal Continuity which is the one and only mystery we shall never be able to fathom or understand.

But when the time has come to surrender that spark of Energy which one has been allowed (for a shorter or a longer period) to borrow from the great store-house of the Eternal Force, there are certain unmistakable evidences of the impending change, such as occur in nature just before a thunderstorm or just before the eruption of a volcano. What these consist of, I could not possibly tell. I have never been able to classify them as I am able to classify the flowers in my garden or to describe them as I can describe the symptoms of an affliction of the throat. But I have met people in the street or in some merry company and suddenly I have known that "that man" or "that woman" would not live much longer and very shortly afterwards I have heard that he or she had died before the end of a month or a week. And I have had the same experience with animals and even with plants. Once I remember a young couple who had but one child (and could never have another) and who concentrated every thought upon their small offspring. The boy was guarded day and night by two maids who had been carefully trained never to let him out of their sight. He was not allowed to go to school lest he breathe the air contaminated by the breath of the other pupils, but he was taught by private tutors. He never even was taken for a walk, but was made to play in the garden, a very large garden, by the way, so that he had plenty of room for exercise. I knew the father slightly (he had studied law at the University of Leyden while I was taking my course in anatomy there) and he had shown me the boy and had proudly boasted that this son of his some day was going to be one of the greatest people our country had ever produced and that he was going to take no chances with his safety or his health. I knew that he was going to be disappointed and that the poor infant would not live very much longer, but of course I said nothing. A few weeks later the boy, while playing in his garden, was stung by a wasp. It hurt him and of course he scratched, as any one will do under the circumstances. And three days afterwards, he was dead from blood poisoning.

Millions of little children are stung every year by millions of wasps and nothing happens. But this particular boy was doomed and if it had not been a wasp it would have been a bee or a stroke of lightning or a falling beam, but something somewhere would have arisen across his path to bring about this unexpected result. I have never seen it to fail and the moment I entered this house on the Anthonie Breestraat, I knew: "Here the eternal process of change is about to take place and there will be crape on the door before the passing of another year."

And then I ceased to think any further upon the subject (this whole meditation which fills so many pages of script had flashed through my mind in less than two seconds) and I assumed that air of grave concern which sick people expect in their physicians and which often proves itself much more beneficial than barrels of powders and hogsheads of pills.

The patient was lying in a big bed that had been built within the wall, for only the very rich have thus far taken to the French custom of sleeping in those four-postered affairs that stand in the middle of the room and are exposed to all the draughts of the night. By her side there was a cradle and I had to move it before I could come near enough to examine her. I asked the husband to let me have his candle and whispered to him to ask if his wife were asleep. But ere he could answer, the woman had opened her eyes and in a very low and listless tone of voice, she said, "No. I am not asleep. But I am so tired— so dreadfully tired."

And then I sat down by the side of the bed and went through the examination which is customary upon such occasions and asked a number of questions, but these seemed to exhaust the patient so terribly that I made the ordeal as short as possible, felt her pulse, which was very weak and very irregular but much too high, put my hand on her forehead and found it to be cold and moist and then covered her up with her blue counterpane (I had noticed that everything in the room was blue, the walls were covered with a bluish tapestry and all the chairs had blue seats) and told her to try and sleep and that I would soon send her a potion which would make her rest. Then I turned to her husband (and where had I seen that man before? While I was sitting by the side of the bed, it had suddenly come over me that I had seen him somewhere before—but where?) and beckoned to him that I wanted to speak to him alone and he once more picked up his candle, went to the door and said to the nurse (the woman who had called for me and who had waited all this time in the hall and who now acted in a somewhat guilty way, as if she had been listening at the keyhole):

"Geertje, you watch over your mistress and take care of the child, while I go upstairs a moment with the doctor."

And together we climbed the stairs and went into a big room in the front of the house which was so full of vases and plates and pewter tankards and old globes and bits of statuary and strange, outlandish-looking swords and helmets and pictures . . . pictures everywhere . . . pictures on the walls and pictures leaning against the chairs and leaning against the table and leaning against each other, that for an instant the thought struck me, "This man is a dealer in antiquities, and not an artist at all."

But a moment later he bade me be seated (on a chair from which he had first removed a heavy book bound in parchment, a dozen or so etchings or sketches, and on top of it all a small Roman bust of some ancient emperor or general), and he did this with so much grace and ease of manner that I came back to my first impression of a painter or an engraver, only I could not quite remember ever having heard his name before, and yet all the while I felt that I ought to know who he was and furthermore, I knew positively that this was not our first meeting.

He then carefully picked up a large lacquered box and a small cup and saucer which together with two small porcelain figures had been balancing perilously on the seat of another chair, placed them on a table crowned with the grinning head of a blackamoor, and sat down, folded his hands, threw back his head with a curious gesture (which is so common among short-sighted people) and said in an even tone of voice:

"You need not lie to me. Her illness is very dangerous, isn't it?"

To which at first I made no reply, and then in order to gain time, I said, "It may be dangerous or not. But before I draw any definite conclusions, you had better answer me a few questions," and I asked him about his wife's previous history with considerable detail and what I heard, confirmed the worst of my fears and suspicions. They had been married seven years. No, his wife was not an Amsterdam girl. She came from Friesland, across the Zuyder Zee. He himself was born in Leyden. His father had been a miller and had died eleven years before at the age of sixty-two and his mother had died only a year ago at the age of fifty-one and there had been six children, two girls and three other boys besides himself. They had all of them been well enough as far as he knew. "Of course," he said, "that had really nothing at all to do with the case of poor Saskia, but I am thinking of my Titus, for the baby does not look very strong to me and I want you to know that from my side at least he comes of fairly healthy stock."

But from his wife's side the report was not quite so favorable. "You see," he explained to me, "she is really of much better family than I and I have noticed that somehow or other, such children don't seem to get along as well in the world as we who slept three in a bed when we were very young and who were left to shift for ourselves."

I might have heard her father's name. He was that Rombertus van Uylenburgh who had been lunching with the Prince of Orange when Gerard murdered him. He had been Burgomaster of Leeuwarden and had been sent to the Prince to talk about the political situation in the North. He, van Rijn, had never known his father-in-law, for the old man had died in '24 when Saskia was just twelve. There had been eight other children in the family but after the death of the parents (the mother had died a year or so before the husband) the home had been broken up and Saskia had come to Amsterdam with her cousin Hendrick who had a curiosity shop and occasionally dealt in pictures and there he had met her and then she had sat for him for her portrait a couple of times. "In the beginning, the Uylenburghs had been a little aloof," the painter told me, "but Hendrick, who was not much of a business man, borrowed some money from me and he probably felt that I would not dun him quite so easily if his young relative posed for me and, besides, the poor girl knew very few people in Amsterdam and was rather bored and liked a little excitement and coming to my studio with her sister was quite an adventure, for you know what the respectable world thinks about us painters." The end had been that they had become engaged and then they had been married. "And now," he continued, "I am afraid that I shall lose her, for ten months ago, a short time before our boy was born, she had a hemorrhage and she hardly lived through the confinement and this evening, just before we sent for you, she had another one, not quite as bad as the first, but it showed that there still is something the matter with her and the surgeon who usually tends her has himself fallen

SASKIA AS FLORA (PAINTING)

Rembrandt van Rijn

sick of some malady of the lungs and until he recovers, I wish that you would look after her, for you live near by and she often has such terrible attacks of suffocation that I think she will die and I would like to have a doctor who is not too far away."

This did not seem the most fortunate of grounds for the choice of a physician, but the man interested me (where had I seen that face before?) and he was such a strange mixture of a rather arrogant grand seigneur and a helpless child and the whole house with its jumbled masses of pictures and furniture and china and Roman senators struck me as so utterly incongruous in our respectable city of Amsterdam, that I agreed to accept the case and told him so.

And he said, "Thank you," though without any great show of gratitude, and apparently wanted to go back downstairs, but I bade him to be seated again, for what he had told me was all very interesting, but there were a few other questions I wanted to ask him before I could express any opinion upon the chances of recovery.

"Have there been any other children besides the boy downstairs?"

"Yes, several. A boy who was born a year after our marriage and who died while quite small, and two girls who also died soon after they were born."

"What did they die of?"

"Nothing in particular. They just did not seem to have strength enough to live. Their mother was too weak to nurse them and that may have made some difference, but even after we had found an excellent wet-nurse, they did not gain. They never cried. They just lay very still and then they died."

"And the present child was strong when it was born?"

"No! Not very. For several hours after he was born, the boy looked as if he too were going to die right away." Then the midwife had given him a cold bath and he began to cry and that apparently had saved him. But his mother had never been able to nurse him. They had a nurse now, the woman who had been sent to fetch me, and who was now taking care of the sick woman downstairs. But the child did not gain and it cried a good deal and it looked terribly pale.

Then I asked him a question: "Have you another room in the house, except the big one downstairs, where you could put the child up for the time being?"

13

"Yes, several. There is one downstairs and there is this room and my studio and the room with the etching-press."

"Which one has most sun and air?"

"The one in which my wife is."

"Is there no other?"

"A small one where my press stands."

"Let the child sleep there."

"But then it will be impossible to work there. I have four boys who do my printing for me. They have just started on a new plate of Dominie Anslo. Yesterday I pulled the first three proofs and changed the plate a little. But to-morrow they are going to begin work on it. I have had orders for twenty-five copies. It will be a great nuisance if I have to turn that room into a nursery."

"Nevertheless, the child had better not be in the same room with the mother for some time."

"Then you know what she has?"

"No, I don't. I am not certain. I may know within a day or two. Meanwhile, the nurse had better take the little boy to your printing room. She can probably fix herself some sort of bed in there."

"We have an extra cot."

"Very well."

"And you will come again to-morrow?"

"I certainly will."

"And there is nothing you can do now?"

"Nothing. She will probably be very tired. She ought to sleep as much as possible. I will pass by the apothecary on my way home and will order him to make her a sleeping potion. If she is restless you can give her two small spoonfuls in some water every other hour. But don't give it to her more than three times. I don't want to tax her heart too much. And now I had better be going."

The painter got up from his chair and opened the door for me. Once more I noticed the powerful shoulders underneath the blue linen smock and the broad forehead and the sad, troubled eyes, together with the common nose and the broad chin that was almost a challenge to the world to come and be damned. A strange mixture of the gentleman and the hod-carrier and where had I seen it before?

On my way out I passed through the sick-room but the poor woman seemed to be asleep. I put my hand upon her forehead, which was

CORNELIS CLAESZ ANSLO, MENNONITE PREACHER (ETCHING)

cold and clammy. She had apparently no longer any fever, but her color had grown worse. When I had first seen her, she had been very pale with a brilliant red spot on both cheeks. Now the red spots were gone and the color of her skin was an unhealthy gray. Her pulse had grown so weak that I could hardly notice it. I put my hand upon her heart. It was beating, but very faintly. She was a very sick woman indeed and seemed to have reached that point of exhaustion when the slightest shock might be fatal. If she could sleep through the night, we had a fine chance to bring her back to life in the morning, but I was not very hopeful.

Just then I heard the angry voice of the woman who had come to fetch me and who was now talking to the painter in the hall.

"I won't do it! I just won't do it!"

And when he answered, "Sh-sh! Not so loud. My wife will wake up," she continued even more sharply, "Sh-sh yourself! I just won't do it."

"But the doctor says you must."

"Bah! Doctors don't know anything. The idea! I have taken care of children all my life. I never heard such nonsense. It is just a little cold your wife has caught. All this fuss about a little cold! But of course, doctors must give you their fool advice so that they can ask you for more money."

At that moment, the sick woman woke up and softly whimpered. I tiptoed to the door and spoke sharply to the nurse. "You will do what I say," I told her, "or to-morrow I shall report you to the medical guild. You may not care for my opinion, but you will care if you never get another case."

She looked at me with great arrogance.

"All right, Doctor," she said sweetly. "I shall do what you tell me," and she went into the room to get the child.

Van Rijn saw me out to the front step.

"I am sorry," he apologized, "but it is so terribly hard to get a good nurse just now."

"Yes," I answered, "but if I were you, I would get rid of this woman as soon as I could. I don't like her eyes. She looks as if she might go crazy any moment."

"I will try and find another one to-morrow," he promised me, and then I bade him farewell and turned to the left to go to the Oude Singel where I knew that there was an apothecary who kept late hours, as he was an amateur musician and had once sold me a viola da gamba of his own making.

I found him still at work in a little room at the back of the house. He had a theory that the tone of fiddles depended upon the sort of varnish that was used and had for years been experimenting with different sorts of oil and resin. He had just obtained a new sort of resin called "copalene" or some such thing—a funny-looking yellow mess which he had ordered from England. He wanted to tell me all about it and how now his fiddles would sound like those of the great Nicolo Amati of Cremona. But it was late and I was tired and I bade him wash his hands and go to his dispensary and mix me the dose which I meant to prescribe for my new patient. While he was busy with his bottles, I asked him whether he had a boy who could run an errand and deliver the bottle.

"Is it far?" he asked.

"About ten minutes. That big house in the Breestraat. The second one from the Saint Anthonie Lock."

"You mean the new house of Rembrandt?"

"I thought his name was van Rijn?"

"So it is. I think he comes from Leyden and his father owns a malt-mill on the old Rhine. But he is usually known by his first name."

"Then he is well known?"

The apothecary looked at me in wonder. "They say he is painting quite a number of pictures for the Prince of Orange. He must be pretty good."

"Yes," I answered. And then I went home and when I passed by the Breestraat, I noticed that there still was a light in the upstairs room.

"A strange man," I said to myself. "And soon he will be a very unhappy man. But where did I ever see that face before?"

THREE HEADS OF WOMEN, ONE ASLEEP (ETCHING)

Chapter 2

UNDER WHAT CIRCUMSTANCES I HAD FIRST MET
REMBRANDT

THE ARTIST AT WORK (DRAWING)

DURING the last ten years, the pictures which Rembrandt had painted of his beautiful wife and which had come to light after his belongings had been sold by the sheriff, have attracted so much attention that I (as her doctor) am constantly being asked what sort of woman she had been. Alas, poor Saskia was such a colorless person that she could not make herself interesting even on her death-bed while her husband came to play such a rôle in my life that every detail connected with our first meeting had become important to me. When I left his house that rainy evening, I was worried by a vague recollection of having seen the man before. I will now tell under what circumstances this happened and then it will be seen that my strangely assorted companions had something to do with it. Besides, they were such wonderful people, it does me good to write about them. And in a private diary that is not meant for publication, such little excursions ought to be allowed.

And so I continue my story once more by going a few years back (which is the way most stories in life are told) and it is April of the year 1626 and this time it does not rain, but the sun is shining and it is Easter morning and the good people of Amsterdam have all gone to church, but my three friends, Selim and Jean-Louys and Bernardo and myself have decided to start forth upon a new venture this day and hire ourselves a small yacht and sail to the island of Marken. This was quite an undertaking, for the people of that isolated sandbank were of a savage nature and enjoyed a reputation as amateur pirates and highway robbers which made most travelers keep far away from their shores unless they were itinerant ministers of the Gospel, when they could count upon a most cordial welcome.

But Selim declared that he had had great experience along that line from a trip which he had once taken as captain of a Turkish man-of-war to the northern shores of the Black Sea, a desolate and swampy region inhabited by wandering tribes of a strange race, called the Slavs. How Selim had ever got himself appointed commander of a war vessel, when he managed to be seasick while crossing the harbor on a ferry-boat, had always been a puzzle to me. But by that time I had learned not to wonder at anything pertaining to the morals, the habits or the customs of the wily follower of the Prophet. Furthermore we were accompanied by Jean-Louys and his ability to win the good will of almost any creature on either two or four legs was such that I thought him capable of taming even those wild men of the Zuyder Zee.

Anyway, we had arranged that we should meet at ten o'clock near the Montelbaans Tower, the old tower near the harbor which twice a month was the scene of great gayety and great misery, when the soldiers and sailors who had signed up for service in the Indies embarked from there for Batavia amidst the beating of many drums, the singing and shouting of a thousand tipsy women and the general jubilation of the crimps who felt that they had done their duty as soon as they had delivered this latest batch of human cattle into the hands of their new master and were now entitled to a few days of drunken relaxation. The rest of the time, however, the tower stood in dignified silence and it seemed an ideal meeting place for four respectable citizens bound upon a peaceful picnic.

I was a little earlier than the others, not having to come quite so far, but as soon as I had reached the Oude Schans, I had felt that there was something unusual in the air. Excited men and women were standing in small groups along the side of the canal, and all of them had their eyes fixed on a single house (a perfectly commonplace, respectable house such as you might find in any street in Amsterdam) and occasionally some one would shout, "I saw one of them!" or "The whole place is full of them!" or again, "There is one now! He is trying to get across the roof!" followed by a cry of "Look out! They are going to shoot!" Whereupon every one would run as fast as possible to find safety behind a tree or the bales of merchandise that were lying beneath tarpaulin covers awaiting the return of the stevedores on Tuesday morning.

The whole thing seemed too absurd for words. Our town was famous for its orderliness. The militia was a heavy-fisted organization and Their Lordships, who could under certain circumstances be persuaded to overlook ordinary misdemeanors of a private nature, knew no mercy when it came to rioting. If one rioted and one was caught, one was hung from one of the windows of the Town Hall and that was all there was to it. "Go as far as you like," the Burgomaster seemed to say. "Rob each other occasionally and even kill each other occasionally, but keep the peace of the community and do not upset the system of law and order as laid down by our wise decrees."

The idea therefore of a riot and of all things, on Easter morning, seemed little short of preposterous and I turned to a tight-lipped individual with mean yellow eyes, who was standing by my side and who was apparently drawing great personal satisfaction from this unusual proceeding.

"Pray tell me," I asked him, "what is this all about?"

He at once grew suspicious.

"Oh, don't you know? Why, that is curious, that you shouldn't know!"

I assured him that since I had only come a few minutes before, I had hardly had time to know.

"Well," he said, "the house is full of Arminians. They are holding a service there and they just tried to kill a child and use its blood for their ceremonies."

Of course, if I had been sensible, I would not have continued this conversation. But in those days, I suffered from a dreadful spiritual complaint. I simply could not get over the notion that since all men

21

had been created after God's image, they also must be endowed with certain primitive faculties for logical reasoning. Of course I knew that some people were not quite as bright as others, but I always told myself that that was merely the result of different backgrounds and different opportunities for development. "Give them a chance," I would tell my friends when they informed me that I was a silly-minded old fool. "Give them a chance. They have never had one. No one has ever appealed to their higher instincts. Talk to them! Reason it out with them and sooner or later you will find their vulnerable point and they will be forever grateful to you for having shown the right way towards the Truth."

I was so thoroughly convinced of the correctness of this point of view that almost every week I would waste endless valuable hours in utterly futile discussions with people to whom even the proposition of 2 x 2 = 4 was an unfathomable mystery and something to be regarded with profound suspicion, as it did not occur within the pages of Holy Writ. And no one short of a perfect lunatic would have undertaken to start an argument with that type of religious zealot and under such circumstances. But I was not very bright in those days and still believed in the efficacy of orderly argumentation and I answered:

"But surely, my dear sir, the people have not revived that silly old lie about the Jews for the benefit of the Arminians?"

Good Lord! how the fellow bristled! But he was the typical coward. He turned to a group of men and boys who had stationed themselves carefully behind a dozen big wooden boxes.

"Hey, boys!" he shouted. "I have caught one of them. This fellow here is a black Arminian. Come and get him."

Wherefore the crowd left its shelter and swooped down upon me and no doubt would have attacked me, when suddenly the door of the house opened and a dozen men and women, like frightened rabbits, made a dash for life and liberty toward the left of the street, which did not seem to be so well guarded. With a howl of joy, the mob rushed after its victims and I was left standing alone, looking as sheepish as one does when one is conscious of having done something very foolish.

But a pleasant voice behind me said: "Trying to solve the problems of this world by the usual appeal to reason, or just merely a

friendly little argument?" And there were Jean-Louys and Bernardo
and they said: "Selim was here a moment ago but he left, as he said
it always hurt his tender Moslem heart to see Christians murder each
other and he is waiting for us in the Ridder Straat and you had better
leave before these brutes come back."

But ere we could turn into the next side street, we heard the beating of drums and from the north a company of militia was coming
marching along, and so we found ourselves caught between the rioters
and the soldiers and not contemplating our position with any pleasure
(for the mob looked as if it wanted to fight) we stood aimlessly still
for a moment and then when Bernardo said, "There! Look, there is
a tavern!" we made for the door of the inn just as some one from the
other side was trying to lock it.

Indeed, our attempt to force our way in almost led to another
violent encounter, when suddenly and by a stroke of great good luck,
I recognized the innkeeper as an old patient of the city hospital and
he recognized me too, for he said: "Come in as fast as you can, for
there is going to be trouble and I don't want them to plunder my
house."

For the moment at least we were safe and having nothing better
to do we sat down and ordered three glasses of gin and asked our host
what had caused all the trouble and he said that he was not quite sure
either but apparently one of the houses further down the street belonged to a member of the Arminian community. Since the followers
of Jacobus Arminius had been read out of the Church by act of the
General Synod half a dozen years before, they had been in the habit
of meeting at this house on the Oude Schans to listen to one of their
ministers and fortify each other in their misfortunes by common
prayer and an avowal of faith. These clandestine meetings were of
course against the law and the clergy of Amsterdam had protested
violently, but the Arminians or Remonstrants or by whatever name
they were called, were industrious and respectable citizens and Their
Lordships of the Town Hall refused to proceed against them, even
if those black-souled sinners publicly confessed that they had serious
doubts upon the subject of predestination and infant damnation. As
long as they paid their taxes and were discreet about their weekly
gatherings, they could sing and pray and preach as they liked and
Their Lordships would most certainly not interfere.

Well, this morning some boys who had stayed away from Sunday-school had used the stoop of this house for a game of knuckle-bones and they had been very noisy about it and some one had come out of the house and had told them to go and play somewhere else. But of course, no other stoop would do and half a dozen times they had been told to go away and half a dozen times they had used vile language until the poor Arminian, forgetting all the precepts of his creed, had lost his temper and had boxed the ears of a young lout who had called him a name which I shall not here repeat. The youthful mucker, instead of taking his medicine, had shrieked that he had been murdered. A few passers-by had taken his side as is the habit of our common people who, regardless of the merits of the case, will always support one of their own class. Some one else then had raised the cry of "The Arminians and the Papists are in that house!" and the fat had been in the fire. For by this time the angry horde had been augmented by those who were returning from early service and they were in no mood to obey the orders of the officer of the guard who marched up to them all alone and bade them disperse.

I was looking through a little peephole in one of the blinds which had been hastily pulled across the windows, for the rattle of breaking glass told us what was happening a few doors away. I saw the officer parley and then hesitate. Evidently he did not want to use force, but that one short moment of trepidation was enough to decide the fate of the besieged worshipers. The crowd set up a terrific yell and a fresh volley of stones and sticks and mud was directed against the offending house. But one of the stones, either intentionally or accidentally, hit one of the soldiers who were waiting at some distance. He was perfectly willing to see the dirty Arminians get their just rewards, but he would be damned if he would stand there and have his nose broken by a brick and just stand there and do nothing about it. I saw him level his musket. At the same moment, one of the leaders of the rabble, an evil-looking ruffian with a cobble-stone in each hand and a long knife held between his lips, in a sudden outburst of fury turned on his heels and made for the officer who still alone, and with his sword undrawn, was absolutely unable to defend himself, and undoubtedly he would have killed him, had not the soldier fired his gun and caught the assailant right between the eyes. The man dropped his knife, threw up his arms, stones and all, jumped about four feet in the air and fell down dead.

This was the sign for a general mêlée and during the next half hour there was a great deal of desultory fighting and several of the crowd were taken prisoner and since the danger of a bombardment was now considerably less, we persuaded our host to let us open the blind, for such outbreaks of popular fury are very interesting to people with a philosophical turn of mind and we did not want to let the opportunity go by of studying our neighbors in the act of breaking skulls and windows for the greater glory of their mysterious God.

And then suddenly I saw something that struck me as most extraordinary. Leaning against a tree and standing there as unconcernedly as if he were all alone in the park drawing a bird or a squirrel, a young man was making a sketch of one of the inevitable beggars who had hastened to be present when the plundering should begin (our beggars have a very sensitive nose for that sort of thing) and who now with some of his colleagues was debating whether they had better go on or whether they should retreat as the game had been spoiled anyway by the arrival of the guards. A few evidently were in favor of seeing the thing out, but others of a more cautious nature seemed to be in favor of flight.

While they were still debating this point, the battle between the rioters and the soldiers suddenly took a fresh impetus from the arrival of a number of sailors from some near-by East Indiamen, who armed with cutlasses were all for showing the damned heretics that they could not preach their stinking doctrines in their city and hope to get away with it. It was a bitter fight and many heads were broken and many fingers were split and stones flew to and fro, but through it all that strange young man kept working away at his sketches and appeared totally unconscious of the fact that at any moment he too might be killed. All three of us were fascinated by the sight of him. He was very simply dressed, like a student or a better-class artisan and he wore his hair long as was then the fashion. But he had eyes, and all three of us remarked on those eyes.

"We must speak to him," Jean-Louys cried out, delighted with so much sang-froid, "and we must invite him to accompany us on our trip. He will be very useful in our negotiations with the natives."

Rembrandt van Rijn

But finally, when the soldiers had swept away the rabble and we could open the door and go out on the street, the young man was gone. We looked for him everywhere, but could not find him. And so we gave up the search and thanked our host and gave him a handsome tip (for maybe he had saved our lives) and went to the Ridder Straat and at the appointed tavern found Selim busily engaged in explaining the mysteries of a ring he wore to the serving girl, who was so fascinated that she had let him put an arm around her—"So that she should be closer to the subject"—as he explained to us when we entered.

Of course, our picnic and our sailing party had been spoiled for that whole part of the town remained smoldering with anger for several days and it was not safe to get too close to a pleasure yacht. The people felt full of righteous indignation. They had tried to protect their homes, their families, their children, against the pollution of a terrible heresy and as a reward for their devotion to the cause of True Religion they had been shot down like dogs. The idea that any one under such circumstances could be so utterly indifferent to the interests of the community as to go sailing for pleasure might have caused a new outbreak and at the suggestion of Jean-Louys we went to his tower and he made us an omelette in the true French style (they don't use flour in France for their omelettes as we do and get something much lighter and much more digestible than our own domestic pancakes) and Selim made us a strange dish of little bits of meat and rather pasty-looking flour which he called Ish-kebab, which he informed us was the favorite dish of His Majesty Murad IV and Bernardo mixed us a salad after the true Portuguese style which was not unpleasant although a little too oily and garlicky and I sat wondering who this strange young man might have been who could lose himself so completely in his task that he kept on drawing pictures while all around him, people were killing each other.

For a long time his face continued to haunt me. But I never saw him again. Until that rainy evening in the month of November of the year 1641 when suddenly it dawned upon me, as I lay tossing in my bed. The strange young man of the riot of fifteen years before was none other than the husband of my new patient. It was Rembrandt van Rijn.

26

Chapter 3

A DISAGREEABLE WOMAN IS AS A RULE A
VERY DISAGREEABLE WOMAN

BEGGAR IN A HIGH CAP (ETCHING)

WHEN I called again at the house in the Breestraat, I mentioned the riot of fifteen years before as we sat in the studio after I had visited my patient. I had been right. Rembrandt had been there. Just by chance. For at that time he was not living in Amsterdam. He had been there for a short time in '23, studying with Lastman, but in '26 he had been back in Leyden, and he had only been in Amsterdam for a fortnight to try and sell some of his pictures. The trip had not been very successful. The pictures were bad, but not quite bad enough to find a customer and he had returned to Leyden, as he explained, "because the meals at home cost nothing and because I could send my laundry to the family wash."

As for the incident of the riot, yes, he remembered vaguely that there had been a lot of shouting while he was drawing, "but I really have forgotten," he added. "All I remember is that I found myself face to face with one of the most picturesque hoodlums I had ever seen. I have always had a secret liking for those wandering vagabonds, who obey neither God nor man. They neither spin nor weave or whatever it is that they are supposed to do. They lie and steal and cheat and loaf and gamble and get hung or die miserably by the side of the road, but they make no pretense to be anything else and when they are dirty, they are dirty, and when they are drunk, they are

27

drunk, and one knows what one is painting. I will show you the one
I saw that day. I have done him in an etching. Some other time—
when I have not got this worry—then I will look it up for you—
some other time—when Saskia is better."

"Better!" I thought. "You poor devil, I ought to tell you right
now. But why should I? She won't live a day longer for my telling
you. No! You might as well have hope until the final end." And so
we talked of this and that and the other thing, but mostly of this and
that, as the "other thing" (taking it to mean the events of the big
world) did not interest my new friend in the least.

I sometimes tried to bring up the sort of subjects that were of importance to the average run of my patients, the trouble the King of
England seemed to have with his people and how it would affect our
own trade if there should be war between the King and his Parliament, and the difficulties that never seemed to come to an end between Sweden and Denmark about the tolls in the Sund, and how
it would mean a great loss to our own grain-trade if there were an
open outbreak of hostilities and how it might force us to take sides
just when our navy was needed for a final attack upon Spain, and
what a lot all that would cost and how some one had written a book
to prove that somewhere between Asia and America, in the southern
part of the Pacific, there must be a large piece of land and how certain
merchants in our town were interested in the idea and wanted to
send out an expedition to discover this mysterious land and take possession of it and exploit it, which would mean a wonderful new
source of revenue, but to all these problems he nodded a polite "yes"
without ever offering a suggestion of his own.

And then I talked of art, of which (with the exception of music) I
am entirely ignorant, and I told him of two pictures by an Italian,
whose name I had forgotten but they represented the Colosseum
by moonlight and the ruins of the Forum early in the morning and
I said what an inspiration it must be to any young man to be able to
go to that wonderful country for a short while and study the ancient
masters, and he said, yes, perhaps it was a good thing for a few of
them. If they were born to be bad painters, they had better be bad
painters on the other side of the Alps than on this side, and of course,
the old masters had been wonderful, the greatest painters that had
ever lived, but the story they had to tell was best told by their pic-

tures and these one could see in Holland just as well as anywhere else.

For it really did not matter much where one painted, but it all depended upon how one painted and all these hundreds of young men, ruining their families because they had to learn their art abroad, had better stay home and join the bakers' guild or become tailors or longshoremen, for if they had talent, it would show itself even if they never left their own little alleyway or their own room and if they had not, all the Italian sunsets and French sunrises and Spanish saints and German devils would not turn them into real artists.

And when he was still quite young and had only painted a few pictures—it must have been in 1630 or '31—My Lord Constantin Huygens, who had seen his work and that of his friend Jan Lievens had told them that what they were doing was very nice and really very promising, but they were an arrogant couple of brats who thought that they were so smart that no one could teach them anything, and if only they would go to Italy for a while and study Raphael and Michelangelo, they might really amount to something. But they had answered that they could not afford to waste their time on such a long voyage and they had stayed right where they were and after all they had learned their trade just as well as the others and they had never lost the habit of working, which was one of the worst sides of the life 'neath the pleasant Italian skies, with all the women in the world at one's disposal and even more wine.

So that was that, and invariably after a couple of minutes our minds went back to the sick woman in the Big Room downstairs and the baby in the Small Room upstairs and what the chances were for the mother's speedy recovery and whether the child had inherited her weak constitution or whether he would pull through. As for the child, I really knew nothing about it. It looked strong enough but it was restless and wept a great deal and this annoyed the mother and tired her. For of course, as soon as I was out of the house, the nurse would find a pretext to move the child from the etching room upstairs back to the living room downstairs.

If I happened to come in upon such an occasion, there always was a vague excuse. The Master had to use his press that morning, or the room smelled so badly of ink that it had to be aired and they were afraid that the child would catch cold or she had to tend to the baby's laundry and could not leave the child alone while she was in the garden. And so on and so forth.

The reason for this opposition was not hard to find. The old-fashioned dry-nurse holds a curious position in our community. She is usually a woman of very simple origin, but because she spends her days in the houses of the rich, she has acquired a certain dignity of manner which deceives a great many people. There are undoubtedly a number of members of that profession who are faithful and efficient and competent and who render exceedingly useful services. But there are all too many who are lazy and indifferent and who do more harm than good with their superstitions and their methods which go back straight to those Middle Ages when men knew sometimes how to die but rarely how to live.

These women are really a menace to the community. They come into people's houses when everything is topsy-turvy and when the husband is half crazy with fright. They quickly succeed in surrounding themselves with a nimbus of indispensability. "If it were not for them, of course everything would have gone wrong, but they saved the mother and they also saved the child," and more of the same sort, until the poor male parent believes that a fat, complacent woman with the mind of a cow is the savior of his domestic happiness, and bows to the creature as if she were a goddess. And the relatives too fall a victim to this nonsense and the dry-nurse shows them the beautiful new infant and pockets her tips and allows everybody to wait on her as if it were she and not the mother who had gone through the ordeal of child-bearing.

Whenever she sees that she is in danger of losing her exalted position, she draws upon her large stock of so-called "nurse's tales" and frightens the poor parents with stories about children who suddenly grew an extra couple of hands or who died of mysterious diseases or who were eaten up by werewolves because the dry-nurse was not there to drive away the devils and spooks and the bogeymen which cause those afflictions with one of those mysterious but efficacious abracadabras of which they alone possess the secret.

Yes, I have known of cases when the dry-nurse, who felt that she was being neglected, deliberately doped the child with a weak solution of gin and milk so as to "save it from a horrible death" and thereby gain the everlasting gratitude of the entire household, which did not know that the "cure" consisted in substituting milk for gin and allowing the child to sleep off the effects of its youthful debauch.

The nurse in the painter's family belonged to this latter category. She was an unpleasant-looking person with large, coarse features and an arrogant voice with a whine in it. Such a combination may seem impossible but she really was possessed of it and reminded me of certain curs which are able to yelp and bark at the same time. She was (as I afterwards discovered) the widow of an army-trumpeter and often talked of the days when she had had her own place and had not been obliged to eat other people's bread. Her game was so simple that any other man would have seen through it right away. She knew enough about sick people to understand that the man for whom she worked would soon be a widower. She meant to fill the empty place. She probably felt that I, as an outsider, might not be so easily deceived and would try to warn the husband, for the whole thing was so transparent that it could not well remain hidden from the patient to whom any sort of excitement might prove fatal. Hence she had a double reason to hate me. In the first place, because as a doctor I was bound to disapprove of a great many things which to her were part of an ancient ritual and an easy way of getting some extra money, and in the second place because I might upset her plan of becoming the second Mrs. van Rijn.

It may seem that I pay more attention to this woman than she deserves, for the world is full of hysterical and scheming females and they are rarely very interesting. But soon after the death of Saskia it appeared that I had been right in my diagnosis of Geertje's hidden intentions, and for years the poor painter's life was made miserable by this former servant and her lamentations and complaints.

From all this Rembrandt might have saved himself if he had done what I bade him do and had sent her packing. But this man, who was without mercy for himself when it came to his work, who would actually live and sleep and sit and paint and walk in his clothes for weeks at a time if he got interested in a problem of light and dark, who would content himself with a slice of bread and a couple of herrings as his only meal for months at a time because he was too busy with an etching to think of anything else, this slave-driver who kept his mind and body going full tilt until he pitched himself head-long into an early grave, was weak as butter when it came to women.

Rembrandt van Rijn

He did not understand them and in his heart of hearts, I think he rather disliked them. He was a vigorous fellow with the strength of a bull and other qualifications which are usually associated with that useful animal. And therefore he was sometimes in dire need of a woman, just a woman, any woman would do. He was by nature exceedingly kind-hearted and, of course, the other sex was quick to recognize this defect in his armor and to use his vulnerability to its own advantage. As a result Rembrandt was forever in some sort of trouble about his domestic relations.

The truth of course was that a man like him should never have been married at all. For no matter what sort of union he contracted, the moment he promised that he would love and cherish a certain female for the rest of his days, he was uttering a lie. He had already given his word to some one else, years and years ago, and she was a most jealous mistress and would never let go of him.

Once shortly after Saskia's death I tried to explain this to one of her relatives, a respectable Frisian dominie. He was horrified.

"Then you mean to say," he stammered, "that my poor niece was married to an adulterer?"

"Yes," I answered, "just as much as any other woman who undertakes to become the life-companion of a man who is more in love with his work than with anything else."

For that, alas, was the truth. And it caused a vast amount of misery to a few human beings and brought inconceivable beauty into the lives of millions of others.

This balance sheet will please a few and others will throw it away in disgust.

But nature ofttimes chooses strange ways her miracles to perform. And who shall say that she is wrong?

Chapter 4

SASKIA'S ILLNESS

SASKIA WITH PEARLS IN HER HAIR
(ETCHING)

YES, Saskia was a very sick woman but like so many sufferers from phthisis, she was totally unaware of the seriousness of her condition. She felt weak, of course, desperately weak at times, and the fever slowly burned up her strength. She was losing weight at a terrible rate of speed, but she felt no pain, no discomfort, and except for an occasional fit of coughing, she would hardly have known that there was anything the matter with her at all.

Perhaps the Gods, who are not renowned for their mercy in dealing with the ailments of the human race, recognized that this affliction was just a little more than most people would be able to bear unless mitigated by some spiritual anesthetic, consisting in this instance of an irrepressible form of gayety and a steadfast optimism which makes it impossible for them to believe that there is no hope and that death is merely a question of weeks or months, or at the best, a few years.

Every time I visited the house on the Breestraat, Saskia was doing "just a little better than the last time you saw me, dear Doctor." She was so lovely and so pathetic and so patient and so totally ineffectual that my heart was full of pity for her and sometimes I bought a few flowers for her from the flower-woman just around the corner of the Anthonie Sluys, a strange old creature who was said to be the widow of a ship's captain, who had been eaten up by

33

the savages of some mysterious Indian island, but who as I found out
one day was the relict of a plain sailor hung for insubordination and
who had invented the story of her romantically consumed spouse
in order to attract more customers.

Upon such occasions, Saskia was as happy as a child and one day
I remember I had brought her a bunch of country violets and she
made a little wreath and put it on the head of the baby, for of
course, no matter what I might say the child continued to live in
the big downstairs room where the mother lay dying. She even tried
to make little Titus dance on her knees while she was sitting propped
up in her chair in front of the fire. But the effort was too much
for her and she had a coughing spell and when I tried to make her
lie down, she refused and said she would be all right as soon as she
had taken some of her medicine.

This puzzled me, for I had given her no medicine except a sleeping potion, knowing only too well that in the whole of the pharma-
copoeia no drug was to be found that could prevail against the
onslaughts of this dreadful disease. And then I discovered to my
horror that that unspeakable nurse had prevailed upon her to try
the mixture of a well-known mountebank who had come to Amsterdam a few years before and pretended that he was a Babylonian
prince who had discovered the secret formula of King Solomon's
elixir of life, hidden among the ruins of the temple of Jerusalem. He
was an absolute fraud. But he wore a long bright red cloak and a
green turban and he was a very clever scoundrel who had had an
enormous amount of experience in almost every city of Europe and
had worked his way out of at least a dozen jails and he played upon
the emotions of his patients with as much agility and virtuosity as if
he had been the late Jan Sweelinck trying out the organ of some
humble village church, and his waiting room was always filled with
eager crowds of suffering mortals who listened to him with great
awe and declared themselves cured before they had even left his
house.

He advertised that since he had been sent by God he was not
allowed to charge for his services and indeed, the consultation itself
was entirely free of charge. But in order to prevent a relapse, he
persuaded most of his customers to buy a couple of bottles of his
famous "Elixir Vitae" which he sold at a florin apiece. I now had

a chance to examine this mixture for as soon as we had put Saskia back to bed and she was resting quietly, I took my departure, but was careful to remove the bottle. At home I examined the contents as well as I could and found that it consisted of licorice, camomile and water with a dash of sugar to make it a little more palatable. No wonder this quack could afford a handsomer carriage than any of the regular members of our Surgeons' Guild.

I spoke to the husband the next day about this incident and told him what I had discovered, that this licorice water might not be directly harmful to his wife, but neither would it do her any good, as she needed plenty of milk and eggs, but that she must avoid all things that would tend to upset her stomach or spoil her appetite. He was very angry and promised to dismiss the nurse at once. When I returned the next day, I found her gone. I expressed my joy and asked where the child was.

"Oh," the painter answered with a somewhat sheepish look, "the nurse is taking the child out for a little walk. She said that she thought it needed some air and it was such a lovely day!"

A lovely day indeed! A sharp eastern wind was making the blinds rattle. The streets were full of dust. When I came into the sickroom I found it filled with smoke. And the mother lay gasping in her bed.

"The nurse said it would be all right," she whispered to me hoarsely, "but there is such a storm and it is blowing down the chimney and I could not get up and I called, but no one heard me." And she wept bitterly for this was one of the rare days when her customary cheerfulness had left her and she felt very sorry for herself.

I was thoroughly angry with van Rijn and I made no attempt to disguise or hide my feelings. He had remained upstairs in his studio as I knew he would, for he felt so utterly helpless in the midst of these domestic upheavals that most of the time he tried to persuade himself that they did not exist by locking himself up in his studio and keeping his mind engaged upon his work. I now told him in no uncertain tones that something had to be done or I would no longer be responsible.

Then I suddenly realized that he had never yet understood the seriousness of his wife's illness. His thoughts had been so completely

Rembrandt van Rijn

concentrated upon his paintings that nothing short of a brutal and point-blank announcement of imminent disaster could break through the man's "unawareness" of his physical surroundings. Now he went to the other extreme. He accused himself bitterly of his neglect, called himself his wife's murderer, carefully washed his brushes in a jar of turpentine, carefully wiped them upon a rag, took off his painter's blouse, turned his easel away from the light, went out of the door, locked the door behind him, went downstairs, sat himself down by the side of his wife's bed, took her hand and said: "Saskia sweet, now I shall be thy nurse." And as far as I know, he never left her room again until she died.

For he loved this woman very deeply and very tenderly. Indeed, he loved her as much as he was ever able to love anything made of flesh and blood, and not of canvas and paint or the gold-gleaming copper of the etcher's plate.

A WOMAN READING (DRAWING)

SASKIA WITH A RED FLOWER (PAINTING)

gerekent door Rembrant van Rijp naer sijn Selvet
soo als hij in sijn schilder kamer gekleet was.

REMBRANDT IN HIS WORKING DRESS (DRAWING)

Chapter 5

I BEGIN TO LEARN SOMETHING NEW ABOUT ART
WHEN REMBRANDT INVITES ME
INTO HIS STUDIO

SASKIA AND HER NURSE (DRAWING)

AFTER this there was some sort of order in the big house on the Breestraat. Van Rijn had put a cot up in a corner of the Big Room. A cleaning woman had been called in and the bottles of acid and the pans with rosin had been removed to a small cabinet to the left of the front door. One or two paintings which smelled too strongly of fresh varnish had been temporarily relegated to the studio upstairs and the peat-fire had been changed for one of wood. It cost a good deal more, but as the man seemed to be making plenty of money, there was no reason why he should worry over a little extra expense. The nurse Geertje was still on the premises, but she carefully kept out of my sight. Three times a day she was permitted to bring the child to see its mother and on those occasions, if mere looks could have killed, I would have died as miserably as Saint Sebastian, for her eyes were as powerful as a whole regiment of Roman archers. But as long as she obeyed my instructions I did not care how little she loved me or how much she hated me. It was my duty to try and prolong the life of my patient for as long as it could be done. She needed rest and regular hours and she now had both,

37

for van Rijn guarded her day and night with a patience and care which were as touching as ineffectual.

For once in his life he had escaped from the dreadful mistress who heretofore had never given him a moment's respite. He did not touch a brush and although I had heard that he had been ordered to do a large piece for the new clubhouse of the Town Guards, I never saw him busy with any sketches. I asked him whether it had been finished and he said no, it had been begun, but it could wait and that people would like it anyway and that he did not care a tinker's dam whether it was ever finished or not if only he could keep his wife alive and get her better. And he used to sit by her side for hours and speak to her softly, which seemed to be the best way to make her go to sleep, for after ten or fifteen minutes she would close her eyes and lie very still with a smile upon her lovely face and she looked so young, not a day older than twenty, that it seemed incredible that she was going to die very soon; but our art has never yet found a way to combat this affliction and so the winter passed and the new year came and I knew that it would be Saskia's last one and I was quite miserable about it when something happened in my own life that made me completely forget the difficulties of the van Rijn household. For we human beings are so complicated that the miseries of our neighbors mean nothing to us the moment we ourselves get into trouble. And it was during this winter that an event occurred which for a time threatened to upset the whole of my existence and which made me an exile from my country for almost a dozen years.

Now it was customary in those days for each of the members of the Surgeons' Guild in town to give a course in anatomy for the benefit of the students of medicine and those leeches and barbers who wanted to prepare themselves a little more thoroughly for their daily tasks. The last time I had given this course of lectures and demonstrations had been in the summer of the year 1636, and now I was told by the Dean of our Guild to prepare myself to teach elementary anatomy once more during the months of March, April and May of the coming year. As I had devoted myself almost entirely to the study of drugs during the last decade, I was a bit rusty and felt the need of refreshing my memory and so I went to Anatomical Hall of the Surgeons' Guild, situated these last eight years on the second floor of the Saint Anthonie Gate, right above the local meat-market, a somewhat unfortunate location as it gave the ribald-minded a chance to make rather pointed remarks about this close proximity between butchers and doctors.

I must confess that I had not been near the place since my last lectureship and I was surprised to find one side of the wall entirely filled with a large picture, showing Doctor Nicolaes Pieterszoon in the midst of his students. Pieterszoon had gone far since the day he posed for this portrait, for he had been High Sheriff of our town and had been elected Burgomaster two or three times. Also he had taken the name of Tulp after a large tulip that stood carved in the façade of his house on the Keizersgracht.

The picture struck me very forcibly for in it I found something which I had rarely discovered in any other painting—though I must confess at once that this form of art had never been my strong point. As a child I had always wanted to draw, but my father, with his narrow religious ideas, felt convinced that young people should be trained to do that which was most distasteful to them, rather than be allowed to follow their natural bent. Therefore when it became apparent (from my eternal scribbling on slates and walls and rarer pieces of paper) that I had not only some gift for drawing but an absolute urge to express myself in lines and curves, representing a large variety of subjects from our old maid Jacoba to Jonah being spewed out by the whale, my father then and there decided that I must become a musician.

He did not ask whether I had a good ear, whether I had the sort of fingers one needs to become an experienced player of the violin. He "decided," and in my youth when a father "decided" a child obeyed and that was all there was to it. And so from the age of six until I was fourteen I went twice a week to the room of Signor Tomasso Staccato, player-in-extraordinary and virtuoso of the Chamber to his Grace, the late Marquis Ercole II of Este.

The little Italian, if he spoke the truth, must have been about a hundred years old, for Ercole, as I happened to discover one day in a history of architecture, lived during the first half of the sixteenth century. But such small lies, due to the vanity of simple-minded and otherwise lovable people, are easily pardoned and Signor Staccato was one of the most charming men I have ever met. He played the violin, the viola da gamba and viola da basso with equal dexterity and was besides no mean performer on the clavecin, an instrument of great charm and much more dependable than the viols which in our wet and damp climate are apt to be as moody as the spoiled wives of indulgent husbands.

There was a tradition, when I was a child, that all music teachers were fair game for naughty little boys and that it was the holy duty of the pupils to make the lives of these poor creatures as miserable as they possibly could. And of course music teachers were supposed to be artists and artists could not handle the birch like ordinary school-masters, for it would have been beneath their dignity to spank any one. Signor Staccato carefully stuck to this rule, that there must be no physical violence mixed with his teaching. But at one time in his career he had acquired a bow made out of steel. Good God! I still shiver when I think of that long, thin steel bow which used to descend upon my fingers with unexpected violence whenever I did not pay sufficient attention. "B flat," he would say in his falsetto voice, "and you played B sharp," and both B sharp and B flat were accompanied by a short, sharp whack across the knuckles with that fatal bow. If that seemed too mild a form of punishment he would discover that the left hand was not in the right position and then it would be hammered into the correct place with a quick succession of rapid blows. "There!—a leetle further back if you please, my child—a leetle further back—still a leetle more!" Bang! Bang! Bang!

It was a strange system to make one learn to play the violin. But somehow or other, it worked, and although I had very little talent, I learned to render some of the simpler pieces of Orlando di Lasso and Arcadelt with a certain degree of accuracy. But my playing was something I had learned out of a book. It was not something that came out of the heart, and whereas if I had been allowed to follow my natural inclination, I might have developed into a fair draughts-man, I had now reached the age of forty, an indifferent performer on the viol and hopelessly ignorant of that form of graphic self-expression towards which I had always felt so strongly inclined.

I had in the meantime seen a great many paintings. Our city was full of them. It sometimes seemed to me that our town would burst from sheer riches, like a sack too heavily loaded with grain. Our harbors were more crowded than ever. The streets near the Exchange gave one the impression of a continual county-fair. During the morning hours, when the musicians played on the Dam, one saw as many Turks and Germans and Blackamoors and Frenchmen and Britishers and Swedes, and even people from far-away India, as one did Dutchmen. All roads appeared to be leading to Amsterdam and the great rivers of the world flowed no longer towards the North Pole, but carried their ships right to our port—ships bulging with spices and with silks and with grain and with whale-oil and every product from the shores of the Seven Great Seas.

There were those who believed that these wonderful blessings were being poured into our laps because as a nation we had found special favor in the eyes of God. How or by what means, I failed to understand, for it never struck me that we were much kinder or more generous or more humble than many of our neighbors and those surely were the virtues which ought to have appealed most directly to the Almighty Ruler of Heaven. And as far as I could reason things out (though I was careful to keep this opinion to myself) we owed this prosperity to the fortunate circumstance that we had been obliged to fight so long and so bitterly for our mere existence. The weaker ones among our people had died long ago. They had not been able to survive the endless sieges, the hunger, the anxiety for parents or children who at any moment might be hanged or burned or broken on the wheel. The strong ones had survived. And when the enemy was driven off our territory, those strong ones were so full of energy and enthusiasm, that they had to find some new outlet for their surplus of high spirits. The sight of a map would drive them crazy with excitement. Our small country could no longer hold them. They had forced the King of Spain to his knees. Old Charles of England had his hands full with that psalm-singing rebel called Cromwell. Louis of France was just nobody at all, and his mother and her dear friend the Cardinal, who ruled France between their quarrels and their bickerings, did not count except as agreeable topics for scandal and rather ribald tavern songs. The Swedes and Danes might be bothersome with their silly quarrels, but somehow or other, the straits that led to the Baltic grain fields would be kept open and a curse upon both of them if they tried to interfere with our honest trade. Finally there were the minor potentates of Germany and the Mediterranean, but they were just funny without being bothersome.

And so, for no other reason than that they must ever and again prove to themselves what fine fellows they were, my neighbors must go forth to pull the pigtail of the Emperor of China and singe the beard of the Sultan of Turkey and pull the tails of the polar bears in Spitzbergen and make love to the daughters of the Cacique of Virginia and drink beer in the pagodas of India and light their pipes with the eternal lamp of some holy shrine in Calicut and do any number of scandalous, dangerous and altogether outrageous things which ought to have cost them their lives, but which on the contrary filled their pockets with ducats and made them twice as foolhardy and brave and devil-may-care as they had ever been before. But of course after ten or twenty years of this sort of life, they would grow a little too old for this sort of pastime and then they would retire from the business of storming the gates of Heaven and Hell and would turn respectable and they would buy themselves large and uncomfortable houses in one of the newly laid-out parts of the town (and how they were robbed by our good burgomasters who speculated in this sort of real estate as if the whole city were their private property and they were responsible to no one no matter how much they stole from the community) and of course they must show their neighbors how rich they were (what is the fun of having bags and bags and bags of money if no one knows it?) and so they filled their houses with elegant French chairs that weighed a ton and with Spanish chests that only a mule could move and with pictures—rows and rows and still more rows of pictures.

I don't suppose that most of them knew what those pictures were about or cared a straw for them either one way or the other. But they knew that in the older days the abbots of the churches and the princes of Italy and Spain and the barons of England and the nobles of France had adorned their houses with paintings and so of course they must have paintings too. As a result, wherever I went, whether my patient happened to be a simple butcher from the Voldersstraat or a rich Indian merchant living on the fashionable side of the Heerengracht, I found myself surrounded by miles and miles of colored canvases. Some of them were probably very good and a few of them were undoubtedly very bad, but most of them were of a very decent quality, as the Guild of St. Luke maintained the highest possible standards and no one could hope to qualify as a master until he had

Rembrandt van Rijn

spent years and years in a very exacting and very difficult apprenticeship.

But for one reason or another, I had never known much about this form of art until I met Rembrandt.

Of course there always had been certain pictures I liked and others I did not like quite so well. I had taken them more or less for granted. A portrait of a man or a woman was that same man or woman made of linseed-oil and divers pigments instead of flesh and blood. A landscape in a golden frame was not in any way different from that same landscape as I could see it from my own front windows. A lamb-chop or a dead fish in color was still a lamb-chop or a dead fish. It was all very fine and very clever, but it was dead.

And now I suddenly made the discovery that such things could have a soul.

I don't like that word "soul." It smacks too much of those theological discussions I have heard going on around me ever since I was a child, but just now I can't think of any other expression that describes equally well what I mean and so I shall let it go at that and repeat that I suddenly came face to face with the animate quality of supposedly inanimate substances (for what else is a picture but a bit of hemp covered with a messy layer of vegetable matter?) and I was forced to realize that the terms "dead" and "alive" were a little less definite than I had always presumed them to be.

This dawned upon me not slowly and gradually through my conversations with Rembrandt (who however could rarely be induced to talk about his work) or through the contemplation of those paintings by different famous masters with which the walls of his house were covered. The first revelation came to me quite suddenly that morning I went to the rooms of the Surgeons' Guild and stood in front of the portrait of Nicolaes Tulp and half a dozen of my colleagues, busy with some anatomical demonstration. I had known Claes Tulp ever since I had come to Amsterdam and was on pleasant speaking terms with most of the other men whose faces appeared in the picture. During my student days I had attended hundreds of dissections. I understood that it had become fashionable among the better-known among my colleagues to have themselves painted carving up some unfortunate victim of the gallows or the poor ward. Together with the whole town I had laughed when one rather vain old physician, who had engaged in a bitter professional quarrel with one of the young men, had ordered a portrait of this sort and had bribed the artist to make one of the "students" look like his hated rival, thereby drawing attention to his own superior position in life. And together with the whole country I had roared when the younger man, not to be outdone in civilities of this sort, had favored the Surgeons' Guild with a large canvas (not particularly well done, I am sorry to say) in which he himself was shown "demonstrating" the entrails of a very unappetizing corpse, which bore a striking if somewhat greenish resemblance to the learned professor who had humiliated him in picture No. 1.

But all of those popular "anatomical lessons" were mere records of past events. They told the spectator that "on such and such a day, in such and such a room, Doctor A., surrounded by Doctors B., C., D. and E., had dissected the mortal remains of the late F. and had found that the praecentral gyrus was still situated between the post-central gyrus and the superior frontal gyrus (as it ought to be) or had opened up the abdomen and had decided that the patient had died of a distemper of the liver, brought about by years and years of assiduous toping."

Well, I don't know how to explain it, but Rembrandt's picture of Nicolaes Tulp was different, quite different. It did not merely tell a story. It gave tangible expression to an abstract idea—an idea so all-preponderant that the story connected with it dwindled down to insignificant proportions, like the piece of inconsequential parchment upon which the original of the Sermon on the Mount was first written by those who heard the great prophet lay down the law of human forbearance.

Nicolaes Tulp ceased to be a distinguished and fashionable practitioner in the most opulent town of that period—the brilliant son of a rich father—a clever politician who four times in succession got himself appointed to the highest office in his community—a distinguished anatomist and an executive of no mean talent who had re-organized the entire pharmaceutical system of his own time. Instead, he became the living symbol of that divine curiosity which prying into the secrets of nature may some day set the human race free from most of its manifold ills and miseries.

And the faces of the men around him were no longer those of

humdrum hard-working leeches, come hither to learn a few things and perhaps improve their standing in the medical world and charge a little higher fees than before and buy their wives new silken dresses for going to meeting. Those eyes looked beyond the corpse stretched out before them. Those eyes saw more than the tendons of a single arm. They were gazing into the mystery that underlies all existence—the one hopeless and eternal mystery: "What was it that made those muscles move?"

I am trying to make my own impression clear to myself and I am afraid that I am not succeeding very well. Nor did I derive much support in my speculations from Rembrandt when we were sitting together one night in the etching room. (Saskia had had a bad attack of coughing but at last she had fallen asleep.) I told him what had happened to me and I grew rather rhetorical and used big words and spoke of art and the mission of art, the way I had heard certain painters and sculptors speak when they spent an evening together at a tavern and some one paid for their drinks.

He was interested, but not particularly interested or surprised.

"You always impressed me as an intelligent person, Doctor," he said, "and those little sketches which you have shown me are quite nice. You may not have learned as much as some of the boys who went to art-school, but the Lord was good to you at birth and you started out with a whole lot more than any of those poor devils will ever get, no matter how hard they work. And yet, here you are, forty years old, or even more, and you have never yet discovered what all truly intelligent people have known since the beginning of time."

"And that is?" I asked him.

"That nothing counts in this world except the inner spirit of things."

"Meaning the immortal soul of man?"

"Meaning the immortal soul of everything that was ever created."

"The immortal soul of tables and chairs and cats and dogs and houses and ships?"

"Just so."

"And the immortal soul of books and scissors and flowers and clouds?"

"Exactly."

45

I was silent for a while. Then I looked at this strange man with the tired eyes and the tired droop of the strong unwieldy shoulders.

"How many people in all the world will be able to understand that?"

He smiled and lifted up both hands in a gesture of resignation. Then he answered me slowly: "Well, perhaps three or four in every hundred. At the most, four. In very exceptional cases, five."

"And the others?"

"They will never know what we are talking about, but they will have their revenge."

"In what way?"

"They will let us starve to death."

The conversation was rapidly getting beyond my depth.

"Good night," I said, and held out my hand. He took it.

"Good night, Doctor, and thank you and if you have a few moments after dinner to-morrow, say at three or two-thirty, I wish you would come here. There is something I want to show you." And with that he showed me through the hall and bade me good night.

It was a dark night and it was raining. In the house of the Rabbi, a few doors further down, a light was still burning. Menasseh ben Israel was busy with his presses. He was always busy with those presses and people said he printed his books from golden letters. He was a clever man of great learning, a simple and lovable character. For a moment I thought that I would drop in and see what he was doing. But just then the tower of the South Church struck twelve. Bang—bang—bang—bang—

One could write a book about that, I thought. The spirit of the hour-glass, the spirit of the clock. Bang—bang—bang—bang—birth, life and death—happiness, sickness and health—hope and despair—bang—bang—bang—bang.

It was a good mood in which to go to sleep. I pulled my cloak around me a little closer and I turned the corner.

The door of a tavern opened and closed. Drunken voices filled the street.

"Lemme tell you," a man was drooling into the ear of another. "Now, what I am talking about, when a thing is so, it is so, and not otherwise, see? and when a man is so, he is so and that is all there is to him, see?"

"Sure, Jan, I see," the other answered.

"That's good," the tipsy philosopher volunteered, "for if you didn't agree with me that what is so, is so, I'd have knocked your damn head between your shoulders, see?"

The other one said that he did.

I left them to their discussion and I went home.

It was still raining when I lifted the latch.

MENASSEH BEN ISRAEL (ETCHING)

THE "GREAT JEWISH BRIDE" (ETCHING)

Chapter 6

REMBRANDT PAINTS A VERY LARGE PICTURE
WHICH HE EXPECTS TO MAKE
HIM FAMOUS

THE ARTIST AND SASKIA HIS WIFE
(ETCHING)

THE next morning I spent at the hospital. Then I went home for dinner and a little after three I called at the Breestraat. The patient was having one of her bad days. Nevertheless she had insisted upon leaving her bed and was sitting in a chair, propped up with many pillows. The child was on her lap. The nurse was busy hanging some clothes to dry near the fire. I had told her not to do the washing in the same room with the sick woman, but of course she had not obeyed my instructions. She grumbled something when I entered, picked up the baby's things, threw them into a wicker basket, slammed the door behind her and left.

"She has one of her terrible days, when I can do nothing with her," Saskia complained. "Sometimes I almost think she is mad."

"I am sorry," I replied, "your husband ought to have discharged her long ago."

"I know it. But he hates to be bothered with such things. He is a good man and he tries to interest himself in the household. But his heart is in his work. And she is very devoted to the baby and you know how little I can do. But soon I shall be better. I feel ever so much stronger than I did a few weeks ago. I looked at myself in

49

the mirror to-day. My cheeks were as red as before I had this attack of a bad cold. Don't you think I look well?"

I assured her that I had never seen her look so beautiful. Nor was it necessary for me to lie. The poor woman had a raging fever and her cheeks were flushed a deep, dark crimson. What she had taken for a sign of new health was merely the harbinger of death. Four months from that day, or at least five or six, she would be resting beneath a slab of granite in the Old Church. It was our duty to make her last few days on earth as happy as possible. I said something nice about the child, who was a very fine boy, but like all children, had an instinctive dislike of sick people and was trying hard to get away.

"Isn't he lovely?" she asked, trying to lift him up but finding him too much for her slender arms. "Oh, he is such a darling! And we are going to make a sailor of him."

"Not a great painter, like his father?"

She slowly shook her head. "No," she said, "I want him to be happy and carefree, and I don't believe artists ever are."

"But surely you cannot doubt that Rembrandt is happy! He has his work. He has you"—I noticed my mistake and hastily tried to correct myself—"he has you and the baby and . . ." But here she interrupted me. "You were right the first time," she said. "He has his work and in his spare time, he has me and then he dresses me up to look like a princess (which I am not) or like a fairy-queen (which I am even less) and I become part of his work!"

"The most beautiful part," I suggested with a smile.

"Oh, well, it is very kind of you to say that but all the same, I am only part of his work, and never part of his life."

"You became part of his life when you gave him this lovely child."

She looked at me with a puzzled expression. All her cheerfulness left her and her high spirits made way for a sudden fit of melancholia. "Do you really believe that?" she asked me with a puzzled look. "For if I didn't think so myself, I would want to die to-morrow. Now I am contented to wait until the day comes, and I am afraid it will come soon enough."

I tried to contradict her with the usual foolish stories which are the stock-in-trade of our profession, but just then Rembrandt entered the room. He was in great anger and was swearing most heartily.

"The idiot!" he shouted. "The perfectly hopeless, clumsy idiot! I thought that I had at last shown him how to use that press. The last time he soaked the paper until it turned to pulp as soon as one touched it. And now he has put the plate underneath the roller without using any felt. The copper is bent like a hoop. I shall have to do the whole thing over again. I might easily have sold a hundred copies. Old Dominie Anslo is always good for a hundred copies, and the Mennonites don't mind what they spend when it comes to pictures of their preachers."

Saskia held out her hand, a very white and very thin hand, but lovely of shape. "Come and sit down here for a moment, my dear," she asked him. "Why don't you tell the boy to go home? If he is just a common nuisance, you surely don't want him around in your place."

At once her husband's anger vanished. "I had thought of it," he answered, "but the next one would probably be just as bad or even worse. And this one pays me a hundred florins a year for the privilege of being one of my pupils. But I will tell you what I will do. Don't we need some kindling for the fire?"

"We always do."

"Very well. I shall turn him out into the yard to cut wood. I shall tell him that the exercise is good for his biceps and that a painter needs strong muscles. A brilliant idea. And I owe it to you. If I had been left to my own devices for another two minutes, I would have fired him, and now, my good doctor, you and I will take a little walk and I will show you something and perhaps I will tell you something—that is to say, if my wife will let you go for a few minutes?"

Poor Saskia made a faint effort to smile, but it was not a very successful one. The color had once more left her cheeks. She looked wasted and coughed terribly while we carried her back to bed.

"She ought not to be doing so much," I warned when we were out on the street.

Rembrandt shook his head. "I know it," he said, "but how can I keep her in bed when she insists upon getting up? Besides, if I didn't help her, she would call for the nurse."

"I thought you would get rid of the woman."

"I wanted to. And I tried to. Really, I tried very hard. But it was rather difficult. You see, I am very busy and it would have taken a great deal of time . . ."

I understood. This man knew only one thing in the world and that was his work. He had acquired a household. Sooner or later, we all do, and most of us manage to muddle through. But this poor devil, who was a giant when it came to his own particular form of art, was a miserable little dwarf as soon as he found himself face to face with the silly troubles of daily life. He was willing to try and solve problems of light and dark which no one before him had ever dared to tackle. But when he was called upon to read the riot act to a shrew of a nurse who was a menace to the health of his wife and child, he got frightened and ran away.

Well, we all are as we are and what we are and there is no use trying to change the human race from one thing to another, for it just can't be done. And with this wise reflection I followed my host into the street when he stopped and asked me:

"Do you mind if before we go to the Amstel we take a short walk through the Jewish quarter? You will see some rare sights." And I answered, "Of course not," and so instead of turning to the left we turned to the right and soon we found ourselves in a world that was as different from the rest of the city as the moon from the sun.

The reason for this strange development in our city was a very simple one. Forty years ago this suburb had been a swamp. Later on it had been drained after a fashion but the houses were still very damp and so they could be rented to no one but the poorest among the poor. Of these there were vast numbers, for ever since we had declared ourselves independent of Spain, our town had been a haven of refuge to tens of thousands of people from every part of the world. Some of them had come because they had heard that we were rich beyond the wildest dreams of avarice and that therefore it was much easier to make a living in Holland than anywhere else. Others belonged to one of the innumerable sects that had sprung up immediately after the Reformation. These had hastened to the

SASKIA (PAINTING)

SASKIA (PAINTING)

SASKIA AS FLORA (PAINTING)

SASKIA (PAINTING)

great and free Republic because they either hoped to escape persecution at the hands of their enemies or (as happened quite as frequently) because they thought that in a country where the magistrates were reported to be very lenient, they might be able to do a little persecuting of their own.

Then during the eighties of the last century, Portugal had been annexed by Spain and of course the first thing King Philip had done was to pass an edict by which he had deprived his newly acquired territory of the only people who ever thought it worth their while to do a little work.

My grandmother used to tell me how in the nineties, when the first of the Portuguese immigrants began to arrive, people used to flock to the shores of the Y whenever it was reported that a ship with fugitives was about to enter the harbor. And she described the terrible conditions on board those vessels, men and women and children all huddled together with their few belongings (they never were given more than twenty-four hours' warning before they were expelled and were obliged to sell their houses and real estate and their merchandise during those hours besides doing their packing) and how quite often when the hatches were opened it was found that half of them had died or were on the point of passing away from lack of food and drink and fresh air and how the survivors would be taken on shore and given milk and bread and were taken to the houses of private citizens to recuperate, among great manifestations of horror and pity.

And my grandfather, with a noble oath, was apt to interrupt her recital at this point to fulminate against the Reverend Clergy who denounced that sort of public charity because the Jews, some fifteen hundred years before, had killed one of their own prophets. "As if," so the old man tried to defend the Sanhedrin, "there has ever been a people that has not murdered its great men!" And then the old lady would bid him remember that he was a Christian and must not say such things and he would roar with laughter and would say, "A Christian? Me? I am a rebel, a good, honest rebel, and I have fought all my life and I have cursed all my life, and I never let a chance go by to get hold of an honest drink or a dishonest woman, and I have killed my enemies and I have loved my friends and I have hated the

Pope of Rome and that bastard Pope of Geneva. Long live the Prince! and when I die, I shall go straight up to God and I shall tell him just what I think of him, and everything he has done to all those I loved, and then undoubtedly I shall go to hell and I shall be a rebel there as I have been on earth, but thank the Lord, it won't be as cold there as among the harp-strumming little angels with their freshly laundered petticoats!"

And then these two charming old people would look at each other with great and sincere affection and being very ancient and rather feeble, they would smile a pleasant smile and before you could count three, they would be fast asleep, holding each other's hand as if they had been married only day before yesterday.

They have been dead now for a good many years and the former immigrants have grown rich and have moved to a more fashionable neighborhood. But every year some new recruits arrive from foreign lands and in the part of the town through which Rembrandt took me, one still hears more Spanish and Portuguese and Yiddish and German than Dutch; the shops still look like bazaars and the food continues to smell like the devil. And as for the women who live there, for reasons unknown to the astonished Gentiles, they still persist in shaving their heads and bedecking themselves with wigs that are as silly as they are unbecoming.

I had rarely visited this Little Jerusalem, for these people have their own doctors (very good ones, too, though they favor some extraordinary remedies) and whenever I had time for a little fresh air, I preferred to go to the harbor and watch the ships come in. But Rembrandt seemed to know this part of the town by heart and was apparently on speaking terms with half the population, for wherever we went, he was greeted with great obsequiousness and caps were taken off to "der Meister" as if he had been a burgomaster or some great official instead of being merely a painter.

But he explained it to me at once. "Don't think for a moment that they are so civil because they have the slightest understanding of my work. I am a good customer. I pay cash whenever I can and I don't bargain more than is necessary. That is all." And then he told me that this ghetto was a veritable treasure-house and contained more color than all the rest of Amsterdam put together.

"You know how it is," he said, stepping aside to avoid the contents of an unmentionable piece of domestic furniture which was being emptied from a second-story window, "our civilization is drab and gray. We seem to regard color as an expression of the sinful flesh. Our men are dressed in black, our women are dressed in black, our children are dressed in black, our churches look like white-washed sepulchers. When we give a party, we all sit around with sour faces until we get very drunk, and then we behave as Jan Steen shows us in his pictures, and a clever boy he is, too, even if he came from Leyden, the same as I do. I wish that I knew something more about my own family. I don't mean my brothers and sisters. They are good people, but they don't interest me, and to tell you the truth, they are pretty commonplace. My grandparents, too, were dull, small tradespeople from a village near Leyden. They had never been anywhere. They had never seen anything. But how about my great-grandparents or still further back? Was there ever an Italian in our family or even a Fleming? For they tell me that the Flemings are much more lively than we are. I bought a picture of Rubens once and it was wonderful! Then again, our religion may have something to do with it. It is hard to tell. I have known a few old people who could remember back to the days before Amsterdam and Leyden had gone reformed. They say that life was much gayer then than now. It was not very pleasant to have quite so many priests and deacons and monks wandering aimlessly through the streets, but if you left them alone, they left you alone and provided you went to mass once in a long while, no questions were asked. To-day, every time you smile, some one comes around to read you a couple of chapters from Job, just as a warning. Of course, in the end, the Church had to go. We are a slow-moving people and we don't think very fast but at least we think. All that had to disappear, but I sometimes wonder whether I would not have been happier if I had been born in Italy."

"Did you ever think of going there?"

"Of course I did. Every youngster who paints thinks of going to Italy at some time in his career."

"But you never went?"

"No. I thought of it seriously in '31. I even talked it over with Jan Lievens when we were studying together in Leyden. We could have got the money too. That malt-mill of my father was not doing badly at all and there were some rich people who were taking an interest in us. But it seemed a waste of time. I was very unhappy in those days and did not think that I would live long. I wanted to use every hour of daylight and could not afford to waste a couple of months trying to get to a place where the daylight probably was not so very different from what it is here. Of course there have been some great masters in Italy. But I can see their work just as well in Amsterdam as in Rome. They bring it to us by the shipload. I have copied quite a number of them. They are being sold as genuine, but, then, our art-dealers would sell pictures by St. Luke himself if they saw a chance to make a profit. Funny that the only apostle who was not a Jew should have done so much to make the Jews rich, with all due respect to my dear cousin Uylenburgh, for he is in the art business too. And so am I, in a way, for a few days ago I let him have another thousand guilders. What he has done with it, I don't know, but I will sell you my claim for half of what I paid!"

While this conversation was going on, we had almost reached the outskirts of the Jewish quarter and I asked Rembrandt whether he hadn't forgotten that he was bound upon some errand.

"I know," he answered, "but that is in still another part of the town. I just instinctively turn to this warren whenever I go out. But I am after something better to-day than I can find here. I think that I have got hold of a genuine bit by Michelangelo. I have only seen it once. Then they asked too much for it. It is a small thing, the head of a child. If they will let me have it for fifteen hundred guilders, I shall take it."

He mentioned the sum as casually as if it had been a couple of shillings. I had heard that he got a great deal more for his portraits than any one else and of course everybody knew that he had married a rich wife, but I was not quite prepared for such nonchalance. The habits of my very simple childhood stuck to me pretty closely and I asked whether that was not a great deal of money for one picture. He seemed a bit surprised at the question but answered that he did not think so.

"I suppose, when you look at it from one point of view, it is a good deal of money. But Michelangelo was a very wonderful painter.

No, I don't think fifteen hundred guilders is too much. I am getting more than that myself."

"For a single picture?"

"Yes, and if you will have patience with me for a few minutes longer, I will show it to you. But first I must go down the cellar for a little light."

The "cellar" to which he referred when we came to it proved to be the basement of the old archery-house on the Singel. The archers had long since been blown out of existence by the musketeers and their clubhouse was now merely a sort of better-class tavern, where one was allowed to look at the pictures of famous old warriors in exchange for a bottle of wine or a few glasses of beer. The top floor of the building was rented to a glove merchant who used the attics to dry his skins and in the basement (as I now saw for the first time) there was an antique shop, run by a Jew whose name was mentioned on a sign outside the door, but it was so covered with dirt which obliging children had smeared upon it that I could not read it. This worthy man was garbed in a long cloak that reached to the floor and beyond, so that he was continually tripping over his own garment. It looked like a relic from the flood and had seen very little water since the day Mount Ararat once more raised its summit from among the waves. As the rooms were very dark and the owner of the premises hid his face behind very black and very bushy whiskers, one was continually bumping up against him and he was forever begging one's pardon in a jargon compounded of two-thirds Portuguese, one-sixth German and one-sixth Dutch with a liberal sprinkling of what I took to be the original language of King David's psalms.

I discovered to my great amazement that Rembrandt not only understood this home-made dialect, but actually spoke it with great fluency, for once the product of Michelangelo's brush had been produced from a corner where the darkness was not only visible but also tangible, he addressed himself to the hirsute dealer in such an eloquent mixture of all the less current vituperations of the different tongues just enumerated, that I was quite sure the two men must come to blows at any moment, in which case I decided that I would not take sides, but would make for the exit with all possible speed.

But nothing happened. On the contrary, after half an hour's animated conversation, during which (as far as I was able to comprehend) frequent references were made to the immediate ancestors of the contending parties, they separated in the best of spirits. Rembrandt had succeeded in forcing the price down by one hundred florins. But the art-dealer on his side had persuaded him to buy the frame, which he swore was worth two hundred guilders, but which he would let him have for half the amount. The whole transaction therefore, as far as I could see, remained *in statu quo ante*. Each party to the deal, however, seemed profoundly convinced that he had got the better of his opponent. Wherefore everybody was happy and we parted with mutual expressions of esteem and a promise to return as soon as there was another bargain to be had.

The fresh air was pleasant after this entrance to purgatory. I awaited some explanation of the mysterious proceedings that had taken place in the catacombs of art, and I got one.

"I wanted that picture," Rembrandt confessed, "and I wanted it badly. The old Jew asked too much. I got it for a hundred guilders less."

"But the frame! How about that frame? He charged you a hundred guilders for it."

The poor painter looked puzzled, like a child that has been caught in some foolish expenditure of a hard-earned stiver. But he quickly recovered. "After all," he asked in a somewhat querulous tone, as if I had unjustly accused him of wasting his son's patrimony, "what is the money for in this world of ours except to spend it? Fifteen hundred guilders is rather a large sum. But next week, next month, at the very least, I shall have eighteen hundred florins coming in for some work I have just finished. And I did want that painting and I wanted it badly!"

With which irrefutable piece of logic we retraced our steps whence we had come, crossed the Rokin and then turned to the right until we reached the Amstel. In the olden days, before the great expansion that followed in the wake of our declaration of independence, this had been the outer limit of the city's territory. There had been only a few scattered houses along the banks of the stream (it really was a canal, but our poets loved to compare it to the Tiber or the Seine or the Thames) and the gardens and open spaces had been much in demand by the archers of the old militia companies who used to come together here on Sunday afternoons for target practice.

During the latter half of the fifteenth century, when all the little cities of our country fought each other (just as the nations nowadays are forever making war upon their neighbors) a heavy bulwark had been erected at this point. The name of one enormous stone tower which still stood intact and was called "Swijght-Utrecht" or "Keep-Quiet-Utrecht," showed only too clearly from what side danger had threatened our forefathers. The Bishop of Utrecht was no longer a menace for he had ceased to exist shortly after the construction of this dungeon and the walls now extended far beyond the other side of the Amstel. But the brick monster continued to stand where it had been built in the year 1482. But it was now a perfectly peaceful part of the famous Kloveniersdoelen, the meeting-place and club-house of the culverin-carrying town companies which had succeeded the archers of medieval fame as soon as gunpowder had been invented.

During the great war of independence, those town companies had rendered the most signal services. Without them we never would have been able to gain our freedom, for the German and Swiss and English mercenaries whom we hired to fight for us from time to time were professionals who had nothing much to gain and everything to lose and in nine cases out of ten they disappeared when the fighting began and did not return until the signal had been given to begin looting.

Of course twenty years ago, when all those things I am here writing down happened, there was no longer a single enemy within a hundred miles of Amsterdam, except an occasional prisoner of war, brought in by the fleet. But every self-respecting young man thought it his duty to join one of the town companies and devote some of his spare time to the practice of arms. That many of those militia regiments were rapidly degenerating into mere social organizations, without the slightest military ambition or strategic value, was becoming more evident almost every day. But such a development seems inevitable (if the history I have read means anything at all, which I sometimes doubt) and in order to be perfectly fair, I ought to state that several crack companies took their duties just as seriously as their fathers and grandfathers had done before them and certainly in the year 1650 when William II made his dastardly attack upon our beloved city, they proved that they were fully able to handle the situation and forced the foolish princeling to return whence he had come with no other glory than a pair of wet feet. And during the early forties (and please remember that I am telling you about certain events that happened in the year 1642 and therefore a very long time ago) there was a sudden return of interest in the noble profession of arms.

The different companies were trying hard to attract desirable recruits and all the social and economic advantages of associating one's self with this or that or the other captain were carefully enumerated and made a subject of conversation in all of the better-class taverns. (The more notorious dram-shops were equally interested, but from a somewhat different angle, as the town militia was also the town police and the sworn enemy of all lawbreakers and rioters.)

Now since the beginning of time, it has been the proud privilege of the children of Mars to be more resplendent in their outer raiment than ordinary citizens, who follow a peaceful if more lucrative and useful profession. Nature, when she began her interesting task, bestowed her gifts of beauty and attractiveness almost exclusively upon the male members of the different sorts of animals. I do not claim that I have an inner knowledge of her secret intentions, but she probably thought that it would be better for the future development of her menagerie if the males should be more attractive than the females and if the competition for favors should not come too exclusively from one side. But when she finally came to the human race, she had either grown tired or had become discouraged, for she changed her policy completely and arranged things in such a way that among us mortals the woman should be the attractive member of society, while the man might look like anything or nothing at all. The women of course have made the best of their advantage while we poor men are still trying (though mostly in vain) to find some compromise by which we would be able to make ourselves a little less painfully plain than we were apparently meant to be. Scholars and other learned doctors put on beautiful silken garments whenever they can find an excuse for doing so. Judges affect scarlet and ermine. I have never seen a priest of the old church in his official garments, for they are not allowed in our city, but from the stories of my grandmother, I judge that the multi-colored coat of Joseph was as nothing compared to an archbishop or a cardinal in full canonicals. That old church, by the way, was very wise in more ways than one and it recognized the need of the average human being to revel in color once in a while by providing a special season when every clod-hopper and lout was allowed to dress up like a royal duke and strut about like a lovesick peacock.

But the soldiers have understood the value of a gaudy appearance better than any one else. With them, it probably was a matter of necessity. Their profession, except in times of peace, offered few advantages. Endless marches along hot and dusty roads, bad sleeping-quarters, poor food and the danger every moment of losing an arm or a leg or getting a ball through one's brain. There had to be some compensation to attract the unwary and beguile the simple-minded into taking the king's shilling.

Of course this could have been accomplished by raising the men's wages, but then the officers no longer would have been able to regard their regiments as profitable sources of revenue and they would have asked for better pay for themselves and all the royal treasuries of Europe would have gone bankrupt. Also as an inducement to enlisting discipline might have been slightly relaxed and there might have been a little less flogging and hanging, but this would have been impossible in view of the sort of people who took most readily to the business of organized murder. The easiest way out was to allow these honorable jail-birds and paupers (and when I call them that I surely offer no insult to the average members of a regiment of mercenaries) to garb themselves as if they were really fine fellows, instead of being mere deplorable cannon-fodder. This gave them a feeling of superiority and the average man will go through almost any hardships and will suffer every form of indignity and degradation if in the end he is allowed to feel himself (if only for a moment) superior to his fellow-beings.

This incidentally accounts for the noble behavior of so many criminals on the scaffold. By assuming an attitude of noble resignation, they place themselves hand and foot above the mob of jeering hoodlums who surround the gallows and they jump off the ladder, saying to themselves, "Ah, what a fine fellow I am, compared to this rabble!" It also accounts for the readiness of hundreds of thousands of poor yokels who leave their plows and the simple pleasures of an humble rustic life to prance about dressed in plumes and gold braid for one hour each day, though they are forced to obey the whims of a drunken and bullying drill-sergeant for the other twenty-three.

I hope that all my medical diagnoses may be as correct as this estimate of the motives that inspired the brave heroes who used to strut down our streets whenever we were obliged to hire extra troops for our operations against the Spaniards. It will be understood that I am not now talking of the ordinary citizen who, exasperated by the endless hangings and quarterings of our dear Liege Lord, finally rose in open rebellion.

They fought because they had to, just as they would go and work on the dikes whenever their city was threatened by floods. It was a matter of live or die and quite naturally they preferred to take a chance at living, even if they had to expose themselves to a little occasional dying in order to accomplish this very sensible purpose. But there was very little outer glory connected with their martial careers. I am too young to have known many of these men myself, but I have seen their pictures, honest, simple citizens, butchers and bakers and shipowners with honest, plain faces and great big hands that could cleave an ox or pull a sail as well as the best of them. Their officers would perhaps wear an orange scarf to set them apart from the rest of their men, but that would be the only bit of color in the whole picture.

But to-day, whenever a company sallies forth to guard a gate that really needs no guarding, or patrol a wall that is as safe as my own back yard, both the common soldiers and the lieutenants and captains resemble warships on parade. They have plumes on their hats and gold braid on their coats and they wrap themselves up in yards and yards of colored scarfs and every sixth man waves a flag that is as big as a house and the servant girls and the scullery maids leave their kitchens to stare at these gallant heroes and to admire them and to giggle at them and the poor fools feel flattered by these basement attentions and spend a night shivering in a guard-house (instead of snoring comfortably by the side of their spouses) and they will repeat the performance next week and week after and week after merely for this short period of popular glory. And when they get themselves painted, they pose around a table that looks as if great King Louis of France were entertaining the Ambassador from the Republic of Venice, and they are all of them dressed up as if they were the keepers of the harem of the Grand Padisha of Turkey and they dine on dishes that our grandfathers would have regarded as the last word in useless luxury and altogether they disport themselves as if they were the sort of young British lords who once in a while honor our city with their visit and they tell me that the artists have to send to Paris to get some of the gilt that has to be laid on the swords and arquebuses.

All of which many and varied meditations passed rapidly through my brain as we were walking in the general direction of the Kloveniersdoelen, for I knew that it was used as a meeting place by some of the smartest regiments and that the captains' rooms were filled with pictures by van der Helst and Govaert Flinck and Claes Elias and I feared that Rembrandt, having started the day bright and early by buying himself a genuine Michelangelo, might wind up the afternoon by dragging me through one of those things I dread most of all—a picture gallery.

And when he stood in front of the entrance-gate and he said: "Let us go in here a moment," the worst of my fears was about to be realized. These buildings had been added to so often and they were by now composed of so many remnants of walls and towers, bits of old walls and decapitated pieces of even older private houses, that one almost needed a guide to find one's way. But Rembrandt opened the door of the tap-room (no military club-house has ever been perfect without a well-provided bar) and said: "It has been quite a walk. You will like a glass of beer. I am not a member of this honorable guild, but I have worked here on and off for quite a long time and they let me use their common-room. Come in."

We sat down and Rembrandt ordered two mugs of beer. Then he said: "You must be hungry! You are not? Do you mind if I eat something? The meals at home have become a little sketchy since Saskia was taken sick, and I have had nothing all day and so if you will pardon me . . ." and he asked that they bring him a plate of fried eggs and one of fresh herring and some bread and he went after the food with a most excellent appetite and between the beer and the fish he told me why he had brought me there.

"I don't want to talk about myself," he said, "but these last four years have been rather lonely and I have had a pretty hard struggle, what with an ailing wife, a pretty difficult family-in-law, a new house which is really much too big and expensive for me, and a few other little items with which I shan't bother you, as you probably have troubles enough of your own. But I shall tell you something and then you will know what is going to happen. It is always pleasant to be on the inside of things. It makes one feel that one really is somebody. And something very interesting is going to happen here soon. Are you sure you don't want any of this herring? It is exceedingly good. But never mind, and here is my story.

"You know that I come from very simple folk. And you know how they look upon such things in our Republic. In Flanders, they think so much of Rubens that they make him an ambassador. They tell me there is a man in Spain by the name of Velasquez who is said to be the greatest painter that ever lived. I have never seen anything he did, but I have heard that he can make an empty room look really like an empty room and that is the hardest thing of all. I may learn to do that too, but it will take me another twenty years of practice. But I hear that this Don Diego Velasquez is held in such great esteem that he is allowed to sit in the presence of the King, when all other courtiers, even the highest nobles in the land, must stand and do homage. And when he is in Rome, the Pope is happy to receive him and invite him to live in the private villa of the Medici family.

"Well, we can't all be the same in this world and every country handles such matters according to its own notions of what is right and suitable and what is not. Here people look upon an artist as a better-class laboring man. Some of us make money. None of us are rich, but some of us get fairly good wages, not any better than those which a dike-worker or a book-keeper or a baker's assistant makes with much less trouble. And so our parents don't mind and are rather proud of their little boy who is sometimes allowed to associate with gentlemen, that is, when he is allowed to paint their portraits, though of course they always fear that in the end he will share the fate of Roghman or old Hercules Seghers and die in the alms-house or break his neck in a grog-shop.

"That these poor fellows came to such an end because their neighbors were too dull to appreciate them, that never seems to dawn upon them. They think it a good joke that Hercules finally had to paint his pictures on his old shirts and the back of his old breeches and had to sell his etchings to the butchers of the Rokin for wrapping-paper. 'My steak came this morning, packed in Tobias and the Angel,' says one, and his friend roars with laughter and answers: 'I bought a landscape the other day, paid five guilders for it—it was on a piece of the old man's pants. Ha! ha! ha!' And they go and put a thousand or ten thousand guilders in a 'sure' investment that some one sells them on the say-so of his grandfather who knew a man who had met a Spaniard or a Pole who had told him that he had heard from some one, whose name he could not remember, that it was a good thing.

"You know this to be so and I know it to be so and all of us know it to be so, but I for one had seen enough of poverty not to want any more of it than I had to have. Some people can stand misery better than others. I loved old Seghers. He was a great man. Hercules has forgotten more about painting and etching than most of us will ever know. I was a youngster and he was quite an old man when I first came to Amsterdam and I did not see him often. But one night I went to his place with a few friends. A bare room with a horrible-looking woman in one corner doing something to a large stone jar filled with vegetables. She seemed to be his wife. Half a dozen dirty children on the floor and the old man with a pleasant bun on, completely oblivious of the mess around him, working at a storm, as fine a piece of painting as I have ever seen. He had fastened it against the wall with two nails and he stood in front of it. The wife wanted to know what we had come for and asked me whether we were sheriffs.

"That afternoon, the Jew with whom he did business had brought him back his last etching, the finest piece of work he had ever done. Sorry, but he could not sell it. And Hercules had taken a copper file and had cut the plate into four pieces because he could not afford a new one and must work. He was crazy with work. He worked morning, noon and night. They say he was a drunkard. Well, drunken people don't paint the sort of pictures he did. But sometimes it got to be too much for him and then he would take a glass or two, just enough not to hear the bawling wife and the howling infants.

"That afternoon, it seemed, while she had gone out to pawn his easel, he had stolen the last sheet out of the children's bed and had cut it up to be used as canvas. I shall spare you the rest. I was not very rich then and, anyway, he had nothing for sale as everything had been either pawned or had been bartered away for butter and eggs and milk for the children. Afterwards, with a great deal of trouble, I got hold of six of his pictures. You may have seen them in my house. One of them is hanging in the front hall and one in the side room and a few others in the little alcove behind the side room. I keep them all over the house, in the first place because I like them immensely and in the second place because they are a constant reminder. They take me back to the day when I stood in Seghers' stable (it really wasn't a house he was living in) and said to myself: 'Rembrandt, my boy, you are a good deal of a dreamer and you are apt to do foolish things. Well, do all the foolish things you want, but see that you get paid well in the meantime. A plumber and a copper-smith get paid for what they do. See to it that you get paid too.'

"Besides, I need a lot of money. I like color around me. I need it. I would have died in a place like that of Hercules in less than a week. I want to buy things. I hate haggling. I hate to beat old Jacob down for a couple of guilders. And when I go to an auction and see something I would like for my collection, I go ahead and let them push up the price and I know that in the end I will probably pay more than the thing is worth, but I have to have it, and that is all, for when I want something, I want it then and there and not next week or a year later. I must be able to make experiments if I am to do good work. Saskia is a lovely woman. You ought to have seen her a couple of years ago when she was still a girl and before she got so sick. But I must try her out, test her, so to speak, see what is in her, dress her up in silks and satins and hang pearls on her and rubies, paint her a hundred different ways. Poor child, I don't think she always enjoyed it. But she was very good-natured about it. I needed that sort of foolishness to find out what I could do and she said yes. She is really very sweet. She always says yes and I suppose at times I am very unreasonable. All that is, however, beside the point and I will tell you what I am going to do. Want to smoke?"

Rembrandt van Rijn

PORTRAIT OF CONSTANTIJN HUYGENS (PAINTING)

The herring was gone and the fried eggs were gone and the beer was gone and I said: "Yes, I would enjoy a pipe." And so Rembrandt ordered two fresh mugs and two pipes of tobacco and then he leaned his elbows on the table and leaned over to me and went on: "You know that I have been doing a great deal of portrait work. I could give you names, but they are neither here nor there. People came to me to sit for their portraits. I painted them and they paid me four or five and sometimes even six hundred guilders. I don't know why. Even van der Helst never got more than that amount for a picture as big as a house with a dozen or twenty figures and that meant a lot more work than I had to do, for each one of those twenty fools would think that he was the handsomest of the crowd and would insist upon being done in great detail. So you see I was about the only one who had no kick coming. I was even asked to do some pictures for the Prince. I don't think he liked them any too well for I believe that His Highness is more interested in the pretty ladies of Jake Jordaens than in religious subjects and I hear that he is going to build himself a new palace in the woods and that he is going to use no one but Flemish painters. But that may be just studio gossip. You know how much there is of that nowadays and I finally got paid, though I had the devil's own time collecting and I would never have got a penny if it had not been that My Lord Huygens, who thinks all the world of my work, had got the bills approved.

"But what I mean is this: everybody had heard of me and it became the fashion for rich people to have themselves painted by me.

" 'Very well,' I used to say to myself, 'I shall paint you and sometimes I shall even paint you as you want to be painted.'

"For I needed the money. Our first child was coming. There was the new house into which I wanted to move (I had to mortgage it rather heavily) and there were all the other things I wanted. People used to say that I was a lucky devil because I had married a rich wife. But Saskia was not rich. There were nine children and old Uylenburgh had been too busy with politics to pay much attention to his estate. I have never seen him, for he died some eight years before I met my wife.

"The old fellow was quite a famous character. You must have heard of him. He was dining with Prince William the day he was called away from the table and was shot by what's-his-name, that friend of the Jesuits whom King Philip hired to murder him. Then he was burgomaster of Leeuwarden and sheriff but he was so busy with public affairs he had very little time to look after his own interests.

"When he died, each of the children was supposed to get about forty thousand guilders. Quite a sum, I grant you, and my neighbors of course added an extra couple of zeros and made it four hundred

PORTRAIT OF A JEW (PAINTING)

PORTRAIT OF JAN SIX (PAINTING)

thousand. They might have made it forty million florins, for all the actual cash we ever saw. For everything was invested in farms and houses and as soon as we wanted to divide the estate, the farms could not be rented and the houses could not be sold. And of course I am living here in Amsterdam and the other heirs are living in Friesland, a couple of days away.

"Did you ever have anything to do with Frisians? A strange race. The most obstinate and pig-headed people there are in the world. And stingy! My God! Only a couple of years ago I had to go to law to get a few thousand guilders that an aunt had left her in '34. Six whole years of waiting. When we finally got it, the other heirs tried to cheat us out of the interest—out of six years' accumulated interest—and I had to hire a lawyer and spend two hundred guilders on fees before my wife could pry a penny loose from those dear relatives of hers.

"They are a nice tribe! They kiss every stiver a dozen times before they spend it and when I made a lot of money painting portraits and bought a few pictures and statues and things (just because I liked them, and after all, it was my money I spent and not theirs, so why should they worry?) they must jabber to all the neighbors about the 'scandalous way in which I was squandering Saskia's patrimony' and I had to go to law once more and sue them for libel and then they perjured themselves all over the place and the judge said that he could not do anything and threw the case out of court.

"Did that stop them? Of course not. They went right on and I had to bring suit once more in Friesland before I heard the last of this famous 'squandering of my wife's patrimony.' Squandering, indeed! When I need thirteen thousand guilders cash to buy the house in the Breestraat, I have to give notes that will keep me busy for the rest of my days. Do you think I would have done that if I could have laid my hands on a little cash? No, that story of the poor painter and the rich wife is so much moonshine. We are not poor, and I have enough to keep living the way I want to live, but I intend to be careful.

"Only you know how it is! I get interested in a subject. I see or rather I feel a lot of things others don't see or don't feel. I put them into my picture and the man who sat for his portrait and considered himself a fine fellow gets angry, says the likeness is not there or I have given him a look in his eyes that will prove to his neighbors that he is a miser or mean to his wife, and in the end he either refuses the picture or he will offer to pay me half of what he promised.

"This won't do, for just now I am not only painting for the sake of my 'art'—whatever that may mean—though you will hear a lot about it if to-night you will go to the Dirty Towel or the Dark Cellar and will listen to the brethren of the brush who come together there every evening to drink their beer and talk of their plans. No, just now I want to make all the money I can. I have got to pay for that house and Saskia will probably be sick for quite a long time and the boy will have to go to a good school and to the University afterwards.

"Besides you know how it is; there exists a fashion in portrait-painters as well as a fashion in women's clothes. I have been the fashion now for several years and I know what many people are hoping to say soon: 'Oh, yes, that man van Rijn! He was quite good a little while ago, but he has lost something of his old—well, what shall we call it?—of his old pep and stamina.' And what they mean of course is that I am beginning to paint them as they are and no longer as they want to think that they are and now I will show you— Hey there, Hendrick, bring me the bill for what we have had. Thank you!—I shall now take you upstairs, and I shall show you."

Hendrick dutifully brought the bill, observed that it was remarkably good weather for the time of year (since it had not rained for almost three entire days), pocketed the change without Rembrandt paying the slightest attention to him, and bowed us out of the door. We then turned towards the left, walked up two flights of broad and comfortable stairs and came into a large room which was used as an assembly hall whenever some important matter made it necessary to call the entire company together. It was quite dark when we entered. The high windows were covered with green baize curtains. On the walls I vaguely noticed one or two pictures—large pictures— the usual company-portraits that one would expect to find in such places. Then, when my eyes got accustomed to the dim light I saw that at the other end of the hall there was a vast wooden structure, supporting an enormous canvas, the most gigantic picture I had ever seen, but what it was meant to represent I could not make out.

Suddenly Rembrandt pulled the curtains aside and the room was flooded with brilliant sunlight and I suffered a physical shock, as if I had been struck in the face by a palette full of the richest colors ever devised by the hand of man. Homer, who undoubtedly was the greatest master of the word that ever lived, might have been able to revaluate an impression like that into terms of words. Dante would have mumbled something divine but obscure. Montaigne would have smiled and kept silent, but I, being only a humble leech, and a simple Hollander, could only say one word: "Damnation!"

Whereupon Rembrandt, who was not given much to outward manifestations of affection, threw both his arms around me and shouted: "Splendid! For now at least I know that one person has understood what I meant to do."

And then he pulled a heavy bench in front of the picture, once more closed the curtains that were furthest away from the picture (thereby fairly forcing the figure in white in the center of the painting to march right out of the frame), made me sit down, himself sat down with his elbows on his knees, rested his chin in the palms of his hands (a favorite position of his whenever he was thinking very hard) and said:

"Now you know why I dragged you up here. This is my chance! My great chance! It came to me by accident. The company of Captain Banning Cocq was going to have its portrait done. First they talked of van der Helst doing it and then some one wanted Flinck and some others wanted some one else again but one day My Lord of Purmerend came to me and said he had seen the portrait I had done of the mother of Jan Six and the one of Dominie Anslo and his wife and he liked the way in which I had arranged the good dominie and his wife, with the books on the table and the man talking to the woman—not two people just sitting, but a husband and wife really talking to each other and being interested too in what was being said —and he had had an idea. His company wanted to have its picture painted. Most of the men wanted the usual thing—soldiers and officers all grouped around a table with a couple of pewter plates filled with dead oysters and a lot of wine bottles—everybody looking

PORTRAIT OF THE MENNONITE MINISTER ANSLO AND HIS WIFE (PAINTING)

very proud and very brave and slightly the worse for having eaten so much. What he wanted to know—hadn't this sort of thing been done a little too often? Wasn't there some other way in which such a picture could be painted?

"Well, at first I was a little frightened by the idea. For I had never tried my hand at large groups of people. But then I said that I would try if he gave me a few days to think it over. He answered that he would be delighted, and would I come and see him when I was ready.

"So I set to work, but most of the sketches I did not like at all and I threw them away. And then suddenly it came to me, as I told you coming up here, that those regiments of volunteers don't mean so very much in our day. As a rule they are just an excuse for pleasant social gatherings. But that is because we are living in times of peace. Probably if there were another war— (Of course I know we are still at war with Spain, but who cares? The Spaniards are broke and we are rich and we can hire all the men in the whole wide world and let them do our fighting for us.) If there were another war they would once more amount to something. And there is a very definite ideal hidden somewhere in the idea of an 'armed citizenry.'

"It is easy to poke fun at those pompous house-painters and gin-distillers and fishmongers marching forth in plumes and feathers, toting heavy swords and lances and carrying gigantic arquebuses and powder-horns as if they were going to drive the Turks out of Europe when all of us know that they are going to spend the greater part of the night throwing dice in the guard-house and drinking small beer for no more serious purpose than to prevent the peasant women from Buiksloot and the Beemster from smuggling their butter and eggs and chickens past the revenue officer at the city gate.

"But that is only part of the story and by no means the most interesting part. Those men are the sons and the grandchildren of just such house-painters and gin-distillers and fish-dealers as got hanged and burned and broken on the wheel, fighting for something that was on their conscience, something that had nothing at all to do with selling gin or codfish or painting houses, for God knows they could have done that just as well while they were being ruled by a king as while they were being ruled by Their Lordships of the Town Hall. There was something in them somewhere, that made them rather fine and noble. Well, if it was there, I was going to find it and paint it.

"And so I went to see My Lord of Purmerend one evening in his house on the Singel (you know the big one with the dolphin which de Keyser built originally for his father-in-law, the old burgomaster) and he was most kind to me and even introduced me to his family and then we sat in his office and I took some paper (I can't talk without drawing at the same time) and I explained to him what I wanted to do—paint him and his men just as they were leaving the arsenal for a turn of duty—everything still in great disorder, one old fellow beating the alarm and some of the soldiers taking down their pikes and others getting their guns ready and little boys and little girls getting out from underneath the feet of the men (there are always a couple of kids running around on such occasions) and the inevitable dog that is present at every parade and always in the midst of it and one man who is The Leader—one man who has himself in hand and who knows what he is doing, who is quietly going ahead because he realizes that the others will follow no matter what he does.

"I am not quite sure that I am making myself clear. But you told me that you had liked my picture of Nicolaes Tulp. Well, in that case I did not paint a learned doctor giving a lesson in anatomy. I tried to make it mean something a little more general—a little more abstract, if you allow me to use one of the big words of your French friend, the Count. I tried to paint science, rather than a group of scientists. Just as here I have done my best to give one an impression of 'civic duty' rather than merely show them a number of inconsequential citizens doing their own little particular duties. Do you follow me?"

I did follow him. I followed him so well that for a moment I could say nothing in reply. It is strange that anything that is really "perfect" affects me that way. Most people when they see a perfect sunset or hear a perfect song or see a perfectly beautiful woman, grow eloquent—shout—wave their arms—climb on chairs—feel that they must do something, anything at all, to let the world know how deeply they have been impressed.

With me, it works the other way.

I grow absolutely dumb and can't say a word.

If anybody interrupts my gloomy meditation, I will curse him as if I were the stevedore of some Indiaman who had slipped on the gangplank and had dropped a bale of rice on his own feet. Then I fall back into that utter silence of desperation which overtakes me whenever I happen to find myself face to face with something really beautiful and only after hours of silent wandering along the back streets or sitting alone in a darkened room, am I able to regain my normal composure.

But Rembrandt, who was not always the most tactful of men and apt to be rather brusque and short-tempered, seemed to understand what had happened to me, for he found an excuse to bid me farewell.

"It is getting late," he said. "I just heard the chimes play and I think the clock struck six. I shall run back home and see how poor Saskia is faring. I am sorry that I have taken so much of your time, but

Rembrandt van Rijn

now you will understand why I brought you here. I had to do something really big, something tremendous, to make the people see what I can accomplish when they give me free rein. And this picture will do it. The world will hear about the trick. I shall have more customers than ever. I shall be able to make experiments. I shall have greater freedom than ever before and all through this picture, for, mark my words, it will make people talk."

THE ANATOMY LESSON OF PROFESSOR NICOLAES TULP, DETAIL (PAINTING)

DETAIL FROM THE "HUNDRED-GUILDER PRINT" (ETCHING)

Chapter 7

AND AS A RESULT OF THIS PICTURE REMBRANDT
BECOMES THE JOKE OF AMSTERDAM

REMBRANDT IN A CAP,
LAUGHING (ETCHING)

R EMBRANDT was right.
People talked about his picture. As a matter of fact, they have not stopped talking yet.

The first result of this "new departure in artistic arrangement," of this attempt "to put an idea into colors" and "translate an emotion into lights and shades" was a gigantic roar of laughter. The members of Captain Cocq's company started it. Their wives and children laughed next. Then their sweethearts laughed. Soon the whole town laughed and then quite suddenly the victims of this "unseemly hoax" ceased to be quite as hilarious as they had been in the beginning. For a joke could be carried too far and they were the ones who would have to pay, weren't they? And pay for what? That is what they asked each other and asked all those willing to listen.

Pay a hundred or two hundred guilders apiece for the privilege of having the back of their heads shown or their feet or one hand or one shoulder?

Pay a hundred or two hundred guilders for the honor of being a dim, unrecognizable figure, amidst a number of dim, unrecognizable figures in the dark recesses of an enormous gate, "a piece of animated shade," as one funny observer remarked, while others who had not paid a penny more had been placed right in the center of the stage and in the full light of day?

What had that poor fool tried to do, anyhow?

What had he been thinking of while he was painting this picture?

Surely one man's money was as good as the next!

And when one had paid one's share, one was entitled to as good treatment as one's neighbor. This business of showing favors would never do. Not if they, the soldiers, knew anything about it. They were not such simpletons as this stranger seemed to think. There had been pictures of boards of regents and military companies in Amsterdam long before this smart young man had left his native mill in the distant town of Leyden to come and tell the benighted people of the metropolis how (in his opinion) the thing ought to be done. All he had to do, if he really cared to find out (but he probably thought that he knew better than any one else), was to pay a visit to the Town Hall or to the orphan asylums or to any of the guild houses. He would then see what the customers who paid him their hard-earned guilders had a right to expect from the artist they employed, and so on and so forth, with a great deal of talk of "going to law about it" and downright refusals to pay money for value not received.

But it was not only the rabble in the street who talked that way. Men and women who surely ought to have known better joined in the chorus of abuse. Vondel, our great poet, driven to despair by those bright peasant lads who, disguised as ministers of the Gospel and shepherds of the human soul, were every whit as narrow-minded and intolerant as the worst of the ancient Inquisitors, had bade farewell to the Calvinist community a year or so before and had boldly proclaimed his return to the church of his fathers. I can't exactly say that his friends were pleased. My Lord Hooft of Muiden bade him never darken his door again. That seemed rather superfluous and I made bold to tell him so one day when he had asked Jean-Louys and myself to visit him at his charming old castle where he kept open house over the week-end and with a rare gift for the social amenities of life entertained poets and painters and musicians without every letting them fly at each other's throats.

"How happens it," I asked him, "that you, My Lord, a true liberal in mind and thought and act, now take the side of those who think a man's conduct should be judged by the religious company he keeps?"

"Stuff and nonsense!" he replied. "I got irritated because that foolish old poet made such a great to-do about his so-called conversion. Calvinism is a curse. I agree with him fully. It is a curse which eventually will destroy us. But the Roman creed that went before was just as bad. Neither of them ever seemed to have heard of a certain Jesus of Nazareth who bade us love each other and be of good will to our neighbors. Now I can understand a man who comes to me and says: 'Sir, I have the measles. I don't like them. And so I want to go ahead and be cured.' But I can't follow him when he whines: 'I have got the measles, I don't like them and therefore I think that I will exchange them for the smallpox.' "

That being more or less the attitude of most of his former friends, the poor fellow, who besides had just lost his wife and had found himself all alone in the world with a good-for-nothing scoundrel of a son, began to growl and snarl at everybody and everything, as an outlet for his own misery and self-reproach. Besides, like so many of his kind, the poor poet was of a very jealous disposition, and being some twenty years older than Rembrandt, he had never forgiven him that he, the upstart, had gained fame and riches, lived in a noble mansion and had married a beautiful woman, while he, the modern rejuvenated Homer, the divinely inspired bard, acclaimed by all the world as the greatest word-painter of modern times, was obliged to sell stockings for a living. He now saw his chance and composed a ditty in which Rembrandt's work was compared with that of his rival, Govaert Flinck (a perfectly competent manufacturer of "official" pictures, but without the slightest touch of originality) and was of course found wanting on account of its "artificial gloom and its pedantic use of shadows and half lights" and he wound up by dubbing the former "the Prince of Darkness," a witticism that stuck to Rembrandt for all the rest of his days.

The other painters, also dearly loving a colleague who had done pretty well in a worldly sense, were not slow to catch up with the general chorus of disapproval. They talked of their poor, misguided friend, who seemed to have shot his bolt in this latest picture and let it be known that they had of course always thought him a great man, but that it was a pity he had reached the limits of his art at such a comparatively tender age. Still others, especially the art-dealers with whom Rembrandt had refused to do business, were even more to the point.

"The temporary infatuation of the public, which had made this eccentric young man the fashionable painter of the hour, has now probably reached its end," was one of their more good-natured comments. While in their less guarded moments, they simply shouted: "Another bubble that has burst!" and rubbed their hands in anticipatory glee.

Why go on with this sad recital of human stupidity?

My wise doctor-friend, who three thousand years or so ago wrote that very wise book which we call "Ecclesiastes," summed it all up in the words: "Vanity of vanities, all is vanity."

Here was a man who had dared to think a new thought and tell a new truth. Proudly he had turned to his fellow men saying these noble words: "Behold! a little yellow and a little black and a little green and ocher and red and presto! I change them into an Idea." And the Philistines had loudly guffawed, had poked each other in the ribs and had shouted: "The clown! The mountebank! He wants to show us! Teach us! Tell us! As if we were not bright enough to know what we want for ourselves!"

And from that moment on, Rembrandt was doomed.

He might have returned to fame at some royal court, and indeed, it would have been better if right then and there he had moved to England or France. But in a Republic, such a thing is impossible. He had set himself up to be better than his neighbors. There was only one answer—death and oblivion.

The only question was: How long would it take the pack to get and devour him?

SKETCH (DRAWING)

Chapter 8

REMBRANDT MEETS MY FRIENDS AND SASKIA
GROWS WEAKER

MOTHER AND CHILD (DRAWING)

THE meeting between Rembrandt and my friends took place much sooner than I had expected and this is the way it came about.

A couple of times a week I would go to the painter's house and we would spend the evening playing backgammon. I don't know whether anybody still takes an interest in this game, but thirty years ago it was quite popular.

Saskia had now reached the stage where she could no longer leave her bed and Rembrandt used to sit by her side and read to her from the Bible. For she no longer expected to get better. The optimism of the first four months had been replaced by a profound and very pathetic form of melancholia. She did not complain. She did not rage against her fate, as so many of her fellow-sufferers do. She had resigned herself to the idea that she must die young and must leave her child to the care of strangers. She was almost too weak to care very much, but she sometimes complained that it lasted so long. She was tired. She was most dreadfully tired and she wanted to go to sleep, but she was too tired to come to rest and she used to beg me to give her something that would make her forget, at least for a short while, and I sometimes let her have a little theriaca, but that compound seemed to have little effect upon

81

her and the poor girl would lie tossing in her bed all day and all night long, her cheeks flushed and her lovely eyes wide open—a picture of abject misery and yet there was nothing that we could do for her except sometimes read to her from those chapters in the New Testament which she remembered from her childhood and which brought back the days of her youth when she had been as strong and well as the best of them.

After an hour or so, however, even listening to the quiet voice of her husband would exhaust her and she would whisper to him and ask him to cease. But at the same time she would beg not to be left alone.

"I shall be alone so long," she once said to me with a little smile. "I shall be alone so long before either Rembrandt or the boy joins me. I want their company every minute of both day and night as long as I can still have it."

And so every evening the baby's cradle was carried to one corner of the room (I insisted that the child be placed as far away from the mother as possible on account of the danger of contagion) and Rembrandt would light the candles on the table that had been pushed against the wall, so that the light would not disturb the patient and he would read to her for an hour or so, until she showed signs of exhaustion and then he would occupy himself quietly with his own business. He would sharpen a steel needle for his dry-points or he would examine a plate and correct some corner that had not come out as he wished or he would sign the pictures his pupils had printed that day in the little alcove upstairs. But his eyes were not very strong, he had suffered slightly from near-sightedness since early childhood and drawing or etching by candle-light would give him a stinging pain right behind his eye-balls, and so whenever I could join him for a game of backgammon he would be most grateful to me and he would go down into his cellar and return with a bottle of a very wonderful Rhenish wine which was called "The Milk of Our Lady" and which most certainly was worthy of that name.

But after a short time, the clicking of the dice as we threw them upon the boards got to be too exhausting for Saskia. We then threw them upon a heavy wad of fine muslin, the muslin he used to wipe his plates with, but even then sometimes one die would slightly touch another and the patient invariably complained that the noise sent shivers all through her and as we could not talk either, and neither of us had the slightest liking for cards, we were hard put to it to find some way of passing the evening without just sitting and staring at each other.

Then one day I happened to mention to Rembrandt that I had just learned a new game from Jean-Louys which was very interesting and took a considerable amount of thought and foresight and which was called "chess" and which was so old that some people said it had been played by the heroes outside of Troy and which originally had been a war game, devised for the amusement of the Shahs of Persia, who used to be great potentates and who had ruled Asia until great Alexander had come and had deprived them of their power and had taken away their land to give it to his own generals.

The very name, calling forth visions of Oriental tyrants with beautiful diamond-studded turbans, lying in tapestried tents in the heart of some wind-swept desert, surrounded by dashing knights and armor-covered elephants bearing turreted castles on their ponderous backs, appealed to his imagination and he at once asked me to introduce him to my friend and let him learn the game too.

I waited until Saskia was feeling a little better and then one evening I invited both men to my house for supper. They took to each other at once and became fast friends. And this was rather curious, as they represented two entirely different classes of society, and as Jean-Louys treated even the most distinguished among the Dutch patricians with that mixture of civil aloofness and amused condescension which the rich Amsterdam merchant would bestow upon a former butler who had gone to the Indies, had done rather well by himself and had now returned to the city of his former activities with a couple of million rupees and who had become a personage whom one must treat with a certain amount of economic respect, while at the same time keeping him at a respectable social distance, never for a moment allowing him to forget that the gap between inherited and recently acquired wealth was a divinely ordained institution across which no earthly wealth could ever hope to build a means of escape.

The Count de la Tremouille was the incarnation of what is commonly called "good breeding." Never during all the many years we spent together have I heard him give offense unintentionally, which surely is the highest tribute one can pay to a man's standard of courtesy. Like all wise people, he moved through life vertically rather than horizontally, but no matter in what company he found himself, I have never known the occasion upon which this unpretentious exile was not sitting "at the head of the table" or when anybody felt inclined to offer the man with the funny accent the slightest familiarity.

How and in what way he had acquired this gift of dominating his surroundings without in any way trying to dominate his audience, I do not know. But he had it and as a result, while he himself never seemed to remember that he had been born the Baron de la Tremouille, his surroundings were never quite able to forget it and even his fishdealer would insist upon selling him sixpence worth of shrimps as if he had been a foreign potentate, come to negotiate a great international loan. Upon very rare occasions, however, the invisible courtiers who seemed to watch every one of his thoughts and actions were given a day off and silently departed for a quiet evening in town. Then his brain resembled a munificent, royal palace, from which all the guards had fled. The doors and windows stood wide open and one could enter at will, to wander through the vast halls and admire the accumulated treasures of recollection and observation, or to find a quiet nook in the formal gardens at the back of the edifice and there meditate upon the strange vicissitudes of the great adventure commonly known as life.

But in order to enjoy this privilege, one had to be recognized as a blood brother of the mind. Mere physical relationship counted for nothing, affinity of feeling for everything. I have seen a first cousin of M. le Baron come all the way from Gascony in connection with some question of an inheritance, sit for hours in the little kitchen that lay just off the study, cooling his heels and swearing impatiently because Jean-Louys was talking to the first mate of a whaler who could neither read nor write but who had observed curious irregularities of behavior on the part of his compass while passing those extreme northern shores of Lapland where it is said that there are a number of vast iron deposits.

And it is a well-known fact that the Baron de la Tremouille forgot to attend the dinner which the Burgomasters of Amsterdam were giving in honor of a cousin of the King of Denmark (in the vain hope of obtaining a slight reduction of the Sund tolls by getting His Royal Highness disgracefully drunk on Dutch gin) because he had promised to sit up with his sick shoe-maker, an amateur philosopher of a singularly amusing trend of thought, who had made a careful study of the anagrams by means of which the Reverend Jacobus Bruinesteek had proved that the Psalms of David had really been written by King Solomon, who had applied these to the Revelation of St. John, and the Gospel of St. Luke, and had come to the somewhat startling conclusions that Judas Iscariot had written the former, while the latter was the work of Pontius Pilate.

One never knew therefore what reaction to expect from a meeting between one's ordinary friends and this strange product of French feudal practices and neo-mathematical theories except that his outward manner would always be in inverse ratio to the respect he inwardly felt for his new acquaintance. When he was sublimely polite, the case was hopeless. When he was just every-day polite, there was hope and one might give the candidate another chance. When he dropped all reserve, the victory had been won. During the first five minutes after I had introduced Rembrandt to him, I was in great fear that the encounter would be a failure. For the painter, conscious of his own low birth (his Uylenburgh in-laws had seen to that), was awkward and surly and ready to take offense at the slightest provocation, or even provide a little of the provocation himself.

The dinner was to be at my house, but Jean-Louys had promised to do the cooking. He held that cooking, after mathematics, was the greatest contribution towards human progress. "After all," he often asked, when, his sleeves rolled up to his elbows, he walked between his study and the kitchen beating his eggs and his oil and quoting profusely from Ennius and from Simonides of Ceos, "after all, in what consists the difference between man and beast except in the possibilities of the former to learn the art of dining, while the latter is forever doomed to feed? I grant you that most men still are in the state of savagery when they take food for the mere pleasure of filling their bellies. I grant you that the vast majority of our fellow-citizens still handle their forks and spoons as if they were a farmer loading a wagon of hay. But a few have at last seen the light. A few of them 'dine.' Whereas my dog Nouille, the noblest beast that ever pulled a fox out of a hole, a creature of such intellect and refinement that if he could only have worn a wig and cassock they would have made him Cardinal-Archbishop of Paris, had the table manners of a hog and unless he were very closely watched, would regale himself with delicacies which were more fit for a starving hyena than for an over-fed turn-spit."

And unless he were interfered with at this spot, he would proceed to explain that a man's table manners were the safest index to his general character, that one could measure the degree of a friend's greed or honesty by watching the way in which he moved his fork or knife to his mouth. If the progress of the food from the plate to lips were even and uninterrupted, one could trust that guest for any amount up to a hundred thousand francs. If, on the other hand, the moment the food approached the mouth, there was a snatching movement on the part of the teeth and a hurrying on the part of the fingers, then that person had still a few hundred thousand years to go before he was fit to associate with civilized people.

All of which was very amusing, but a little dangerous in view of the "catch as catch can" method of eating which was still being practiced by the majority of our neighbors. And alas! Rembrandt was no exception. When he was hard at work upon some new picture or when he was struggling with a new idea for an etching, he could be terribly absent-minded. Upon such occasions he seemed to be completely oblivious of his surroundings. As I have already written down in a former part of my diary, I have known him to go without either food or drink for as long as two days and two nights at a time. Then when he finally broke his fast, his table manners were rather painfully reminiscent of the days in the Weddesteeg, when the six van Rijn infants were all of them standing around the paternal table, dipping their spoons into the common bowl of pap and fishing out the few chunks of meat left behind by their father and mother. Now he not only had his work to worry him (I knew that he was finishing a portrait of the Widow Swartenhout and the old lady, who had a will of her own, despite her seventy-five years, was not the easiest of sitters) but also had a very sick wife on his hands and a rather sickly child (not to mention a hellishly ill-tempered nurse), I had good reason to fear that he might be in one of his vague and irritable moods and then one never could foretell just exactly what he would do or say or how he would react to the simplest remark, if by some miraculous stretch of the imagination it could be construed as a reflection upon his personal behavior.

And when Jean-Louys appeared from the kitchen in his shirt-sleeves, wearing an apron over his silk ruffles (for though he affected no colors in his outer garments, he remained scrupulously faithful to the reigning fashions until the day of his death), carrying a large blue Delft bowl full of batter and loudly quoting Seneca's "Convivae certe tui dicant, Bibamus!" suddenly I had the feeling: this party is going to be the wreck of an old friendship. For Rembrandt, who knew a very little Latin but no French whatsoever, looked as if he were going to say: "Well, my fine young man, and what about it, and have you lived here all this time without learning enough of our language to wish me at least a civil good morning in my own tongue?" But Jean-Louys, without paying the slightest attention, greeted him with a very deep and ceremonial bow and said in the nearest approach to Dutch I ever heard issue from the mouth of a Frenchman, "Mijn Heer, I welcome the successor of Pheidias, who did not think an old woman making pancakes a subject beneath his august dignity. Wherefore with your kind permission, I shall now make you an alemette the recipe of which I got straight from the chief cook of the Abbot of Thelème."

Whether Rembrandt got the allusion to the greatest of all the past masters of ancient France, I had reason to doubt, for as he often told me, he lived for the day and not for day before yesterday. And I am afraid that not half a dozen people in the whole town of Amsterdam knew (or cared) what sort of friars had inhabited the delectable abbaye of old Doctor Rabelais' invention. But the reference to the pancake woman, a rather mediocre etching of his early days which hardly any one knew, greatly flattered his pride. And he at once dropped the bristling attitude with which he had watched the advent of our amateur cook, bowed low and answered with a courtly wave of the hand:

"And if the product of your art, Monsieur, comes up to what certain reports of your culinary powers make me anticipate, then even great Jupiter would consider himself fortunate to be invited to this feast."

Which so surprised and delighted de la Tremouille that he almost dropped his bowl of batter on my instrument case, bowed even lower than before, pronounced himself Monsieur van Rijn's most humble servitor and ever after treated him with such marks of esteem and good will that the French commercial agent (who was supposed to collect business information for his royal master, but filled most of his letters with social gossip of what he supposed to be the better sort of Amsterdam society) filled three entire letters with the details of this famous meeting and hinted in no uncertain terms that M. de la Tremouille was rapidly approaching that stage of democratic debasement where a hint to the judicial authorities of Amsterdam and a Lettre de Cachet held ready at the nearest frontier town might not be out of place—a fine piece of diplomatic reasoning which in the course of its peregrinations towards Paris was duly copied by the postmaster of The Hague, was forwarded by him to My Lord Huygens, and so reached my humble home in Amsterdam with a request for the recipe of that famous alemette, which he spelled wrong and called an "omelette."

But to return to our dinner-party, we really had a very pleasant evening. Selim at first held himself slightly aloof. "The graphic arts," he offered as an excuse, "are not quite in my line. The Koran does not allow me to take an interest in them."

"And in which chapter, my friend, does the Koran mention the graphic arts?" came the voice of Bernardo, who knew that this excellent follower of the Prophet (not unlike a good many Christians) never gave a thought to these holy works except upon those frequent occasions when he needed their authority to talk himself out of doing something which he really did not want to do. For example, whenever he went to the house of friends and was offered beer, which he detested, Selim would solemnly lift his eyes toward Heaven and in a sepulchral voice he would declaim: "Alas and alack! does not the Angel Gabriel in the fifth verse of the second Sura declare unto the faithful: 'In the name of Allah, the compassionate compassioner, abstain, ye lovers of righteousness, from all those things that benumb the spirit'?"

But should his host take the hint and dive into his cellar for a bottle of Burgundy (which the young Moslem dearly loved), then Selim would proceed: "But what does the Prophet himself in the twenty-third verse of the eighteenth Sura have to say upon the duties of those who wander abroad in foreign lands? 'Listen, all ye faithful, and act ye so in all ways that he who offereth you food and drink shall never feel himself slighted, for true hospitality is the foundation-stone of friendship, the bulwark of good will.' " And he would continue to misquote these highfalutin passages until either the supply of wine had been completely consumed or the rest of the guests had passed underneath the table.

He would, however, be a little more careful with his texts whenever Bernardo was present, for the Jew, having spent several years of his life in a Portuguese prison in the company of a holy man from Fez, had used the endless hours of this interminable bondage to learn the greater part of the Koran by heart, in return for which he had taught the poor blackamoor the Psalms of David, the book of Judges and the Canticle of Solomon. He had long since thrown this useless intellectual ballast overboard, but enough remained to allow him to control the more phantastic statements of our amateur Moollah and the quarrels of these two Semites about the relative merits of their ancestral creeds (for neither of which either one of them felt the slightest respect) added a great deal to the gayety of our small society.

It caused considerable scandal among our Christian neighbors (who were never invited to our parties, yet knew everything we had said and done as accurately as if they had been present in person) but they were as a rule too busy fighting among themselves to pay very much attention to our hilarious heresies. And this evening, Selim, true to his custom, had no sooner relieved himself of his noble sentiment about the Koran and the art of painting, than he asked for a pencil and paper and spent the rest of the evening entertaining my small son with accounts of the glorious deeds of Harun al-Raschid, illuminating his talk with very amusing little pictures in which that great warrior was depicted in the act of decapitating rows and rows of Crusaders with such bloodthirsty realism that the poor infant could not sleep for five nights in succession.

As for the rest of us, immediately after dinner we went to my work-room and spent the evening playing chess. Jean-Louys, who claimed that this game was the best remedy for gout and nagging wives (the two evils he most dreaded) had recently taken a very serious interest in it and had made it a subject of careful study.

"What will you?" he used to ask. "I can work at my tables for only eight or nine hours a day. After that the figures put their hats and coats on and begin to dance minuets all over the page. I have got to do something to keep myself from going woozy and I can't live without mathematics, just as others can't live without gin or rum or theology or women. There is music. But that is no longer what it used to be. Too much sentiment in it nowadays. And so let us have the board."

We got the board (a home-made affair, for in the whole of Amsterdam I had not been able to get one and in most shops I had been told that such a thing did not exist) and Jean-Louys got out his copy of Ruy Lopez (a little book which he had ordered all the way from Sevilla in Spain) and he turned to page nineteen and carefully followed all the instructions from opening to attack, and in eighteen moves he had been checkmated by Bernardo, who had learned the game only the week before and who had no more idea about "gambits" and "end plays" than I had of raising pheasants, but who beat us all with a regularity that was as much of a surprise to us as it was to himself.

But what interested me most of all was Rembrandt's reaction to this game. I had already taught him the moves, king one square at a time, forward, backward, sideways—castles up and down the whole line as may be desirable—knights one square forward, two squares sideways—etc., etc., and much to my surprise he had learned it in an astoundingly short time. One or two evenings had been enough to give him a general idea of the game. But he played chess as he painted.

I have said before that he would rarely talk about the theory of his art and used to say that one hour of practice was better than a week of discussion and I do not believe that he ever put a single thought upon the subject on paper, although he had quite a gift for expressing himself in writing. But a few nights after our dinner-party he approached the subject himself and what he said was quite interesting.

"I like your Frenchman," he said in connection with some remark of mine upon the excellence of Jean-Louys' virtuosity as a cook. "I grant you that he makes a most excellent pancake, but these fancy dishes are not very much to my taste. I am accustomed to simpler fare. But I like him for the line he follows in playing that strange new game and it is upon 'line' that everything in this world depends.

"You know that I have a number of pupils. Some of them have been rather successful. Flinck has already made his mark and you will hear of Bol and Douw, for they are sound craftsmen and know their trade. Of course I did not really teach them very much. In their own way they are just as good as I am. It just happens that I am a little older and have had time to learn a few tricks which I can hand down to them.

"But of course, people see that Flinck has got a new commission from the Prince or they hear that Bol is painting a dozen portraits a year and they say to themselves: Here is our little Willem or our little Jantje and he is making wonderful pictures with that box of colors grandpa gave him for Saint Nicholas. We must send him to this man van Rijn and let him grow up to be as great an artist as Eeckhout or perhaps as the master himself and make a lot of money and go about all dressed up in silks and plumes, for you know what foolish ideas there are abroad about a profession which counts so many of its most honored members among the inmates of the poor-house.

"But what can I do? I can't make a living merely painting por-traits. I need pupils. None of those boys are very easy to handle. They are young and models are willing. I have not got the slightest inclination to play the school-master, but I can at least be careful that I don't waste my time upon material that is too absolutely hopeless. And so I have made it a rule that they must bring me their drawings.

"Their drawings, mind you, not their paintings. For almost any-body, if he is not absolutely color-blind and has had a good teacher, can learn to paint some sort of a picture. But a line never lies. Give me a scrap of a man's drawings, anything at all, and in five seconds I will tell you whether he has any talent or whether he had better become a brewer.

"Besides, painting is not merely a question of technique. There has got to be temperament, character, personality. Without those, there is no life and the world is dull enough as it is. No need to clut-ter it up with miles of dead canvas. Yes, a painter should learn his trade and be able to finish a picture, attend to all the details just as

91

a tailor should be able to finish a suit of clothes or a carpenter to finish a cupboard.

"Perhaps I don't make myself quite clear. There are others who could tell you much better what is in my mind than I can tell you myself. But mark my words, a man has a 'line' or he has not. And that Frenchman has a line. He has got it in his manner. He has got it in his manners. He has got it in his pancakes. He has got it in his chess. He has got it in everything. While I . . ."

I looked at him in surprise, for this was a new note I had never heard before.

"While you?"

"While I have got too much of it in my drawing and too little in my life. But I am still young. Give me a few more years of experience, and I too may learn."

SELF-PORTRAIT (DRAWING)

Chapter 9

SASKIA QUIETLY GOES TO SLEEP FOR ALL TIME

DEATH APPEARING TO A WEDDED COUPLE
FROM AN OPEN GRAVE (ETCHING)

REMBRANDT did learn certain things about life and he learned them much sooner than he had expected. It was a fortnight after our dinner-party and the painter and I were spending an evening as usual, watching over Saskia.

I had long since given up all hope of ever being able to do something for her. I had brought in two of my colleagues who had studied her disease in Grenoble and in London. As with patients of this sort a great deal depends upon their own state of mind and they must be encouraged in their strange belief that they will soon be cured (their occasional attacks of melancholia are the worst thing that can happen to them), my learned rivals had been introduced to her as art-dealers from Antwerp who wanted to inspect Rembrandt's etchings and she felt quite flattered that two such distinguished-looking gentlemen should have come all the way from Flanders to pay homage to her husband's genius and had asked a good many questions about Rubens, whether he really had been paid a hundred guilders a day while he was painting a picture for some one and whether his wife had really been as handsome and well-dressed as she had heard and whether she had ever posed for him in the nude, because that was something she herself never could have done, however much she might love her husband.

To which they had answered to the best of their ability and being

experienced physicians and therefore accustomed to the telling of
many innocent lies, they had so well acquitted themselves of the
task that Saskia was quite satisfied and had dozed off, firmly convinced that she was a much better-looking woman than Helen Four-
ment and also, to a certain extent, a much more respectable one, since
she had sometimes appeared in her man's pictures as Flora but never
as Venus.

Then we had bade Rembrandt leave us and the three of us had
examined the sleeping woman, for the short interview had already
exhausted her waning strength, and I had shown them my record
of the case and they both had looked solemn and they both had
shaken their heads and the first one had whispered, "mors," and the
second one had whispered, "mors," and then we had waited a few
minutes to make the husband believe that we were discussing the
matter in detail and that there still might be some hope and the elder
of the two doctors had said: "One month more, at the very most."
And the younger had answered, after the fashion of young physicians who try to show their superior experience before an elder con-
frère: "It seems to me that she might live another six weeks."

But I had said nothing, for I had seen her lose weight steadily for
the last two months and I knew that it was a question of days rather
than weeks and I took them upstairs and we all uttered some platitudes to Rembrandt, who had used that half hour to pull two proofs
of a little etching of the three Magi, on which he had been working
for quite a long time and which he now offered with a few complimentary words to my two doctor friends who were rather touched,
for there was something very pathetic and almost naïve about this
man who kept on laboring as unconcernedly as if his little household
were not, at that very moment, on the brink of collapse and extinc-
tion.

Then they bade him farewell, declining his offer that he show them
some further hospitality in token of his gratitude for their services
and we went downstairs to the big hall and made ready for our
evening's game.

Saskia was still asleep. Her right hand, very white and dreadfully
thin, was resting on the counterpane. She had always been very
fond of flowers and now that summer had come at last, Rembrandt

Rembrandt van Rijn

brought her some fresh roses every morning. One of these she had stuck in her hair to give herself a more festive appearance, before the arrival of the "Antwerp art-dealers." It lay on her pillow. It was a very red rose and her cheeks by contrast looked even more pallid than usual. But she was breathing easily and regularly and there was a smile on her lips. I softly pulled the curtains of the bed together and tiptoed back to the table.

"She seems to be doing very well," I said. "What will you play, backgammon or chess?"

"Chess," Rembrandt answered. "I think that I can beat you to-night. The last time we played, I lost my queen almost at the very beginning. I will do better to-night."

I took two pawns and let him choose.

He pointed to my left hand and got red.

We began in the usual way, king's pawn, queen's pawn, king's bishop, queen's rook and whatever followed. I have forgotten how the game ran, but I remember that after only five or six moves, he had brought his queen out and was using her to force me into a defensive position. I warned him. What he was doing had a certain quality of brilliancy. It might make him win the game in about ten or fifteen moves, but only on condition that I overlooked a counter-attack which I could make with my knights, in which case his lack of reserves would put him into a fatal position. I watched him closely. He was so engrossed in his own calculations that he seemed completely unaware of the danger that threatened him from the side of my knights. I warned him once more. "This is all very fine," I told him, "but you are playing this to win."

"But this is so amusing," he answered. "I know that I am running a few risks but I have the position well in hand. I shall beat you the next move if I can extricate my queen."

"But can you?" I asked him, taking his bishop's pawn and thereby opening an avenue of attack for my bishop.

"I think I can— Why, it would be absurd if I couldn't! I had the game in hand only a moment ago and now—"

"And now," I answered, "I have your queen and you are mate in three moves."

He pushed back his chair.

Rembrandt van Rijn

"Too bad," he consoled himself. "Too bad. I thought that I had you this time. Let me try again. Just a moment till I make sure that Saskia is all right."

He picked up one of the two candles, went to the bed and pushed aside the curtains. Then he turned to me and whispered: "Look how quiet she is to-night! I never saw her sleep so soundly. She must be really getting better."

I stood by his side and put my hand upon her heart.

Saskia was dead.

LANDSCAPE (ETCHING)

96

Chapter 10

SASKIA IS BURIED AND REMBRANDT GOES BACK
TO WORK

THE VILLAGE AT THE LAKE (DRAWING)

I AM writing this in the year 1669 and Saskia died in '42. That is twenty-seven years ago and twenty-seven years are a long time in a man's life. I can't complain about my memory. It is causing me very little trouble, and as I shall be seventy next year, I have no right to expect too much. The greater part of my contemporaries are either dead or rapidly becoming senile and the former are better off than the latter.

What Fate holds in store for me, I do not know. But when the end comes, I hope that it will be sudden and swift and that I shall never have to pass through those periods of slow mental decay which seem to be the inevitable concomitant of old age.

But I have noticed something curious whenever I try to reconstruct the events of my own past. I can recollect the most unimportant details of my early childhood. I still know with absolute assurance what presents I received on Saint Nicholas day when I was seven and eight and nine and ten. I could tell you what we had to eat on the few occasions when we entertained guests. Could I handle a pencil, I would be able to draw you the absolute likeness of all my school-teachers and most of my friends.

The same holds good for the two years I spent studying anatomy and surgery at the University of Leyden. Every detail of every day, almost every detail of every hour of every day, is firmly fixed in my mind. But suddenly after my twentieth birthday, the picture becomes hazy. I still know in a general way what occurred during the years that I practiced medicine in Amsterdam, but I often lose track of the sequence of events. For example, I will remember with perfect clarity that such and such a person fell ill of such and such a disease and I could give you a fairly accurate account of the development of his case. But should you ask me to name the year, I would be hopelessly at a loss. I would be obliged to answer that I did not know. It might have been '46 or '56 and then again, it might have been '49 or '59. I just simply would not know. I could tell you whether the patient had a temperature on the third or on the fourth day of his affliction, but I might be off on the date all the way from five to ten years.

I have often speculated upon the true nature of this curious mental trick and I think that it is due to the increase in speed of both the months and the years as we grow older. When I was ten years of age, a single day resembled eternity, only on a somewhat smaller scale. It was composed of twenty-four hours, each one of which bore a distinct character of its own and offered countless possibilities for new adventures and fresh experiences.

Gradually human existence became more commonplace. One got up, did one's work, ate a few meals, talked to a few friends, worried a bit, laughed a bit, read a few chapters in a book and went to bed again.

The humdrum became the normal. One commenced to accept whatever Fate had in store without murmuring, for what was the use of trying to fight God? At first, of course, there still were the seasons. The spring, when the trees and the plants were in flower, the summer when it was hot, the fall when the grain was harvested, the winter when it was cold and one was obliged to wear heavy woolen coats and mufflers.

But after one's fiftieth birthday, even those natural divisions of the year seemed to lose their importance. One no longer grumbled about the frost or the heat or the rain or the snow. They were there! Impossible to do anything about them, anyway. That was the last great surrender. From that moment on, time ceased to have a personal

Rembrandt van Rijn

entity. It became a smudge. Some gigantic joker had wiped his dirty thumb across the vault of Heaven and that was called life. Then the last final sleep and grateful oblivion for the rest of eternity.

Those thoughts have been continually in my mind during the last twenty years. Hence dates and hours mean very little to me and as I have never been in the habit of keeping a diary until now, as I never saved a single letter or a single scrap of paper that was in any way connected with my own existence (it seemed such a silly thing to do, as if my own funny little adventures were really of the slightest general importance), as, in short, I am writing this entirely from memory, I find it rather difficult to state when exactly Saskia departed this life or even when she was buried.

She died (I am quite sure about that) sometime during the summer of 1642, for I remember that it was during the same year in which Tasman discovered that mysterious island in the Pacific Ocean which was called Nieuw Zeeland, after my beloved Zeeland, and sailed around the great south land about which we had had so many strange reports during the last forty years.

As always I was interested in any reports he might bring home about the narcotics in use among the natives. Everywhere in the world the inhabitants seem to have some favorite way of bringing about temporary forgetfulness. In most instances they were only interested in their miserable hasheesh as a momentary means of escape from lives that were none too happy. But I am convinced that some day we shall find a plant which will enable us to do something infinitely more important to perform surgical operations without that dreadful agony which now turns the operating-room into a torture chamber and makes people avoid the hospital as if it were the lepers' house. And there always is a chance that one of those explorers, coming back from distant parts of Asia or Africa or America, shall bring us the answer to this age-old question. I had therefore made it a rule to keep track of all new voyages and when I heard that this new big island, called van Diemen's Land (after My Lord Anthony van Diemen, the governor-general of the Indies, who also conquered Formosa and who had equipped this most recent expedition)—when I heard that it was inhabited by woolly-haired aborigines who could make battle-axes return to their hands after they had thrown them at their enemies, I decided that people clever

99

enough to invent such a curious device (the true nature of which I never heard explained) might also have discovered some new methods of bringing about a state of artificial oblivion. But the reports that were printed about these new explorations remained exceedingly brief and far from satisfactory. Finally I addressed a letter to the directors of the India Company and was informed that Their Lordships were conducting a business enterprise and were not managing a museum of natural curiosities and had no information to give me upon the subject in which I seemed interested.

Well, that famous voyage happened in 1642 (though I only heard about it two years later) but the date stuck in my memory, for the very silly reason that I had had a dispute with one of Rembrandt's brothers-in-law whether Lutjegast in which Tasman was born was situated in Friesland or in Groningen and finally I had bet him a rijksdaalder that it was in Groningen and not in Friesland and he had taken me up and I had been right and he had never paid me that rijksdaalder, claiming that by rights the hamlet ought to have been a part of his native province. (A pretty feeble excuse, it seemed to me.) And ever since, when some one said, "Sixteen-hundred and forty-two," I instinctively added, "Tasman from Lutjegast and Saskia, too." It was a foolish little jingle and not a very dignified one, but as long as the particular compartment of our brain occupied by our memory resembles a pawnshop the morning after a fire, with everything helter-skelter and in hopeless disorder, I suppose that such absurd combinations are inevitable.

Anyway that terrible rime allows me to remember that the poor girl died in the year 1642 and that is enough for the present purpose. She died in the summer of '42 and if I am not mistaken, it was during the middle of June, for the push-cart venders were selling their first cherries and there were flowers everywhere, and the trees along the Burchtwal looked fresh and green as we slowly carried Saskia to her last resting place.

When we came to the Old Church, we found that the officials had not expected us so early and that the building was still locked. The coffin was put down while some one went to get the sexton and we all stood around in a small group and we wanted to say something and we did not know quite what to say and the noise of the traffic in the near-by Warmoesstraat served as a background for

THE DEATH OF THE VIRGIN (ETCHING)

THE ANGEL APPEARING TO THE SHEPHERDS (ETCHING)

our silence and then all of a sudden, there was the grating sound of heavy bolts that were being pushed aside and the doors opened slowly as if pushed aside by invisible hands, and inside everything was very quiet, but in the distance some one was hammering at a bench that needed repair and I looked at Rembrandt and I saw that he had turned pale, as if they were hammering nails into his wife's coffin.

We buried her right underneath the small organ, not far away from the monument erected to Admiral van Heemskerk who had died off Gibraltar and who had been the first man to try and reach the Indies by way of the North Pole.

The ceremony took only a few minutes. The heavy black cloth which had completely covered the casket was carefully folded up by two of the professional pall-bearers who performed this office with such absurd dignity that they reminded me of my grandmother and her maid Rika, doing the sheets when the half-yearly laundry came home. Then the coffin was placed upon two heavy ropes. Eight men, four on each side, took hold of the ropes. The minister stepped forward with an enormous Bible which he opened and placed on a small wooden stand which had been placed there for the occasion and while he read the one hundred and third psalm, Saskia was slowly and silently lowered into the cavernous darkness of her open grave.

I have gone to many funerals in my day and every time I have been struck by the inability of the creed of Calvin and Luther to express its emotions in anything beyond mere words. The music in our churches is hideous. The singing is atrocious. We cover the walls with a dozen coats of whitewash, we paint the ceiling gray, and we varnish the benches until they are stained a dark brown and then we ask the congregation to come and sit still on incredibly uncomfortable seats while some one talks to them.

In our churches, some one is forever telling somebody else what he ought to think or do. Instead of agreement there is argument. Instead of being urged to lose our souls in quiet contemplation, we are exhorted to follow the intricate subtleties of violent controversies and to take sides in never-ending disputes. Heaven knows, I do not wish a return of those good old days of which our Catholic neighbors are secretly talking. Deprived of their ancient shrines and obliged to worship their own Lord in the attic of some innocent-looking warehouse, they must of course look back to the period before our town went Protestant as a sort of Paradise Lost. But their Church had to go. It was too foreign to the nature of our people and we shall have to continue our present way until we shall be rid of it for all time.

No, it is not that I want. But I can't for the life of me see why we had to go so far in the other direction and why everything we do must be ugly and devoid of symbolic meaning. Most people are starving for a little color in their lives. They hunger for some variety of mysterious emotion that shall (for the moment at least) allow them to forget the all too brutal facts of human existence.

We fortunate ones who are not forever beset by the necessities of finding enough to eat and to drink and maintaining a roof over our children's heads, don't know what the poorer classes suffer. We go in for music or for painting or we write sonnets or study mathematics or lose ourselves in the works of the ancient philosophers. But all those roads of escape are closed to them. The Church alone can give them relief. And I never enter one of these sepulchral places of worship without wondering why our churches are so hopelessly one-sided and always appeal to the brain but never to the emotions.

Take that funeral of Saskia. Surely if there was a tragedy it was the death of this lovely creature. She was young and until a few months before her death, very lovely. She was married to one of the most remarkable men of her day and age, who was devoted to her and could have given her a life full of beauty and interest. She had a child. She had many friends. She was not very bright, perhaps, but no one asked of her that she be able to translate Auveer into Latin hexameters.

And then she died. Died before she was fully thirty years old. Died and left everything she loved behind, to become a mere number in a row of hideous graves and molder away in a threadbare shroud until her poor bones should be evicted to make room for some new candidate.

A ghastly tragedy, the negation of everything that men and women are supposed to live for. But a marvelous opportunity for the Church to stand forth as the prophet of hope, to maintain boldly and in the face of all this incriminating evidence, that life is good and that death is but another form of living, to surround these assertions with beautiful gestures and honest music, with symbols that should speak uncontrovertibly of the Eternal Verities.

Instead of which a young farmhand, speaking an accent that betrayed no breeding whatsoever, read some very fine verses, the meaning of which, however, he did not seem to understand in the least. Then sixteen men, who during the rest of the day were drivers of beer-wagons and eel-fishers, their working clothes badly hidden by long black cassocks and still smelling of the ale-house, took the large wooden box containing all this loveliness and with an ill-concealed "one, two, three!" they hurriedly lowered it into its stone cage. Then they turned away to carry the stretcher to the store-room in the back of the church where such paraphernalia were kept whenever there was no demand for their services, and hastened to the door to gather in the tips of the mourners.

I suppose there were those among us who wanted to linger a moment longer—to say something for the last time to the shadow that lay at our feet. But we were given no time. The minister left. The sexton was rattling his keys. There was nothing for us to do but to go.

And so we returned to the house in the Anthonie Breestraat and the nurse with the help of some of the neighbors had prepared a meal and the table was set in the same room from which they had carried the corpse away only an hour before (a dreadful and barbarous custom which we have undoubtedly inherited from our savage ancestors) and we were all of us bade to enter and regale ourselves.

I remained a few minutes, for not to have done so would have attracted too much attention. Then I looked for Rembrandt. He was not there. Driven by some sort of premonition, I softly tiptoed upstairs to the studio. Rembrandt, still in his mourning clothes, a long veil of black crape hanging down from his hat and black gloves on his hands, but completely oblivious of the world around him, was busy painting. I went up to him and put my hand on his shoulder, but he never turned his head and I don't think he noticed me.

For he was working once more at a portrait of Saskia, a portrait of Saskia as she had looked the day he had married her.

SASKIA (PAINTING)

Chapter 11

REMBRANDT UNEXPECTEDLY CALLS AND BORROWS
FIFTY GUILDERS

THE ADORATION OF THE SHEPHERDS (ETCHING)

I LEFT the studio without saying a word, talked to a few people downstairs, uttered the usual platitudes which belong to such an occasion, went home, changed my clothes and walked to the hospital where I spent the rest of the day. But to my great surprise, just after I had finished my supper, the maid told me that Mr. van Rijn had come to see me, and of course I bade him come in and asked why this formality of having himself announced, to which he replied vaguely that he did not know, and took a chair and sat down. Then I noticed that he was still in the same black clothes he had worn at the funeral and that there was something wild about the way in which he stared around the room.

In the case of any one else, I would have thought: "This man has been drinking." But he was dead sober and indeed it was not until much later, when anxiety about losing his eyesight was added to all his other worries, that he occasionally tried to find a few moments of oblivion by means of that false friend who dwelleth at the bottom of a brown jar of Schiedam gin.

There was but one other explanation for his disheveled looks: he was utterly exhausted.

I asked him whether he had had anything to eat that day, when he had last dined. He tried to remember, but could not. "Two or three days ago," he answered. And so I went into the kitchen and with my own hands prepared a meal of soft-boiled eggs and toasted bread and I sent the maid out for some milk, which I slightly heated, and he ate everything and then said: "I am dreadfully tired," and I took him upstairs and practically had to undress him (for he could hardly lift a finger) and I put him into my own bed and went downstairs again and made myself some sort of a couch out of chairs and cushions and the family Bible, which I used as a pillow, and blew out the candle and it seemed to me that I had hardly slept an hour when I was awakened by a loud banging on the front door, and of course I thought it was a patient and I went to the front door and to my great surprise, noticed that the sun was shining brightly and that it must be between eight or nine o'clock in the morning, and then I opened the door and there stood the nurse of little Titus, her hair hanging down her forehead and her bare feet in leather slippers.

"This is a fine thing to happen!" she began, but I shushed her and bade her come in and said sharply: "Keep a civil tongue in your head, woman. What is it you want?"

"Is he here?" she asked.

"He? What do you mean by 'he'?"

"Rembrandt."

"And since when do you call your master by his first name, or refer to him as 'he'?"

"Oh, well, he isn't so much, and for a widower to spend the night after his wife's funeral outside of the house! It is disgraceful! The neighbors will talk about it. They are already talking more than is good. It is disgraceful. And here I am, slaving myself to death to keep everything going nicely, and I cooked the finest meal ever served in our street after a funeral, and he does not even come down to say 'how do you do?' to a single one of the guests. And he forgets to give me money to buy beer and I have to pay for it out of my own pocket and then he does not come down to the meal and everybody will be talking about it!" and so on and so forth, a hysterical woman feeling very sorry for herself.

As there was no use arguing the case, I told her that she was a very badly used woman, that her master had been sadly negligent in his duties and that I would speak to him as soon as he had rested from the terrible exhaustion of the last few days, and having in this way quieted her somewhat, I prevailed upon her to go back home and take care of the baby and I would return with the master just as soon as I could.

The harpy actually left me and I returned to the dining-room to dress and to make up my mind what to say to Rembrandt, for although his household no longer needed my professional assistance, I felt that it was in even greater need of my services as a fairly sober-minded and not entirely unpractical human being. And when Rembrandt finally came downstairs, a little after eleven, and after he had eaten three ordinary breakfasts, I pushed my chair back (why can't one think with one's feet underneath the table?) and I said: "Listen, my good friend, this will never do! If I have told you once I have told you ten dozen times, that woman ought to go. She is no good. She is irresponsible. I don't quite want to say that she is crazy but she isn't far away from it. Pay her her wages and let her go, but let her go right away, for unless I am much mistaken, she is rapidly losing her mind and she may end by murdering you or your child."

This startled him considerably and he asked: "Do you really think so, or do you say that because you do not like her?" To which I answered, not without some heat, that my personal likes or dislikes had nothing to do with the case, that in such matters I firmly believed in keeping professional and private opinions strictly separate, but that as a doctor who had done his best to save his wife and was now doing his best to save his son, I felt it my duty to warn him against so dangerous a companion, and I ended once more with the admonition: "Pay her and let her go."

But he answered that that was not so easy as it seemed and I asked him why. For the position between servants and master was clearly defined and regulated by the laws of Amsterdam. One might have to pay a servant or a nurse a few weeks' extra wages, but that was all, and as long as the financial obligations were fulfilled, the magistrate took no notice when irate scullions stormed their council-chamber with their complaints and grievances. He might be obliged to give her a full month's wages, but then he would be able to ask her to leave his house at once, and good riddance.

All those arguments, however, seemed to make very little impression upon him. He kept repeating that it would not be so easy as I thought and finally took his leave, but just as I opened the door to show him out, he made a remark which puzzled me a great deal. "You are right," he said, "and I will do what you tell me. I will try to raise the money to-day."

"Raise the money to-day . . ."—a question of twenty or thirty guilders at the very most. "Raise the money"—when one lived in the biggest house on the Jodenbreestraat, bought pictures by Rubens and Raphael as if they had been ten-cent prints and was known to have married one of the richest girls of Friesland!

"I will try to raise the money to-day!" Thus far we had had tragedy. Now mystery had been added. And I decided to have a serious talk with him as soon as he should have recovered from the emotions of the last few days.

A man who any day could lay his hands on fifty thousand guilders in cash (every one knew that Saskia had not had a penny less) telling me that he would try and raise a servant's wages—no, something was wrong there.

But one can't very well ask questions of that sort and so I waited and went the usual rounds of my professional duties, for I knew that when people have something on their minds, they sooner or later must relieve themselves or go mad.

In the olden days, so I am told, one could go to a priest and tell him all about everything. Then came the new dispensation and people were admonished to address themselves directly to God.

Rembrandt van Rijn

And God lives so very far away and a doctor is conveniently near by, right around the corner. And so the doctor often gets the confidences that were really meant for the Almighty. I therefore made up my mind that I would not call at the Breestraat, and would wait, for the patient would appear soon enough.

Rembrandt, however, appeared to be struggling hard to keep his trouble to himself. The days grew into weeks and he never came near the Houtgracht.

And then suddenly one day when I returned from the hospital late in the afternoon I found him in my working-room. He must have been waiting quite a long time, for he had amused himself copying a bust of Hippocrates that stood on my book-case, and the drawing was almost finished.

"I have come to speak to you about something," he said, without offering me the usual salutation. "I am in a rather difficult position. Can you let me have fifty guilders?" And then he told me his story, and it was a strange one, as you shall see for yourself.

SKETCH (DRAWING)

CHRIST, WITH THE SICK AROUND HIM, RECEIVING LITTLE CHILDREN: THE "HUNDRED GUILDER PRINT" (ETCHING)

Chapter 12

I LEARN A FEW THINGS ABOUT SASKIA'S FAMILY

THE WINDMILL (ETCHING)

"I AM just back from the Old Church," he began. "I have bought the grave in which Saskia is buried. It is mine now and she will never have to lie there with strangers. I had to sell two of my pictures to raise the amount. I don't know what has happened. I had thought that they would bring me six hundred florins. I only got half. But the grave is mine. I went to the notary this morning. The papers have been signed and are in my pocket. Now could you let me have fifty guilders? I owe the nurse thirty for past wages and twenty for letting her go without the usual notice. Can I have the money?"

I told him that of course he could have the money, but why did he need it? It was a difficult subject. I decided not to try and be too delicate. Such mental operations are very much like physical ones, and the tender-hearted surgeons, who try to save the feelings of their patients, are the ones who do the most harm. And so I said: "Of course your affairs are none of my business and I would gladly give you a thousand guilders if you really needed them. But there is the house. You once told me that you had paid thirteen thousand guilders for it. You will grant me that I have never pried into your affairs, but one day when you were pulling a proof and I was talking to you in the little room upstairs, you remarked that you made between two thousand and three thousand florins a year from your etchings alone. Then there are your pupils. I don't know how much they pay you, but it ought to be a fairly decent sum. Then there are your portraits. There is the picture of Banning Cocq's company. The other day (it was at the funeral of Saskia, to be exact) young Uylenburgh, her cousin, told me that you had got five thousand florins for it. And then there is Saskia's inheritance. She must have had quite a good deal. Her father was a man of importance. I don't know what became of it, but I suppose you got some of it."

"I got everything."

"Well, you ought to be able to realize on it." (I hated to talk like a damn school-master, but in many ways the man to whom I was speaking was still a child.)

"I can," he answered. "It is merely a question of time. You see, Saskia had made a will about two weeks before she died. We did not tell you, because you had given orders that she must not be disturbed, and as a matter of fact, I did not know about it until it was all finished. But the thing had been on her mind for quite a long time and one afternoon, when I had gone out to talk about a new portrait, she sent the nurse to get her a notary. He came to see her and drew up everything in true legal form. She signed the documents nine days before she died and she left everything to me. It is understood that I will look after the boy and see that he gets a first-rate education and if I ever marry again, which I doubt, all the money goes to Titus. And some other details which are neither here nor there. But the most wonderful thing of all—and I never thought that the poor girl had cared quite so much for me—came at the end. She stipulated that I should never be asked to give any sort of an accounting. It is all mine to do with as I please. Of course, I shall merely regard it as a trust-fund for the benefit of little Titus. I may use some of it to pay for the house. Half of it has been paid already but I still owe some seven thousand florins on it and a few years' interest. In the end it will go to Titus anyway and so that means nothing.

"I am really much better fixed than ever before. But I have no head for business and I would rather paint three pictures than add one single sum of figures. And things have been sort of slow coming in these last six months. I know that people say that I got five thousand guilders for that big militia piece. Well, sixteen hundred is a little nearer to the truth, and even of that, I am not quite sure, for they now tell me that it is too large for the hall and they want to cut a piece off at both sides, and some of the soldiers who stood pretty near the edge of the picture threaten that they won't give me a cent unless they show up as well as the rest of the company. And then there are four or five of that crowd who claim that I have not done them justice. They don't want to be painted with their backs to the public. They say that they had agreed to pay an equal sum, all of them, and that therefore they have a right to as much canvas as their neighbors. One of them stopped me the other day on the Ververs Gracht and caused quite a scandal, and he was a sergeant, too. What did I mean by hiding his face behind the arm of another fellow, who was only a corporal and a man he did not care for to boot?

"Well, I did not lose my temper, though I was sorely tempted to do so. Instead I bought him a beer and took him to the Kloveniersdoelen and I spent an hour trying to show that beetlehead that I had tried to do something more than paint a nice, polite picture of himself and his companions, that I had not tried to paint one particular company of soldiers, but all the soldiers of all the ages, going forth to defend their homesteads. I made quite a speech. Did I convince him? Of course not! All my fine words did not make the slightest impression upon the creature's dumb brain. Whenever I thought that I had made my point clear, he would look at me and shake his head and say: 'I paid as much as the rest of them and I want to be shown as big as the rest of them, or I shan't give you a cent.' And in the end he got quite abusive and asked me whether the little girl in the center had paid her share and what she was doing there anyway, and then I gave up in despair, and I shall count myself lucky if I get half of what they promised me.

"You are right, I used to have quite a number of pupils, but you know how it is. Those who have talent are usually too poor to pay me anything and those who can pay have not got the talent and they are just a common nuisance. They might at least have given me some rest when Saskia died. Well, a few had the decency to go home. But half a dozen came from too far away to go home and they stayed. And one evening I heard a lot of noise in the attic (you know that is where they have their rooms) and I went upstairs to investigate and I heard two people snickering behind a door and then I heard the high giggle of one of the models, who had no business to be there at all, and then the boy said: 'And now we are in good company, for we are like Adam and Eve in Paradise.' So I told them that I would make that wish come true and would play the Angel with the Flaming Sword and would drive them out, and I threw them out of the house then and there, because I have got to have discipline in my own home, but of course people talked about it and as a result three of the other boys have left me.

"And so you see how it goes. I have several thousand guilders still coming to me for portraits I have done. But it seems that it is harder to collect nowadays than formerly. Some people claim that we may conclude peace with Spain almost any day now and that there will be quite a terrible crisis then, but why war should be more profitable than peace is something I don't quite understand. If I had ever kept books I would be able to tell you where all the money has gone, for I must have made quite a great deal these last ten years. And anyway, it does not matter. It is only a question of a few months— as soon as the formalities connected with the inheritance shall have been completed. You know how slow our courts are about such things. There must be a guardian for little Titus and the Chamber of Orphans must be consulted. I hate all such legal complications. I don't understand them. They worry me and keep me from working and so I just try to forget them. But everything will be all right in a couple of months.

"Meanwhile, it will be much better for everybody concerned if that damned nurse goes before the end of another day. I could sell something out of my collection, but then the whole town would say that those Frisian relations who said that I was a spendthrift and was wasting my wife's money had been right. I need fifty guilders and I need them right away and I need them very quietly. I can pay you back in September or October and I shall give you six percent, which seems fair. Can I have them?"

I said yes, he could have them, and went to the little safe in my bedroom in which I kept the East Indian shares I had inherited from my grand-uncle and I took out five golden riders and I gave them to Rembrandt and I bade him forget about the interest—it was just a small loan between friends, and that evening I wrote a long letter to a friend of mine in Leeuwarden, a young man with whom I had studied in Leyden, but who had given up medicine and had gone in for the law. He belonged to an excellent family which had remained faithful to the King of Spain after the outbreak of the revolution and had therefore been deprived of all its possessions. He often declared that while poverty might be no disgrace, it had very little else to recommend it to a sensible person, and he had made no secret of it then that he meant to marry money—a great deal of money— just as soon as he had the opportunity. He had been as good as his word. Almost immediately upon graduation he had married the daughter of a very rich cattle-owner from the neighborhood of Franeker. A former acquaintance who had gone to Franeker to finish his studies (finding Leyden a little too diverting for that constant application to his work which his father deemed necessary) had been present at the wedding. I ran across him one day when he was passing through Amsterdam and he told me all about it.

"The bride squinted and she was slightly lame," he informed me, "but she was an orphan and had two hundred thousand guilders in cash. The groom looked very meek and dignified and kept awake all during the service. He has bought out one of the best notary offices in the capital—specializes in farmers' cases, has become the financial adviser of every honest plowman in all of the sixteen counties—coins in the money almost as fast as the Mint can turn it out— is a very decent husband to the unsightly wife and is just as amusing and honest a companion as in the days before he got rich."

I wrote to this provincial Croesus and asked him to find out for me whether Saskia van Uylenburgh had really been as rich as people said and to give me all the particulars he could lay hands on—that

I was not acting in an indiscreet fashion, but that I had a friend who was greatly interested, etc., etc., and would he please let me know by return mail.

Three weeks later I had his answer and his letter showed that he had not changed a bit from the days when we used to walk to Noordwijk on a fine Sunday afternoon to eat a supper of bread and cheese in the Golden Hyacinth and felt that this world was by far the best sort of a world anybody could wish to live in.

This is what he wrote:

"Ornatissime!

"Magno cum gaudio accepi litteras tuas atque maximo cum—now what in thunder was 'haste' in Latin? But anyway, I got your letter and the question you ask can refer to only one person, the great Maestro Rembrandtus van Rijn, painter-in-extraordinary to the Rabbis of Amsterdam and who not long ago, if I am to believe my correspondents, has given up the use of colors altogether and now distills himself a new sort of picture out of a mixture of soot, lamp-black and coal-ashes.

"For who else could be interested in the affairs of that poor Uylenburgh girl, who left here so long ago that few of her contemporaries remember her? Be reassured, however. I have done a little quiet investigating and here is my general impression of the case.

"I don't think that there is very much money in that particular quarter, or if there be any, that it will ever be of great use to him, as most of the renowned Uylenburgh millions exist only on paper, or wherever they exist 'in naturalibus,' are so hopelessly mortgaged, hypothesized or hypothecated (take your choice), debentured and generally tied up that in case of a sudden sale I doubt whether they would realize one-twentieth of their normal value. I am on agreeable terms of professional cordiality with the notary who has handled the affairs of the family ever since the old man was elected sheriff for the first time and that must have been shortly after the flood. He threw up his hands in despair and said: 'Don't talk to me about that case! It will be my death yet. For now, so I understand, that the youngest daughter has died, the one who married that miller or painter or whatever he is in Holland, the widower will probably write us a letter and ask for a settlement but Solomon in all his wisdom could not unravel that estate.' And then he gave me many details, all in a perfectly professorial manner, and I shall not even try to explain his speech in plain Dutch, but I shall merely give you the gist of his observations.

SELF-PORTRAIT (PAINTING)

SELF-PORTRAIT (PAINTING)

SELF-PORTRAIT (PAINTING)

SELF-PORTRAIT (PAINTING)

Rembrandt van Rijn

"Old Rombertus van Uylenburgh, the father, had been quite a famous man in local Frisian politics. A big frog in a small puddle. During the critical years of the rebellion, he had several times been Burgomaster of Leeuwarden and he it was who conducted the negotiations between the Estates of Friesland and the Prince of Orange about choosing the latter to be sovereign ruler of the new commonwealth. But William was murdered before they had been able to reach an agreement. As you undoubtedly know, old Rombertus was lunching with William the day the latter was shot and held him in his arms when he died. All this had brought a great deal of honor, but he had been away from home so much that he had little time to look after his own affairs.

"The mother had brought up the children, of whom there had been nine at the time of her death in '21 or '22. In '24 Rombertus himself had gone to join the angels. At that moment, two of the sons were engaged in the law and a third one had become an officer in a regiment of the line. Of the daughters, the eldest, Antje, is married to a certain Maccovius, a professor of theology in the University of Franeker, a rather unpleasant person of very violent convictions, but very popular among his neighbors whose views are about as broad as that of a birdseed. The second one, Hiskia, is married to Gerrit van Loo, who holds a political office in a little village north of Franeker. The third one, Titia, is married to a certain Frans Copal, who is engaged in business and who is said to spend much of his time in Holland. The fourth one is the wife of a Frisian gentleman of good family and some fortune, one Doede van Ockema, and the fifth one is the spouse of an artist by the name of Wybrand de Geest, a native of her own beloved town of Leeuwarden, who enjoys an excellent reputation as a portrait painter in this remote part of the world and who has done portraits of practically all of the members of the House of Orange who have ever visited Friesland.

"That, as our friends the French would say, is the 'tableau' of the immediate Uylenburgh family. There also are a vast number of uncles and aunts and cousins and second cousins and third cousins and some of them have remained at home, but others have boldly crossed the Zuyder Zee to try their luck in Amsterdam and of these you probably know more in Amsterdam than we do in Leeuwarden.

"Now as to the financial status of this Gens Uylenburghiensis. It is a most intricate matter, for as far as my informant knew, there never had been a division of the funds, and although the father had now been dead for almost twenty years, the estate had not yet been settled and it was doubtful whether a settlement would be possible at the present time, when the general fear that the war would come to an end has made money so tight that one is glad to pay twenty or even twenty-five percent for a loan of a few thousand guilders. In short, once upon a time there was a considerable fortune which belonged to the Uylenburgh children and of which they received so much per annum in the form of rents. But if any one of them should ever get into trouble and would ask for an immediate accounting, I am very doubtful whether the matter could be arranged without a dreadful sacrifice on the part of all concerned.

"Wherefore [so the letter ended], if your friend should be hard up for ready cash, I would advise him to go to the Jews and the money-lenders. They will give him better terms and they will prove to be more charitable than his beloved relations on this side of the Zuyder Zee. From all I have been able to gather, they are none too friendly towards this 'foreign' connection (any one not born within spitting distance of our beloved tower of Oldehove is considered a 'foreigner' in these parts) whose father ran a mill, whose brother is a shoemaker or some such terrible thing, who paints rabbis and associates openly with Turks and Frenchmen and other immoral races and who (something they will never forgive him) once paid 424 guilders for a picture by a certain Rubens who not only was an out-and-out Papist but who furthermore chose his subjects by preference from some heathenish story book, making it impossible for decent Christians to contemplate the same without a feeling of utter shame and mortification."

Then followed some very intimate and rather ribald remarks about the pleasant habits and manners of the populace among whom my old friend had cast his fortunes and the usual salutations in execrable Latin.

"Vale ornatissime atque eruditissime doctor medicinarum artium atque me miserum in hac urbe taediosissima visitare atque consolare festina.

"P.S.—You might send me some dried sprats as soon as the season opens. I confess to a liking for the lowly, petrified fish. In return for which I promise to keep you faithfully informed about anything that happens here in the matter of the U. family. But my general advice would be not to count on a penny. The money is there without a doubt. But how to get it away from the dear brethren and sistern—ah, my friend— there's the rub!

"P.P.S.—My wife wants to be remembered to you, ignota ignoto. She wonders whether you can find her a good cook in Amsterdam. Such a thing no longer exists in this part of the world. We have grown too prosperous. The wenches all of them marry sailors, become ladies, and go about dressed up in silks and satins.

"P.P.P.S.—I meant bloaters, and not sprats. We can get sprats here by the ton, but the bloater is a delicacy. Ad nunc, vale definitissime atque favere mihi perge. . . ."

I put the document aside and did some fast thinking. Between the lines of his crazy letter, my old friend had told me everything I wanted to know and my heart was filled with sad forebodings. For by this time I had come to know Rembrandt quite well. He lived in a world of his own making and thus far life had been fairly easy to him. Now he had undoubtedly reached a crisis. His wife was dead. He had a small boy to bring up. It would cost a great deal to maintain the house in the Breestraat and public taste was rapidly changing and no longer looked with favor upon what people had begun to call his "phantastic experiments." The fact that he had asked me (still a comparative stranger) for a loan of fifty guilders, showed that he was very hard up for ready cash. Now if he had only been made to understand that he was poor and would have to begin all over again to provide for himself and his son, all might have been well, for he was a hard worker and never spent a penny upon his own comforts. But there was this strange streak of the grand seigneur in him. He must play fairy-godfather to his poor colleagues and whenever he went to an auction, he must outbid all the professional art-dealers, just to show them that he was Rembrandt, the great Rembrandt, who need not bother about trifles.

If only he had been put face to face with the fact that he did not have a cent in the whole wide world! But he had fallen heir to Saskia's fortune! There was that pathetic will, leaving everything to her "beloved man" and leaving it without any restrictions or reservations whatsoever. If only she had insisted upon a guardian for her son, then there would have been a public appraisal and Rembrandt might have discovered what I now knew and what I could not very well tell him without running the risk of being called a busybody— a man who poked his nose into affairs that were none of his business.

My hands were tied and I was forced to stand by and see the poor fellow play the millionaire on the strength of a paper promise which was not worth its weight in lead.

Rembrandt van Rijn

Nevertheless, I might have done something, but just then an incident occurred that upset my own life so completely that it was years before I saw Rembrandt again.

And when I returned from my foreign travels, it was too late.

The bubble had burst, the house had been sold, and the painter was peddling his pictures from one pawn-shop to the next, to buy bread for his children.

THE PHOENIX, OR THE STATUE OVERTHROWN, AN ALLEGORY (ETCHING)

Chapter 13

I RELATE A FEW INTERESTING STORIES ABOUT
MY GRANDFATHER

OLD MAN (DRAWING)

AND now I come to that strange period in my life to which I have already alluded a few pages back, when through circumstances over which I had no control whatsoever, I was an exile for almost eight years.

I have always been exceedingly sorry that this happened. I can never quite get over the feeling that things might have gone differently with Rembrandt if I had been there.

I am not thinking in the first place of the financial end of things. Since the death of my grand-uncle I really had more than I needed for my very simple needs and I might have been able to help him out of a few of his difficulties. But it would not have been an easy task. For Rembrandt (as I have said so often before) was absolutely blind on the subject of money. He was indeed blind upon most subjects related directly or indirectly with the business of living a quiet and respectable existence, as those terms were understood by the vast majority of his neighbors. He was a man possessed of a single idea. Within the realm of color and form, he felt himself like unto God. His ambition along that line sometimes assumed almost divine proportions. He wanted to capture the entire existing world around him and hold it his prisoner on canvas or paper. Life, alas, was so short and there was so much to be done. He had to work and work and work. He was sick. Never mind, he must work. His wife (one of the few persons who ever assumed the shape of a

121

definite human being in his preoccupied mind) died. He must rush through the funeral and go back to work. He was acclaimed the fashionable painter of the hour and made twenty or thirty thousand guilders a year. Put them away in that cupboard over there or go to the Jew around the corner and buy out his whole stock of curiosities or give them to some poor devil of a fellow-painter who lies starving in a garret. Do anything you want with the money, as long as you don't bother him by talking about it. For he must work and life was short and there was a great deal to be done. A letter has just arrived from the sheriff saying that a number of outstanding notes are long overdue and should be paid right then and there or there would be difficulties. Visits from the Honorable Masters in Bankruptcy. Forced sales—fines—imprisonment, even. Fiddlesticks! it is winter and at three o'clock in the afternoon it is too dark to paint. One has to be economical and save every minute in times like these. The sheriff is a fool. Tell him so. Bid him come or stay away, for it is all the same as long as one can only work and work and work. No, a man like that could not be helped with an occasional check—with the loan of a few thousand guilders. They would have meant just as much to him as to a beaver busily engaged upon building a dam, or a bird constructing its nest.

All one could do for an unfortunate fellow like this, mad with the beauty of the outer world, crazy with joy at the myriad manifestations of the mysterious inner spirit, was to give him some understanding and then some more understanding and still more understanding and ask for nothing in return. Amen.

For the lovely pioneers who do the work that the rest of us shirk ask for very little. They are willing to go hungry and to slave for mean wages and to be humiliated by those who in God's own good time, in a thousand different ways, won't be allowed to hold the stirrup of their horses.

But they die unless at least once in a long while some one comes their way who stops in his tracks and bids them a cheery good-morning and casually remarks: "That is a pretty fine piece of work you are doing there."

For such is their nature.

And it is part of the penalty they pay for the greatest of their manifold blessings—the weregild they must contribute for never having grown up.

Here I must call a halt.

I had intended to write about a very dear friend, now dead and gone, and from the very beginning I had meant to keep myself and my own affairs as much as possible out of these recollections.

But when two lives are as absolutely entwined and interwoven as those of Rembrandt and my own, it is very difficult to accomplish this as completely as I meant to do it.

The next few pages therefore will be mainly about myself. But I shall be very brief and above all things, I shall try to be honest.

My grandfather was an almost mythological figure to me. I knew him well, for he did not die until I was almost thirty. But when I was young, the men who had taken part in the great struggle for liberty were fast dying out and the few survivors were regarded with that awed respect which the Greeks would have bestowed upon the Titans, had one of them managed to escape from Tartarus to find his way to Athens.

As a young man, while serving as first mate on a ship that plied between Rotterdam and Antwerp, he had once been caught with a copy of a Dutch New Testament which in the kindness of his heart he had promised to bring to a Lutheran minister awaiting a sentence of death in one of the Flemish prisons. He himself (as far as I was ever able to find out) took very little interest in theological questions. Whenever a dispute of that sort arose (and in our Republic, next to the making of money, people seem to have very few other interests) he would leave the room and whistle for his dog and go out for a walk, if it were daytime, or if it were night, go to bed and read the colloquies of Erasmus, which were an everlasting source of entertainment to him and which he could enjoy in the original, as shortly after the siege of Haarlem he had spent a year in a Spanish prison and had shared his cell with an Anabaptist preacher who happened to be quite a scholar and had whiled away the tedious hours of their common confinement by teaching his room-mate the rudiments of the Latin grammar.

No, he belonged to that vast group of men and women who had happened to be born just about the time Luther and Calvin had started their reformatory activities and who had been so thoroughly exasperated by the cruelty, the intolerance and the bigotry of both Catholics and Protestants that they had been obliged to seek a refuge among the philosophers of ancient days.

Nominally, my grandfather called himself a Christian.

In his heart, he was a contemporary of Socrates. Jesus, if he ever thought of him at all, he regarded as a well-meaning but rather futile and slightly bewildered young Jewish prophet, who in the aloofness of his primitive mountain village and totally ignorant of whatever lay beyond his own poverty-stricken hillsides (peasants always despise what they do not understand), had done more to arrest the normal development of the civilized world than any other agency, either human or divine.

He often talked to me of these matters during the last years of his life, but asked me not to mention it to any one else.

"What would be the use?" he would say. "Our wily old cousin was right. The average man is too weak to stand firmly upon his own feet. He needs some outward support, some pleasant fairy-story that shall make him forget the horrors, the boredom, the dull disappointment of his daily routine. Let him have his tales of giants and gods, his heroes and paladins.

"When you were a boy and believed in Santa Claus, Dominie Slatterius came to your father and said that this old saint was a relic of heathenism and you ought to be told and your father, being a fool, was ready to do so. I took the reverend gentleman by the scruff of the neck and threw him down the stoop and I told your father he would go the same way if he ever tried to substitute one of his dreadful Jewish fishermen or tentmakers for that amiable holy man who has made more children happy than all the church fathers and apostles together. That was not a very tolerant thing to do but look what has happened right here in our own country.

"Who started the great rebellion? A handful of men. What did they have to gain? Very little except the chance of being hung on the nearest tree. Of course, once the thing was under way, there were a lot of ardent patriots who knew that it was good fishing in troubled waters and who came over to our side. But who were the men who planned everything and took the risks and pawned their plate and their wives' diamonds and took extra mortgages on their houses to hire troops and buy guns and powder and ships and everything that was needed? A mere handful of honest fellows who hated to see poor devils of weavers and fishermen and carpenters being hacked to pieces and boiled alive and drowned like kittens merely because they happened to think differently from their neighbors upon subjects of which the neighbors couldn't possibly know more than they did themselves.

"I don't want to claim that we were saints. We were nothing of the sort. We drank and we cursed and we knew the difference between a handsome young wench and a homely old hag. And I don't swear that we would ever have moved a finger if it had not been for those endless processions of men and women, trudging patiently from the jail to the gallows, perfectly respectable citizens, hard-working little artisans with mumbling lips and staring eyes, going to be tied to a ladder and thrown into a slow-burning coal fire because they disagreed upon some utterly idiotic point of divine law with a fat old Italian who lived a thousand miles away, and who needed some money to give his daughter a suitable dowry.

"That is what started me. That and nothing else. And then, when it was all over, what did one see? The same men whom we had dragged away from the gallows by main force—those same men and women for whom we had ruined ourselves that they might think as they pleased—started murdering those who only a short while before had murdered them. The victim turned executioner, and the former executioners were now merrily dangling from a hundred trees. Could anything have been more absurd? We got rid of those hordes of mendicants and begging friars, because they were an obscene nuisance. And then, as soon as they were gone and we thought, 'Now we shall have peace,' our cities and our villages and our cross-roads and our homes were invaded by platoons of even more unpleasant brethren with long brown coats and long black faces, but every whit as stupid, as narrow-minded, as objectionable, as their pestiferous predecessors.

"What is it all about, anyway?

"I am an old man. I have spent most of my life fighting for an absurd ideal of tolerance. And as soon as we had kicked the enemy out of the front door, he came in again by the back entrance.

"Bring me a pipe of tobacco and let me sit and smoke. It is the only sensible thing besides raising strawberries, and for that I am no longer young enough."

These conversations (and we had many of them, and they were all of them more or less alike) were typical of the old skipper and it will give you an idea of the sort of man he was. He must have been a terrific fighter in his day. He stood six feet three in his stockings and weighed well over two hundred pounds. He once figured out that he had passed through six formal sieges and taken part in eighteen naval engagements, not to mention skirmishes and three pitched battles upon those not infrequent occasions when the sailors waded ashore and joined the infantry. Several times he had been badly wounded, but he had the constitution of a young ox and even recovered from the blood-lettings with which in those early days my colleagues tried to cure everything from a broken leg to a case of anemia.

At one time or another in his career he must have accumulated considerable wealth. He once told me that during the expedition against Cadiz, when he commanded the second squadron, his share of the plunder alone amounted to fifty thousand ducats, and that was only one occasion among many when he had a plentiful chance to line his pockets with Spanish doubloons. What had become of all this money, I don't know. Nobody seemed to know. But he was the incarnation of generosity. He was so absolutely open-handed that in the middle of a battle he would have given his sword to his enemy, had the latter asked him for it, and would have continued to fight with his bare hands rather than say no to a courteous request.

Not that he was exactly poor when I came to know him a little better. He lived in a very decent house on the river front near Rotterdam and after the death of my grandmother he kept but a single servant, an old sailor whom he had once saved from being hung for an act of insubordination—a most excusable case of insubordination, as he explained to me, for the fellow had merely gone on shore to kill a landlubber who had stolen his girl from him. The old sailor was not only his devoted servant but also a perfect cook.

To return to my grandfather, he spent very little money upon his personal adornment, but a great deal upon books, and until the last years of his life he kept a small sailing-boat with which he used to putter around from morning till night and which at last was the cause of his death, for one day, leaving the harbor of Brielle, he saw how a small boy, who had been bombarding his craft with chunks of dried mud, lost his balance and fell into the water and was on the point of being carried away by the tide. He jumped overboard, saved the brat, gave him a most terrific walloping and continued his voyage without bothering to change his clothes. That night he had a chill and three days later he was dead from pneumonia, a fitting end for one who had spent his life doing the sort of things he had done.

When his last will and testament was opened, it was found that he had left every cent he possessed to an old sailors' home on condition that once a year a rousing feast be given to all the inmates upon which occasion they were to be allowed to get as drunk and hilarious as they pleased.

On the last day of his life he was visited by a minister. Rumor had gone about that the old skipper was on the point of dying and it seemed inconceivable that any one should go to his final rest without a word of commendation on the part of a duly ordained clergyman. The Reverend Doctor who made his appearance was a genial soul, the only one among the fourteen local shepherds who had sometimes been suspected of certain worldly inclinations. In the language of that day he was a "libertine," a man who took liberties with Holy Writ and who was more interested in the spiritual message of Jesus than in the color of the cloak he had worn while delivering it. Upon this occasion his brethren had probably delegated him to call upon the dying sinner, as the one least likely to be shown the door. And the good dominie acquitted himself of his task with great dexterity, being neither too cordial nor too distant and aloof. He casually remarked that most people when they found themselves on the point of reporting for duty to the Great Commander of us all (a bit of joviality which was not appreciated by the patient) liked to have the opportunity to discuss their past record with some one who devoted all his time to matters of the soul.

"Dominie," the old man answered, "I know who you are and I have heard a good deal about you that I like. For one thing, most of your colleagues wish that you would slip on an apple skin and fall in a canal and drown. In this house, that is a recommendation. But what could you possibly hope to do for me?"

"Well," the reverend gentleman replied, "we might have a little

ILLUSTRATION FOR THE OLD TESTAMENT (DRAWING)

talk about your chances of salvation. What, for example, has been your attitude towards the Lord's most holy covenants?"

"Yes," said my grandfather, "that is rather a leading question, but I like your courage and I will answer you. I think your Ten Commandments are a waste of time."

"But isn't that a dangerous remark for a man who is on the brink of the grave?"

"I don't see why. I am perfectly willing to have this out with the Lord himself. The best proof that he does not believe in them himself is the fact that he has never kept them."

"That is pure blasphemy!"

"Not in the least. But short of keeping the Sabbath, he has broken every one of them."

"I am afraid that I have nothing to say to you."

"Now there you go again, like a good Christian! Have a moment's patience with a dying man and I will explain. How about that idea of not killing your fellow men? My dear friend, the whole Old Testament is full of killing. Your Jehovah is a mean and vindictive creature and suffers from tantrums like any badly brought up child.

128

Rembrandt van Rijn

ILLUSTRATION FOR THE NEW TESTAMENT (DRAWING)

When he has one of his attacks (and almost anything may bring them on) he hits and strikes and thumps and prances like a drunken sailor in a bar-room brawl. Villages, towns, whole nations are wiped off the face of the earth—and what have they done? Often nothing for which an ordinary magistrate would dare to fine them.

"Take that business in Egypt. It has always struck me that the Egyptians were completely in the right. After all, it was their country. After all, the Jews had come to them to keep from starving to death and they had been pretty decently treated too. And according to what I have heard of them, they were a fine people—much nicer than their guests who were like the cuckoo and always put their eggs into another bird's nest. But they must be visited with all sorts of plagues and lose their children and suffer hunger and pestilence because your absurd Jehovah had another attack of anger and wanted to do a little smiting."

The minister looked perplexed. "I never heard it explained quite that way," he remarked.

"I am sure you never did and I am sorry if I should hurt your feelings. But that happens to be the way I look upon it."

"Anyway," in a feeble effort to spar for time, "that happened before he gave us his precious Law."

"Precious Law indeed! But afterwards it was just as bad. I know he kept the Sabbath, but that is about all. It was easy for him to tell us to honor our parents, as he did not have any himself to exasperate him with their everlasting complaints about being an 'undutiful child.' And as for the seventh commandment, have you ever thought of the way Joseph must have looked upon this divine command about respecting the integrity of another man's wife?"

The minister made ready to go, but the sick man held him back. "Don't go, Dominie," he said. "If this hurts your feelings, we will talk of something else."

"It does not hurt my feelings," the minister replied, "but it fills my heart wth grief that any one who has spent his whole life among Christians should speak and think the way you do."

"That is just it! I have spent my whole life among Christians. When I was forty, I made a vow. I said to myself that if I met three Christians who really and truly lived up to the lessons of their Master—three men or women who were truly humble and kind and tolerant and forgiving—yet professed themselves to belong to your creed, I would join the Church."

"And now you are how old?"

"Eighty-two, though I shall never see eighty-three."

"And you are still a pagan."

"No, Dominie, I am not that either."

"Then what do you call yourself?"

"Exactly what I am. Look here," and with great effort he pulled his night-gown from his left shoulder, for he was in terrible pain and very weak. "Look at this. Can you still see it after these sixty years? A big red letter H. The Inquisition burned it on my back so that if they ever caught me again, they would know me as a heretic and could treat me accordingly. When I come to the Gates of Heaven, I will show Saint Peter this and I am sure he will let me in, for what was he himself but a heretic when he turned his back upon the law of his fathers? And I will come to the throne of God and I will show him this and I will say: 'Holy Father, I fought sixty years for what I believed to be right and that red H is all I got to show for my labors. They gave it to me because I felt, like a very wonderful sage of olden times, that the still small voice from within was the best guide to follow in dealing with one's fellow men.

" 'They burned it into my quivering flesh because they said I was a heretic—a person who did not hold with the established opinions. They meant it as a disgrace, but I have worn it as a badge of honor ever since. I don't know, God, what your intentions were with us poor mortals. Perhaps you ought to have devoted another week or fortnight to the business of getting our world started, for although I mean no offense, it is a pretty sad mess at the present moment and if all the history I have read means anything, it has been a muddle ever since you turned your back upon it and left us to the mercies of old Adam. Now I may be all wrong, but the only way in which I can see that anything will ever be accomplished is for some of us now and then to take an unpopular stand. The aye-sayers never get anywhere. But the no-sayers irritate the rest of their neighbors occasionally into doing the right thing. And I am a no-sayer, a heretic, a man who does not hold with the majority. As long as you turned me loose into this world with a mind of my own, I took it for granted that you meant me to do something with it.

" 'But that meant that I had to have doubts, to ask questions, to take every problem apart and see what I could make of it. Blame me and punish me, God, if I have done wrong, but I would have disgraced your Holy Name had I done differently and not used that brain you put into my skull to the best of my ability to show my fellow men the way to a more reasonable world.' "

The old man exhausted himself by this supreme effort and lay panting for breath. The minister, who was really a very kindly person, tried to change the subject.

"Our Heavenly Father no doubt will know how to answer that question better than I can hope to do. But how about this world? You were a mariner. You depended upon a compass to set your course. And yet you lived without a single rule by which to guide your conduct."

The old man opened his eyes and smiled, though very feebly. "I am sorry, Dominie, but once more you are mistaken. I was quite young when I learned that my fellow men had to be loved in spite of themselves, not to speak of trusting them. The only creature that I could depend upon, besides my wife (but she was an exception), was a dog. And I have never been without one since I was a boy of fifteen.

"I know you don't think very much of dogs. You won't even let them have a soul or go to Heaven. Think of golden streets with nothing but holy people and not a single dog! No, I have never spent either a day or a night without one of those four-footed companions. They cost me a lot of time, but they amply repaid me for my trouble. For dogs are very wise. Much wiser than men. People say they can't speak. Perhaps they know how but refuse to use their voice to save themselves an endless amount of bother and vague discussion. But they know all sorts of things we don't know, and they have a finer feeling for the difference between right and wrong than we do. And when I came home at night, or back to my ship, after the day's work (and pretty rough work it was at times), I would look my dog in the face and if he still wagged his tail at me, I knew that everything was all right, but if he didn't, I knew that something, somewhere, had gone wrong. It may sound a bit simple, but it is true, and best of all, it worked."

"And our system does not work?"

"Your system does not work. It merely talks and now if you will pardon me, I will go to sleep. I am not very strong any more and to-morrow, if you are right, I will have to engage in another conversation of this sort, and I still have to prepare my little speech."

"And if I am wrong?"

"If you are wrong, I shall be able to rest—rest for ever and ever."

"Then you are very tired?"

"Incredibly tired."

"Of living?"

"No, just of having been alive," and with this the sick man pulled the blankets around his shoulders and never spoke again.

The next morning the sailor-servant came to open the curtains and ask after his master's wishes.

But the skipper had received an answer to all his questions.

He was dead.

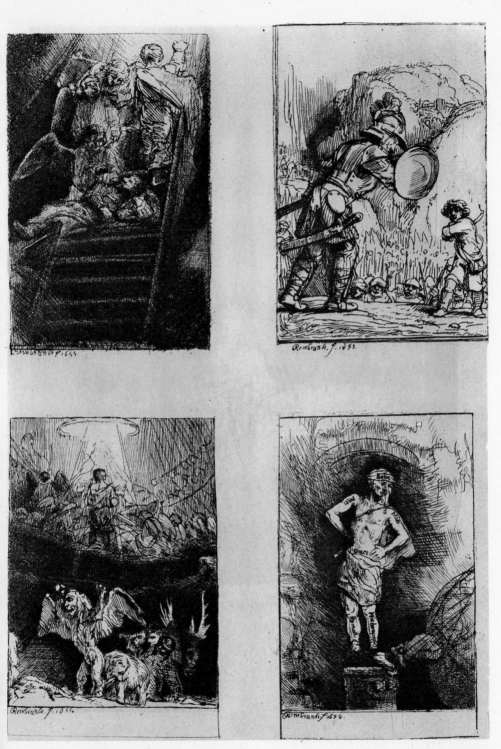

ILLUSTRATIONS FOR MENASSEH'S BOOK ON NEBUCHADNEZZAR (ETCHINGS)

POTIPHAR'S WIFE ACCUSING JOSEPH (PAINTING)

Chapter 14

REMBRANDT ASKS ME TO CALL

THE RETURN OF THE PRODIGAL SON (DRAWING)

A SINNER in our town was a sinner. He had offended the majesty of God and must bear the punishment, no matter how undeservedly.

That same evening I called on one of the Burgomasters who was under some slight obligation to me, as I had once taken care of his oldest boy and had pulled him through a very dangerous attack of croup. I explained to him what had happened and he sent his maid out (very few of our rich people dared to employ male servants, as this smacked too much of foreign manners) with a note for the High Sheriff, asking him to call for a few moments. The Sheriff came and promised that he would do his best to get some information upon the unfortunate incident. Meanwhile, the corpse of my brother remained in the dissecting room, for he was supposed to have come to his end as the result of "being the participant in an act of violence with one or more persons whose identity remained unknown." And according to the laws of Amsterdam, such a person could not be given proper burial but was either handed over to the medical profession or hanged from the gibbet outside the gate until his body rotted away or was devoured by the birds.

Fortunately the Sheriff was a very active man. In less than twenty-four hours, he came to my house with his news.

Two of his assistants had made a round of the different taverns and the first one reported as follows:

Three people, two men and a woman, apparently English, though one of them spoke fluent Dutch, had come to Amsterdam last Monday and had taken rooms in the inn run by an old woman known as Mother Joosten. They had stayed indoors most of the time, claiming that they still felt indisposed from the voyage which had been exceptionally rough and they had had their meals sent up to their rooms. One of the men drank a great deal and seemed to quarrel with the woman, who was apparently his wife. On Tuesday at about five they had gone out. Mother Joosten had asked them whether they needed anything for the night and they had said no, but the smaller of the two men had turned to her and had shown her a piece of paper on which he had written the word Houtgracht, indicating by gestures that he wanted to know where that street was. She had told him as best she could and they had departed.

Late that same evening the husband and wife had returned and had asked that their bill be prepared as they were obliged to leave early the next morning. Then they had told their landlady that they wanted to take another stroll and had gone out in the darkness.

In the morning when Mother Joosten knocked on their door, there had been no answer. The man and the woman were gone. They had left their baggage behind. It consisted of one very shabby leather trunk, containing a few odds and ends of personal apparel, without any value. The bill of nineteen florins and eighty cents (most of this had gone for gin) remained unpaid. (Bill annexed to the report.)

The second constable had followed their track after they had left the place of Mother Joosten. They apparently had started out to find me, for in the "King of Bohemia" where they had eaten and where one of the two men had drunk a great deal of French wine, they had once more asked the shortest road to the Houtgracht. When they left, the smaller of the two men was apparently very much under the influence of liquor and had stumbled across the door-step. He would have fallen if the woman had not caught him, but instead of being grateful to her for this assistance, he had cursed her and the other man had intervened and had suggested that they had better go home. But the smaller of the two men had said no, and had added something to the effect that that night would serve them as well as any other. Thereupon they had departed and it had been impossible to retrace their track.

They apparently had visited several other taverns but the innkeepers, fearing that they might be implicated in a scandal and a scandal connected with murder and highway robbery (for my brother's pockets were absolutely empty when the body was found) had all of them lied like troopers. Yes, they had seen three people who answered the description given of them, but they had only entered their place of business for a moment and then had gone away, apparently in the best of spirits, and that was all they knew, until the moment some highly respectable citizens, returning from a wedding, had stumbled across the dead body and had warned the police.

Under the circumstances and since it was becoming fairly evident that the victim had not been killed in a fight but had been deliberately murdered when he refused to show his companions the way to my house, Their Lordships felt that they might make an exception. They could not very well give me permission to bury my brother in one of the churches, but they had no objection if I could find room for him in one of the yards surrounding those places of worship where occasionally some of the poorer people were interred. I followed him to his grave one drab and rainy morning. But when I reached the cemetery, I found my three friends waiting for me. How they knew or how they had ever found out, I am unable to tell. But they were there and when the coffin had been silently lowered into the grave, Bernardo took a small book from his pocket and opened it.

"This poor man has suffered much," he said. "We will therefore bid him farewell with one short chapter of consolation." And he read the one hundred and thirtieth psalm. Then the sexton and his helpers quickly filled the grave and we went home.

At the bridge of the Saint Anthonie Lock, I bade them farewell, but Jean-Louys followed me.

"Friends," he said, "are the only dependable refuge in time of sorrow." And he came and stayed with me and said very little, but whenever I went out or whenever I returned home, he was there with a pleasant smile and a cheerful word of welcome. God knows how I would otherwise have pulled through those dreadful weeks.

And one evening, a few days later, a small flat package was brought to the house. Inside of it was a copy of an etching of "The Return of the Prodigal," and underneath it, in pencil, the words: "In Memoriam. Come and see me and let me share your sorrow. Rembrandt."

SKETCH (DRAWING)

Chapter 15

I HAVE THE HONOR TO DINE WITH ONE OF THE BURGOMASTERS

THE GOLF PLAYER (ETCHING)

WHEN I was a small boy I was taught that all of life was tragedy, and when I grew a little older I sometimes tried to convince myself that all of life was comedy, but now, when I am fast approaching the traditional threescore and ten, I know that both those definitions were wrong.

Life is neither tragedy nor comedy, it is melodrama and melodrama of such a primitive sort that should any playwright dare to put it on the stage, his work would be hooted off the boards and he himself would be publicly derided as an impostor.

Here was my brother, the most peaceful and lovable of men—a hard-working and intelligent craftsman—just the sort of person to be the father of a cheerful family, spending the greater part of his days in quest of the unfindable and left for dead on the door-step of a mean ale-house. And there I was myself—a person with just one interest in life—to sit quietly in my study and try to find some way to alleviate the suffering of sick humanity—at best a very timid creature—rather afraid of life and perfectly willing to spend all my days in the same house on the same street in the same city with the same faithful friends—suddenly condemned to go to the other end of the earth and to spend eight long and lonely years in a wilderness which no white man had ever visited before.

It was all very strange and yet it seemed so hopelessly unavoidable. The hand of Fate was clearly discernible in everything that happened. I struggled as all of mankind has struggled since the beginning of time. I objected. I fought back. I cursed. I insisted upon an answer. And the gods whispered "Inevitable" and again withdrew behind the high clouds in indifferent aloofness.

Plainly it was impossible for me to continue much longer in a town where every stick and stone reminded me of the calamity that had overtaken me. My friends recognized this. They urged me to take a trip, to visit some of the universities of Italy where I would be able to see and hear much that would be of interest to my own investigations. But I lacked the courage and the energy.

I did my work and went to the hospital at the usual hours and made my rounds and saw my patients, but I resembled one of those automatic machines they make in Nuremberg—one that had been wound up long ago and the key of which had been mislaid by a careless servant.

Every day I felt myself grow a little weaker. Like most people of these northern climes, I had a very decided tendency towards melancholia. Thus far I had always rather despised the infamous "black humor" as a confession of moral weakness. And now, so help me God, I too was fast becoming one of its victims.

A few more weeks or months and I would begin to feel sorry for myself. That, as I well knew, was the beginning of the end. The next step would be a slow trip to the cemetery. Not from any wish to die so long before my time, but from a sheer lack of interest in keeping alive.

And then, just when I was beginning to tell everybody that the music had gone out of existence (I rather fancied that expression) and that the sky had lost its color and the flowers had lost their fragrance, in short, when I was beginning to be a terrible nuisance both to myself and to those who were patient enough to bear up with me, the "unexpected inevitable" or the "inevitable unexpected" that always stands hidden in the wings of the magnificent theater devoted to Human Folly, suddenly jumped to the center of the stage, whacked me gayly on the head with the jawbone of Balaam's ass, picked me up, threw me bodily across a couple of seas and oceans and left me stranded high and dry amidst such strange surroundings that I was soon forced to forget all about my own woes or suffer the indignity of being eaten up by a wolf or a bear. And the beginning of these strange adventures came to me in the form of a note which was delivered to me early one morning and in which

Rembrandt van Rijn

My Lord Andries Bicker requested the pleasure of my company at his house on such and such a date for dinner and a private talk afterwards.

And this in itself was rather mysterious, for the Burgomasters of our good city did not as a rule extend their hospitality to private citizens like myself. It is true that I had visited his house once or twice in my professional capacity, but that was hardly a social introduction. And most of my neighbors still regarded me as a better-class barber. To-day the study of medicine is beginning to be elevated to the dignity of a science, and a few of us actually rank a little higher than mere leeches or pill-purveyors. But thirty years ago no mayor of the sovereign city of Amsterdam would break bread with a humble disciple of Aesculapius unless there was something he wanted to get from him and wanted very much indeed.

My Lord Andries Bicker was one of four brothers, who on the death of their father had inherited his vast fortune and then quietly divided the entire world among themselves as if it had been a parcel of real estate in one of the suburbs. There were those who said that the Republic ought not to be called the United Seven Netherlands but the United Four Bickerlands, and they were right. I have never been much interested in financial affairs. Perhaps that is not quite correct. I am interested in them, but in a vague sort of a way. Figures and statistics mean nothing to me at all. Tell me to-day that last year we imported eight hundred thousand lemons and four million pounds of rice and five hundred thousand pounds of almonds or that ten years ago the East India Company paid a 22½ percent dividend and last year only 18 percent and I shall answer you very politely, "Yes, indeed, how very interesting!" But an hour later, I shall have forgotten all about it. But tell me that Jansen's father died of such and such a disease and his grandfather of such and such an affliction and if I am called in to see this same Jansen, fifty years hence, I shall have half my diagnosis ready before I have even entered the sick-room.

My grandfather, who was what you call a "practical man," more than once had held the Bicker family up for my youthful admiration. "The backbone of our country," he used to say. "Honest, hard-working people. There is no foolishness about them. In any other country they would be dukes and grandees and live in fine castles, and give themselves airs." (Grandfather could play the plain, simple democrat with great effect on such occasion.) "Just look at them! They must have two hundred ships between them and more shares in the big companies than any one else. Their income is a hundred times larger than that of many a German princeling who goes about boasting of his titles and his ancestors. And yet they continue to live right here in the midst of their wharves and breweries and storehouses and they tell me that they eat meat only once a week, like any ordinary citizen."

But these breweries and wharves and store-houses and those shares in East and West India companies and North Pole companies and South Pole companies meant nothing to me. But I had known both the father and the mother of these remarkable brothers and I was a good friend of the physician who had taken care of them for a number of years and I could have told any one of them offhand what he should eat and drink and what he should avoid and (had he been interested) I could have foretold him with a very fair degree of accuracy what illness would eventually take him to his grave. But as body and soul are not two different entities, as the church fathers of the Middle Ages told us, but are different expressions of one and the same mysterious occurrence, which we call life, I felt that I did not go too hopelessly unprepared to this strange meeting and that I would be able to hold my own in the conversation that was to follow, for I would understand the probable trend of thought of my host much better than he could possibly comprehend mine. Not that I expected anything very unusual. His Lordship probably contemplated some change in the conduct of the city's hospitals and wanted to consult a physician before he introduced the subject in the meeting of Their Lordships the Burgomasters.

But it turned out quite differently, as I was soon to experience.

Our dinner too was more elaborate than I had anticipated. The whole family was present and I was introduced to the ladies of the household, which was a signal honor to a member of my humble profession.

I was even taken aside to accept the solemn salutation of a very pretty little girl of six or seven, with a rich abundance of auburn curls. She made me a very pretty curtsey and said, "Good afternoon, Doctor," and I bowed low and kissed her hand with great formality.

(For people are mistaken when they think that children don't observe our manners just as closely as we do theirs.) And I said, "Good afternoon, my dear, and what might your name be?" And she answered, "Wendela, sir, and I am staying with Uncle Andries because my sister has got the mumps," and then made me another curtsey and shyly ran back to her aunt who kissed her and said, "And now good night, little Mamselle, it is time you were in your coach with the white horses," whereupon she asked, "May I have just one pear?" and proudly marched off with her possession tightly clutched in her small right hand, the left one holding her long silken petticoats for fear that she might trip on the stairs.

I was not to see her again for a good many years and then under very different circumstances. For she afterwards married My Lord de Witt, whom many esteem the greatest statesman of our age, and she had a number of children, but after her last confinement in '65 she never quite recovered and I was called in on consultation and I had to tell her that as far as she was concerned, the Book of Life was closed and that another birth would mean the death both of herself and of her child, an announcement which seemed to fill her heart with great grief, "For," said she, "my husband is away so much of the time on business of state, and what shall I do to pass away the lonely hours, when the nursery is empty?"

But to return to our dinner. It was excellent and it was short, the highest praise one can give to that sort of function. It consisted of oysters and soup and a large roasted capon. "We ought to have sacrificed a cock to Aesculapius to-night," My Lord Andries explained while carving the fowl, "but seeing that it is not Aesculapius himself, but merely his trusted disciple, we thought that a capon would do just as well. Besides, these beasts are infinitely more tender than their less incomplete brethren." And he offered me the drumstick, which was another token of honor for which I was not in the least prepared.

"These good people want something from me," I said to myself, and I soon found out that I was right. For immediately the feast had been served, the women bade us good day and my host and his brother Cornelis suggested that I follow them upstairs and they took me to a large room in the front of the house, the walls of which were entirely covered with book-cases and maps, and bade me sit down in a low chair by the side of a large globe, and then the maid came in with a tray containing bottles of French wines and of Malaga and Madeira and glasses, and My Lord Andries filled me a glass and said, "Try this wine. It comes from Burgundy. It grew on the estate of a man who for fifty years faithfully served the King of France. Then he committed an act, most honorable in itself, but which went contrary to the personal interests of his sovereign. He died in the Bastille and my brother and I, who had had business dealings with him, bought his vineyard to keep his wife from going to the poor-house. Here is your good health."

And my Lord Cornelis took a large copper box, filled with tobacco, out of his pocket and, handing me a fresh clay pipe, he said, "Try this noble weed. It is of the same quality as that smoked by Sir Walter Raleigh on his way to the scaffold. He also had wasted fifty years of his life waiting upon a queen who called him an atheist for all his troubles and threw him over to please a silly boy who was her lover and serving a king who cut off his head as soon as he failed to find him that gold mine which everybody knew did not exist."

And then both brothers, lifting their glasses, said, "Here is to ourselves. God knows, we are coming on hard times."

And when my looks showed that I was slightly bewildered by this strange performance, they bade me light my pipe again (I always forget to keep those clay contraptions going and wish that some one would invent us a more agreeable way of inhaling the pleasant fumes of nicotine) and Cornelis said, "Fear not, dear Doctor, we have not lost our reason," and Andries added, "This is just our little joke, and now let us come to business," and he delivered quite a speech, which seemed so important to me that as soon as I returned home that evening, I wrote down everything I remembered of it and here are my notes of that evening.

"Doctor," he began, "we want your help. Perhaps you will think that we are slightly crazy but I can assure you that neither of us ever was in better health. Only one thing I must beg of you. All this must remain strictly between ourselves. Nothing is ever accomplished in an open meeting. God himself could not rule this world if he had to discuss everything he did with a dozen committees of archangels and was surrounded all the time by a mob of common little angels who more than half of the time would not know what he was talking about. What we are about to propose to you can only serve the weal of our own fatherland. But if our plans are to succeed, we must keep them a secret. At least for quite a number of years."

And when I had nodded my assent, he continued: "I don't want to give you a lecture on current politics, but you are no fool. Otherwise I need not assure you we would never have sent for you, which I mean as a compliment though perhaps I am a little too direct, but you have a good pair of eyes and an excellent pair of ears and you know just as well as I what is actually happening and more important still, what is going to happen in a couple of years.

"Of course you have heard what they say about us. That we run the Republic as if it were our own property. Well, what of it? We are business men. It is our duty to show profits. Is there any one who dares to claim that we don't make money? We make it for ourselves, but by making it for ourselves, we make it for every one else. Has this town ever been as rich as it has since the day our father joined the government? Has the Republic ever been as mighty as in these days when I and my brothers tell them how things ought to be done? There are a lot of lazy loafers who spend their waking hours in the taverns drinking mean gin and telling each other that we are tyrants, that we ought to be assassinated, that in ancient Greece and in ancient Rome the people ruled the state. Perhaps they are right, but this isn't ancient Rome nor ancient Greece. This is the Republic of the United Seven Netherlands and we now write the year of our Lord 1642.

"No, that 'vox populi' business and all that nonsense about democracy and Brutus and Caesar won't get us anywhere. Nor, to tell the truth, will it do us much harm. We are in power and we feel that we exercise this power for the common good. We therefore mean to keep it firmly in our own hands and we can do it, as the rabble will discover the moment it tries to start something. We are peaceful burghers. I and my brother would not harm a fly. But we must have law and order and prosperity! Let any one dare to interfere with us and he will swing outside the Town Hall windows and no mistake about it!

"But there is one little item that worries us a good deal. Some day, very soon, the war with Spain will come to an end. We are practically independent now, but when peace is signed, the whole world will have to recognize us as a sovereign commonwealth. What is going to happen then? And what will the House of Orange try to do? We have always been on good terms with those Germans. Old William was a great man. I have heard our grandfather speak about him. He knew him well. And so did our father. A very great man, wise and shrewd and very liberal. Not much of a soldier, but then the world is full of soldiers, and statesmen are as rare as roses in January. A terrible pity he was murdered just when we needed him so badly. A great many things would have turned out differently had he lived just a couple of years longer. But that is the way it goes in this world, and no use crying over spilt milk.

"His sons too have been very useful. But in a different way. Old William was a man of learning, a man of taste. He had vision and knew what was what. He would have made a good business executive. He knew how to row with the oars that were at his disposal. If he needed the support of the church party to further the interests of the land, he would go and associate with the ministers of the Gospel. If he thought that they were going too far and were trying to dominate the situation (and give that sort of people one finger and they will try to take the whole hand), he tactfully but sternly reminded them of their proper place and they went back into Clio's box until they were needed again. When there was fighting to be done, he not only found an army (and mind you, most of the time his treasury was completely empty, and did you ever hear of a professional soldier who fought for the love of the thing?) but he accomplished the impossible by enlisting the good will of all the different elements that under the leadership of a less clever man would have cut each other's throats long before they had seen a single enemy. But once the fighting was done, back they went again into their little wooden box, and that was that. He played on men and their emotions as old Sweelinck plays on his organ and as a result we had a decently balanced form of government. The Republic, as he saw it in his mind's eye, could have lived and might have lasted longer than even Venice or Genoa. But then he was murdered, and we got his sons.

"Excellent fighting men. Old Maurice never had a thought in his head except that it had to do with guns or horses or regiments of foot or ordnance. In the summer he laid siege to cities and in the winter he laid siege to women and I never heard of him to fail in getting whatever he wanted.

"But he was a German. His father had been a German too, but somehow or other, one never thought of him that way. He belonged to the world at large, but Maurice, for all his fine palaces and his courts and his gentlemen-in-waiting, always reminded me of an ordinary landjunker. He always smelled of horses and of stale beer, and when he dined at our house, we had to keep the windows open for a week afterwards.

"I am telling you now a few of our professional secrets. The crowd believes that the Stadholders of the Republic and the Burgomasters of Amsterdam are bosom friends, all coöperating most heartily for the ultimate benefit of our common country. Let them believe what they will. As long as we remain safely seated on those comfortable cushions of the Town Hall, we can afford a few amiable fairy-tales of that sort.

"But how long will we be able to hide the fact that we are really at cross-purposes? How soon before the man in the street discovers that all is not well? It has already happened once, upon one memorable occasion of which I need not remind you. Undoubtedly you are old enough to remember that terrible Monday the thirteenth. The greatest man our country had produced so far was murdered that day and murdered by the people for whom he had slaved for more than fifty years of his life. He had understood what few people before him suspected, that we were fast drifting towards a monarchy, and that the Republic would become another little German principality as soon as the Prince was allowed to forget that we, the people who make this commonwealth what it is, are his employers and pay him his salary as we pay that of any of our other servants.

"But of course Maurice would have been helpless without some political organization to back him up in his plans. I don't know who the bright man was who suggested that he make common cause with the church party, but he did. And ever since, none of us have been quite safe. What happened to Oldenbarneveldt may happen to any of us almost any day. The present Stadholder is not a very strong man. He suffers from violent outbursts of temper and such people are always easily managed. Besides, he is too busy with his army. A marvelous fellow in his own field! Bois-le-Duc, Maastricht, Breda, Roermond, Wezel, he captured them all as neatly and as easily as a good chess-player takes the pawns of his opponent. And not a single false move. But he is wasting himself physically. By the time he gets the last Spaniard out of our last city, he will be dead. He has a weak chest. Mark my words, we will sign our peace over his coffin.

"And then, what will become of all those German junkers who are now making a fine living as officers in our armies? We shall let our troops go the moment the war is over. Those captains and colonels and quartermaster-generals will all be out of a job and they won't like it. They have grown accustomed to three or four square meals a day, and plenty of wine. Do you think they will ever content themselves with the watery gruel of their beloved homeland, the beer-soup of Pomerania? I doubt it, and if all we hear of the way in which the Emperor's troops and the Swedes are chasing each other across the German lands is true, there won't be much even of that.

"Well, you can draw your own conclusions. They will want to remain right here where it is nice and comfortable and warm and where even the beggars won't touch their charity porridge unless it has about half a pound of sugar in it. And how will they accomplish this? By making themselves indispensable. And to whom? To the only man who has any need of their services, to the Prince.

"It is all very well to be the highest paid official in the Republic. But it would be a great deal more agreeable to step out of the salaried class and become an independent little potentate. I am not saying anything against the young prince. He is only a child. But at sixteen, a boy in his position is old enough to give us some inkling about his character and I don't trust that infant. I don't trust him for a moment! If he merely aspired to his father's place, why was he in such a hurry to marry the daughter of King Charles? Charles is hard up for money. He is having troubles with his people. I can't blame the people much, for their beloved sovereign seems a pretty slippery customer and he is costing them the devil of a lot of money. But of course he needs all the help he can get and so our young princeling was able to marry himself a princess of the blood at the moment that dear lady was going cheap.

"Well, what will he do next? He has the army, for as I have just pointed out to you, the officers know on which side their bread is buttered and a pleasant and solvent miniature court right here in Amsterdam or perhaps in The Hague would suit them remarkably well.

Rembrandt van Rijn

"But the army alone is not enough. We still have credit with the banks. We could send to Switzerland for a dozen regiments of infantry or we could buy half a dozen army corps from the Emperor, with cavalry and horses and all, enough to make an end to all this foolishness. And the navy is on our side and if the worst came to the worst, we could bring the men on shore and they are rough customers. But there are still a number of other people in this land of ours who have mighty little love for us and who would rally to anybody who promised them a chance to get even with their betters. That is the church party.

"I am a good Christian myself, as my father has been before me, and my mother too, and as I hope that my children will be after me. But those (and here His Lordship used a number of terms which I had never expected to hear from his lips and which I deem it wiser not to repeat)—but those stupid, narrow-minded, vainglorious plowboys, who have spent four years in some theological seminary and then come to town and frighten the rabble with their cock and bull stories about punishment and Hell and try to tell us—us!—how we should run the government of our own city and our own country! No, thank you, I'd rather flood the land again as they did when old Prince William was still alive and die in the last ditch than give in to these fellows one-tenth of an inch.

"And that, I think, is the way all of us feel in the Town Hall. Well, of course the dominies know it and the Prince knows it and all his uncles and nephews and bastard little cousins know it. And there you have the lay of the land. As soon as the war with Spain is over, the war at home will begin. On the one hand, we, the merchants who have made this country what it is, and on the other hand the Prince, who wants to become a king, and the rabble that believe everything he promises them and that see in him their savior who will lead them out of what they are pleased to call the wilderness of paganism into the promised land of that terrible man, Calvin."

Now when my Lord Andries got to this point, I thought it was time to rise respectfully to a few points of doubt. In the first place, had the House of Orange really ever had such ambitions as he had just implied? Surely, if they had wanted to make themselves the absolute rulers of the country, they could have done so repeatedly ere now. And in the second place, was he quite fair to the humble men and women who had fought and starved and died like flies during the first years of the great struggle for freedom and who had silently and contentedly borne such sufferings as would have broken the spirit of almost any other nation? But the Burgomaster was right there with his answer:

"I follow your objections," he said, "but don't you see that all this has changed completely since we practically gained our freedom? I will say this much for the doctrines of the learned Doctor Calvin, they absolutely suited the circumstances of the time. They were an excellent code of behavior for a town that was in a state of siege. They made men hard and women invincible. They put iron into the souls even of small children. It was a system that even the veterans of that old cut-throat Alva could not break. When he took Haarlem and drowned a couple of hundred of our people, they would grasp at the executioners with their dying fingers and would try to drag them down with them.

WILLIAM THE SECOND, PRINCE OF ORANGE
(ETCHING)

"But that sort of religion is of no earthly use to any one in times of peace. It is like the hammer of a smith that needs an anvil in order to function properly. Take the anvil away and it is just a useless tool that smashes people's toes when it is handed about and gets in everybody's way. Our ministers knew this and they still know it to-day. They must be forever standing on the ramparts of some beleaguered town. They must go snooping through the streets looking for hidden traitors. They must exhort and expostulate and urge and incite their poor disciples as if the enemy were still at the gate, ready to plunder and rape as did the soldiers of His Most Catholic Majesty. They must keep the people in a white-hot rage against some threatening iniquity in their midst or go out of business altogether. And so forever they are keeping the country in unrest and are forever setting the crowd off on a wild-goose chase after a bugaboo that in reality does not exist.

"One day they clamor for the head of Oldenbarneveldt and keep the people happy with the lurid details of his execution. Then they must appoint a commission to examine the old man's affairs and show the world what a scoundrel he has been and behold! the commission reports that never in their lives have they come across so much honesty. That ends the search in that particular direction. But they are right away on the scent of a group of other miscreants and this time it is the members of some unfortunate sect that does not see fit to think of the Trinity as the old man in Geneva did.

"The Trinity is far removed from human affairs and it will be a long time before we shall really find out who is right in the matter. But that is a detail about which they don't bother. Those people don't think the way we do. Therefore they are in the pay of Satan. To the gallows with them! They made poor Hoogerbeets hang himself. De Groot is an exile somewhere in Sweden or France. And a couple of hundred of perfectly harmless preachers, some of the best and kindliest of men who ever trod this earth, are deprived of their livelihood, are making a living as bakers' assistants, have turned cobblers, have fled to one of those dreadful towns in northern Germany where they have to send their children begging in order to keep alive. All that is the work of the men of the Great Synod.

"They are ideal shepherds for those who believe that they have seen the Devil sliding down our chimney on a long black broomstick and that we are making ready to massacre the children of Zion just as soon as the necessary formalities shall have been fulfilled with the King of Darkness.

"You think that I exaggerate? Well, think of what happened when you were young and the fights we had to fight right here in this city before we put an end to the tyranny of these clerical upstarts. What happened then taught us a lesson. This commonwealth was built upon the principle of live and let live, believe and let believe. That was the creed of Father William, and it is our creed to-day. We intend to maintain ourselves upon that basis. If we cannot do it, we shall fight. Meanwhile, like good merchants, we should provide for the future and that is why we asked you to come here. We are delighted to see you as our guest. But we also want to make you a business proposition. I shall light another couple of candles, to show you something. Meanwhile, have another glass of wine and fill yourself another pipe."

My Lord Andries went to a cupboard and took two candles which he fastened into a brass candle-stick and those he put in front of one of the large maps that hung on one side of the walls. He beckoned me to come nearer and I got up and I recognized one of Mercator's charts of the world, one of those new geographic maps that are said to have done so much to further the art of navigation.

"It is quite an old map," My Lord Andries remarked, "but it will do until the Blaeus give us a new one, which they have promised us very soon. Now look for a moment," and he showed me different parts of Asia and Africa and America, "all this belongs to us. Here all these islands," and he pointed to the Malayan Archipelago, "are possessions of the East India Company. Here, Ceylon has been ours for the last four years. Formosa old Carpentier has conquered. We have an open door that leads into Japan by way of Deshima. It is not very much of a door but a mighty profitable one. Here along the coast of Coromandel and Malabar we hold at least two dozen ports, we have a trading station at Mascate and control the trade in the Persian Gulf. Then down to Mauritius, and they say that Governor van Diemen is going to send Tasman to see what there is in this old story of several vast continents somewhere between Java and the South Pole.

"Sorry to bother you with these details. I sound like a school-master teaching a class of little boys their geography. In a moment you will see what I am driving at. Here on the west coast of Africa we possess a couple of harbors where our ships can get fresh provisions, then way up north here, Spitzbergen, where our whaling companies have built themselves a town where the money flows like sperm-oil, and down here is Brazil, where we have a chance to build ourselves a vast empire of coffee and tea and tobacco, though unfortunately all this territory belongs to the West India Company and God knows how beautifully they mismanage it! And then here are all these islands in the West Indies. Old man Columbus surely was off the track when he mistook these bits of rock for part of the realm of the Great Mogul, but we are beginning to grow things on them and in due time they will pay their way. And then here in the north, the land we got from the discovery of Hudson. That is the spot to which we want to draw your attention for the moment, right here at the mouth of the Mauritius River, that one and this other bit of land at the tip of the African continent, right here where it says the Cape of Good Hope.

"I told you that we are afraid of what may happen to us as soon as we conclude peace with Spain and the soldiers join the great army of the unemployed, the people who are now working in our arsenals and navy-yards and powder-mills and who will have quite a hard time finding new jobs. Well, we intend to be prepared. That is why we asked you to come here to-night. You can help us and I will tell you in what way, but first of all sit down again and have some more of this wine and another pipe of tobacco. The pipe will remind you of the fate that awaits those who put their faith in princes. But then, we are only burgomasters."

The glasses were filled and My Lord Andries took a sheet of paper and cut himself a new pen.

"I can think better when I have a piece of paper and a pen in my hand," he said. "You first had a lesson in practical politics and then one in geography. Allow me to add a little mathematics, the only science that should be of any real interest to the members of our merchants' guild. Come over here near my desk and I will show you the conclusions we have drawn from many years of careful study."

With a few rough strokes he drew a picture that looked like a see-saw and two small soup-plates connected with pieces of string.

"What is this?" he asked.

"A pair of scales," I guessed, and I was right.

"That pair of scales represents the Republic," he continued. "That is the situation at the present time. The scales are well balanced," and he drew a small square in each of them and wrote in one of them "The Prince" and in the other, "The Merchants."

"In order that we may continue to be prosperous, this balance should be maintained. We merchants have no objection whatsoever to a strong central government. We are too busy with our own affairs to look after a lot of executive details that can be much better attended to by the Stadholder, who is trained for that sort of work and whose family has made a specialty of it for God knows how many centuries. We need such a man in the Republic and we really don't care very much whether he wants to call himself a Stadholder or a King or anything else, as long as he does not interfere with our affairs and leaves us free to make the money without which the commonwealth would be as helpless as a ship without sails. I am afraid that I am beginning to mix my different figures of speech. I am not a literary man, but I hope that I have made myself clear."

I told His Lordship that he had made himself entirely clear.

"Very well," he went on, and he drew another square in the soup-plate that had already been honored with the princely cargo. Then he wrote "The Church" inside the square and once more showed it to me.

"Suppose I add this extra load to one side of my scales, then what will happen?"

This mathematical catechism was beginning to amuse me.

"Then the balance would be disturbed," I answered.

"And in order to reëstablish that balance?"

"You would be obliged to find a counter-weight."

"Just so, Doctor! You ought to have been a mathematician instead of making pills. And what sort of a counter-weight would you suggest?"

I thought a moment and, not wanting the conversation to become too serious, I said, "You might try moral suasion."

The two Bicker brothers looked at each other and then lifted their glasses. "We must drink to that. 'Moral suasion' to balance the dominies! A fine idea. But you know what became of the first man who tried to outweigh the power of a monarch by moral suasion?"

Rembrandt van Rijn

I said yes, that I thought I remembered only too well.

"And of all the others?"

Again I nodded my assent.

"Very well, Doctor. Now be very bright for once and give us another guess."

"Money," I hinted.

"You are getting there. And how much money?"

"A great deal of it."

"An awful lot of it," My Lord observed.

"And even more," his brother added, and then he went on with his lecture.

"How is money made?" he asked me.

"By industry and perseverance."

"Yes, in the copy-books from which you learned your reading and writing when you were a little boy. But how is it really made?"

I told him that I had never thought of it. I was interested in only one problem, how sick people could be made well again. How was money made?

"Well," he observed in the tone of a schoolmaster who is trying to be patient with a very dull pupil, "in a variety of ways. I don't want to go back all the way to the days of Moses and Julius Caesar or even of those noble barons and knights who are now trying to marry our daughters if we are willing to give them enough of a dowry. I know the Greeks and the Phoenicians, or whatever their names were, used to peddle their wares around the Mediterranean, and in the Middle Ages the Jews did a lot of buying and selling and had their teeth pulled out as often as some twopenny potentate was in need of a small loan. But generally speaking, before Venice and Genoa and Nuremberg and Antwerp and now our city taught them better, people made money by catching a few boatloads of their fellow-citizens by fastening dog-collars around their necks and forcing them to work for their own benefit as if they had been horses or dogs, which undoubtedly they were except that the man who killed a first-class stallion was punished a little more severely than the fellow who merely murdered a serf.

"But all that belongs to the past, at least in the civilized part of the world—which of course means our own part of the world. What the rest of our blessed continent does, hardly interests me. Perhaps from a business point of view, it is just as well that they remain a little backward. Meanwhile we will try and make 'profits.' Now what are profits? I have something that costs me ninety-nine cents and I sell it for a florin and I grow rich. I have something that costs me a florin and I sell it for ninety-nine cents, and I go to the poor-house. Business is really very simple. It merely consists in buying cheaply and selling dearly. All the rest is stuff and nonsense and belongs in one of those pamphlets about the 'rights of stockholders,' etc., that certain clever lawyers write in taverns when they have had a couple of drinks. Buying cheaply and selling dearly is the whole secret, and how can you do that best of all?"

Again I confessed my ignorance.

"You don't know? You really don't know? And yet it is so terribly simple. All you have to do is to get hold of some convenient little monopoly. Once you have got it, your troubles have come to an end. You can sit peacefully in your office and hire some one else to count your profits. Soon you will need a dozen people just to keep track of the figures."

I interrupted him with some irritation. "And that is where you need me? You want me to give up the practice of surgery and become a book-keeper?"

His Lordship jumped to his feet. "God forbid," and he waved his hands in despair. "The world is full of good book-keepers, honest, intelligent, obliging fellows who will work all their lives for five florins a week and will never have a thought or a desire as long as they live. Book-keeper, fiddlesticks! Whenever we let it be known that the house of Bicker needs a new book-keeper, there is a line outside our door from here to Zaandam. No, we don't want you to turn book-keeper."

I looked at him in surprise. "Then, My Lord, how in Heaven's name do I come to figure in your plans and calculations?"

"Very simply. We want you to go and find that little monopoly for us," and once more His Lordship picked up his pen and began to do some figuring.

"In order to hold our own against the political combination we anticipate and fear," he said without looking up from his pothooks, "we need a great deal of added revenue. For this we need the exclusive hold upon one of the necessities of life. Most of these are already in other hands. The East India Company has got all the spices. They are out. The West India Company has got the slave trade. That is out. Besides, it is a nasty sort of business and I am not enough of a theologian to be able to drug my soul with those passages from Holy Writ which elevate slave-raiding to the dignity of a semi-religious duty. Then in the North, there is whale-oil and whalebone. But all this is in the hands of a single company and they won't allow any outsider to look in on their fishery preserves. Besides, I hear that they have gone after those poor dumb whales with such murderous violence that soon there won't be a whale left within a thousand miles of Spitzbergen. And suppose the French dressmakers decree that women shall not wear corsets any longer, what then would become of the whalebone industry? It would lie flat on its back in less than a month.

"That does not seem to leave very much for us, does it? Of course, my brother and I are stockholders in all those companies and directors, and we get our share of the dividends. But the people on the other side of the fence, the partisans of the Prince, are stockholders too and occasionally they are able to outvote us. And that is just what we don't want to happen. We want a monopoly of our own that shall be entirely in the hands of our own family and a few of our relatives, a water-tight and air-tight monopoly that is ours, to use as we shall see fit. And we think that we have found one.

"Let me give you a few more figures. Man has to eat in order to live. Granted! The staple article of daily consumption in most households is bread. Also granted! Bread is made out of a substance called grain. On that point there probably won't be any dispute. Where does that grain come from? Most assuredly not from the territory of the Republic. We have had two of our brightest book-keepers study this problem for three years. They have examined all the reports of the harbor-master and they have carefully gone through the tax returns of the commissioners of internal revenue. Here they are" (and he opened a drawer of his writing table and took out a blue cover which held a number of papers)—"here you are. Last year our city alone needed about forty-two thousand tons of grain, but one-third of that went to the breweries and, as you know, we make the beer for practically the whole of the country. The rest of the Republic used up another forty thousand tons. The total import was 160,000 tons, so that almost eighty thousand tons were exported again and at an excellent profit, I can assure you. For even under the present circumstances, our country has practically a monopoly of the carrying trade of all grain. Our agents in Copenhagen report that of the 793 ships that crossed the sound on their way from the Baltic to the North Sea, 702 flew the red, white and blue of the Republic. That is not a bad showing, is it? Of those 702, not less than 590 were bound for our city and more than half of those were loaded with grain. That grain is grown in Poland and Curland and Esthland, the old possessions of the German Order, and in Ukrania, which is part Polish and part Russian.

"In the olden days, this trade was easy enough. Of course the Danes with their infernal tolls made our lives miserable, but as long as we paid (although often enough we paid through the nose), we got our ships. But the political situation around the Baltic Sea is beginning to fill our hearts with fear. Poland is getting more disorderly every day. A republican monarchy, in which one foolish knight (be he drunk or sober, but as a rule he is drunk) has the power to upset any law that all the others want—such a country is bound to go to pieces sooner or later. The Swedes have conquered Esthland and Livland, but Gustavus Adolphus is dead, his daughter Christina (even if she had had sense enough to send for Grotius to act as one of her advisers) is—well, let us say rather 'unbalanced.' I hear that she has begun to see spooks and wants to travel to Rome to tell the Pope how to rule the world and then go into a monastery. That country, therefore, is out of our calculations, for the present at least. All the Wasas have been a little bit crazy—very brilliant many of them—but always just a trifle unreliable.

"And then there is the famous Grand Duke of Muscovy, who now calls himself 'Caesar' and prattles sweetly of being heir to all the rights and prerogatives of the old Emperors of Byzantium. What all that will eventually lead to, God only knows. We have an agent in Moscow and he tells us that ever since Czar Ivan (you remember? The one who beat his son to death) the Russians have been talking of their 'ancestral rights' to the whole of the east coast of the Baltic. What those ancestral rights are I don't know. But I do know that there are a terrible lot of these wild people and once they are on the war-path, neither Swede nor Pole nor Prussian will be able to stop them.

"A nice little war in those parts that lasted, let us say, two or three years would make all of us starve. We need grain and Spain needs grain and Italy needs grain. We need it because there is more water than land in this country and no one so far has invented a method of growing grain in a swamp like rice. Spain and Italy need grain because they are so full of monasteries that there isn't room enough left to sow a few acres of wheat of their own. But think what it would mean to our carrying trade if we should be cut off from our base of supply in the Baltic! More than half of our ships would lie idle. And the greater part of the other half would be forced out of business because we would not have gold enough with which to buy the things we need from abroad. Now, Doctor, what is the answer?"

I confessed that I did not know.

"The answer is very simple. We must no longer content ourselves merely with transporting and selling other people's grain. We must grow it ourselves. And there are only two places where we can do that. One is on the Cape of Good Hope. But the East India Company would never allow us to settle there. Until now they have not taken possession of it themselves, but I hear that they may do so almost any moment and their charter gives them the right to claim the whole of southern Africa as part of their dominions and then we would have done all our work in vain. I have no desire to be another Le-Maire. That poor devil was no doubt well within his rights when he claimed that he had not infringed upon the charter of the company when he sailed to the Indies via Cape Horn. But old Coen took his ship away from him just the same and young LeMaire died from sheer disappointment and the father took the case to the supreme court and won it, but by the time the last judge had signed the last decree, the old fellow was a bankrupt and that is what would happen to us too if we were ever foolish enough to try it. No, there is but one way out. Come over here a moment," and His Lordship picked up a candle and went back to the map on the wall and pointed to the central part of the North American continent and he said:

"Right here and now we will tell you what you can do for us. All this of course belongs to the West India Company. It was given to them by the charter of 1621. But that company has never done well. I don't exactly know why. I suppose the East India Company has absorbed all our available surplus capital. In the Indies, almost everything will grow and the natives are patient little brown men who all work for you if you treat them badly enough. In America the natives will die rather than work for some one else. And the climate is annoying. No pepper, no cinnamon, no nutmeg. A few beaver-skins and a little dried fish and even for these you have to barter with a naked red man with feathers in his hair and a large battle-ax in his strong right hand.

"And they have been terribly unfortunate with the people they have sent out. They began wrong. That man Hudson may have been a fine navigator (I suppose he was) but he was about as loyal to his employers as those other Englishmen we hired to fight for us, and who sold Zutphen and Deventer to the Spaniards. I will say that he did a fine piece of work in sailing up the Mauritius River, but if Adriaan Block had not lost his ship off Manhattan Island (a strange accident that fire was too, but in this case a very fortunate one) and if Block had not been the man he was, we would know no more about America to-day than we did when Hudson first invited the natives on board his *Half Moon*, and got them so beautifully drunk on Dutch gin. That was a pretty terrible performance and that bad beginning seems to have put a special hoodoo on everything we have ever tried to do in that part of the world. We have had a fine lot of men as governors of the Moluccas and Java, but there on the banks of the Mauritius, one terrible person has succeeded the other. Pieter Minuit was an honorable man. But the others, great Heavens, what a sad collection of incompetent scoundrels! May was a common clerk and not even an honest one. No one knows why he was ever appointed except that he happened to be on the spot when they needed some one in a hurry. Krol was a runaway dominie and absolutely untrustworthy. Van Twiller was a fool who thought that his good connections would keep him out of jail when he engaged in a little private speculation, as they afterwards did. Kieft, who is supposed to rule that colony to-day, is an undischarged bankrupt. You can still see his picture fastened to the gallows.

"He seems to belong to that unfortunate race of 'energetic' people who always must be 'doing' something, especially when they would serve their purpose much better by doing nothing at all. He got the company into a nice war with the natives. I have forgotten their names, Algonquins or something like that.

"The good ship *Fortune* came into port last week with a cargo of beaver-skins and I had a long talk with her captain. He used to work for us years ago when we had more breweries than we do now and needed more grain. He married a wife with some money and he put it into West India shares and then he went into the service of the company because, as he said, that was the only way to discover what they were doing with his funds. He has traded all over America from the Trask River to Cape Hinloopen. We are old friends and he knew that he could trust me. I learned more from him in five minutes' talk than from all the endless written reports of these half-literate but long-winded governors.

"The trouble with the Indians, so he told us, has been absolutely uncalled for. Anybody with half a grain of common sense (uncommon sense is more to my liking but it is so terribly hard to find)— any one with half a grain of uncommon sense would have been able to avoid those difficulties. The savages in that part of the world seem to be harmless enough, a bit dirty and a bit lazy from our own point of view, but rather like children, good-natured until they discover that you have tried to cheat them, when they suddenly lose all control of themselves and slash and burn and kill until their anger is spent and they smile once more as if nothing had happened.

"Our friend had dealt with them for a dozen years or more. He had visited their villages and spent nights in their tents, absolutely unarmed and the only white man within a hundred miles. But nothing had ever happened to him. If it had not been for the slightly embarrassing and not entirely unodorous expressions of affection on the part of the wives and daughters of these poor heathen, he told me that he would rather settle down in almost any Indian village than in the place of his birth, which lies somewhere in the darkest interior of Friesland.

"You therefore need have no fear on that score. You won't be eaten up or burned at the stake or thrown to the dogs. I know that that has happened to a few of the Jesuit missionaries who operate in the neighborhood of Fort Orange. I am sorry for them, but why didn't they stay at home? Can you imagine a couple of priests and sorcerers of those Algonquins, or whatever the name, right here on the Dam near the fish-market, let us say, telling the dear public that is busy buying and selling shrimps and mussels, that they ought to stop buying and selling shrimps and ought to listen to the words of the Great White Spirit from the hills, who bids men and women paint their faces a bright red and stick a feather in their hair and say 'Walla, walla, walla' forty times in succession to escape the disfavor of the Great Black Spirit? Can you imagine such an episode and can you imagine what would happen to the poor heathen? Well, I can and I suppose you can too.

"No, the natives will be the least of your worries. You are a man of tact and we shall give you a shipload of these gimcracks and little mirrors and beads and bangles that seem to delight the hearts of those simple children of nature. And then, at your leisure, we want you to sail across the ocean and go to Nieuw Amsterdam. We have collected a great deal of information about you before we asked you to come here. We know that you are deeply interested in the problem of reducing the pain connected with those surgical operations that take place in our hospitals. Mind you, I don't say that they are not necessary, but I was a victim myself once. It was not much of an affair as such things go, but I still turn green and cold whenever I think of what they did to me. Very well, you let it be known that you are going to take a trip to America because you want to investigate those stories that are coming to us continuously about certain plants which the natives of the New World use to alleviate pain."

I interrupted His Lordship. "I am sorry," I said, "but why lie about it?"

But this rather downright question did not worry the speaker for a moment.

"In the first place," he continued, "it would not be quite a lie. My bookseller sends me every account of American exploration that appears. He has standing offers for such books in London and Sevilla and Lisbon. I can't read those printed in Portuguese, but I have those translated by a bright young Jew, a curious fellow who seems to be the only man who ever got away from the Inquisition and lived to tell the tale."

"I know him," I said. "He is one of my best friends."

"Really? Well, he is a bright fellow and ought to have a better job than he has now. We have offered to employ him ourselves, but he seems to be content to jog along. Well, as I was saying, I read every word that is being printed about those mysterious aborigines and what strikes me most is that they seem to know a great many things of which we, with all our learning, have not the faintest idea. They do seem to be able to deaden their bodies against pain. It may be just a funny story, like that one connected with the famous gold of Sir Walter Raleigh which proved to be some sort of copper, or the Fountain of Youth of that old Spaniard whom they buried in the Mississippi (you see, I know my American geography), and so you won't be wasting your time if you consent to spend a few years collecting shrubs and weeds and interviewing medicine-men with rings through their noses."

I agreed that it would be a wonderful opportunity, but why not tell the truth?

"Because," my Lord Andries answered, "it would be one of those occasions where telling the truth would be fatal. What we really want to do, and now I am coming to the kernel of the business, is to get hold of vast tracts of land where grain can be grown at a very small cost. According to the best of our information, the coastal regions are too rocky and too densely covered with woods to be suitable for that purpose. But a few hundred miles inland, as I have found stated in any number of books, there are enormous plains where grain will grow almost overnight. All the land from the Atlantic to the next ocean (most likely it is the Pacific, but we are not sure yet. Hudson, so I hear, claimed to have found another sea much higher up in the north, a small ocean that may reach as far as Mexico) for all we know. All the land between the Fresh River and the South River belongs to the West India Company, however. That organization is terribly hard up for money and the directors would listen with both ears if we offered to buy a few hundred thousand square miles and pay cash.

"That is what we want to do as soon as you come back and tell us that the soil is suitable for our purpose. We have the money and we mean to keep this a strictly family affair. No one outside of our own city will be allowed to invest a penny. No Committees of Seventeen or Gentlemen Nineteen for us, if we can help it. This time the enterprise is going to be well managed. That is why we shall depend so greatly upon your report. If you tell us that the land will grow grain, we shall buy vast tracts. We are already at work upon a system of colonization. There are thousands of people in the Republic who would go abroad and settle in Java or Brazil or even in the New Netherlands if they were not obliged to go there in a state of semi-serfdom. If we find that we cannot work our farms without slave

VILLAGE SCENE WITH A MULE (DRAWING)

labor, we shall import a sufficient number of them from Africa. I don't approve of it much myself, but if that is the only way to make money, well then, we shall do as the others do.

"But what we have in mind will bear very little resemblance to those trading-posts which are the eternal stand-by of all our Indian companies. We want permanency. We want to turn our possessions over there (if ever we get them) really and truly into some sort of a New Netherlands. So that if things go wrong over here in the old Netherlands, we have another home in another world upon which we can fall back.

"Maybe I am a little too pessimistic. Maybe that young Orange prince is not bright enough or has not got courage enough to try and do all those things of which we suspect him. In that case, if we are successful, we shall have another source of income, and a little extra pin-money is always acceptable even to the best of us. On the other hand, if things go badly we shall have a new fatherland. And new hope and courage for thousands of people."

He stopped abruptly and turned to his brother. "All this seems clear to you?" he asked.

"Perfectly," my Lord Cornelis answered.

"Then," turning to me, "have you any questions to ask?"

"Yes," I replied. "The one at which I hinted a moment ago. Why all this secrecy? Why not let everybody know what the purpose of my voyage is?"

"For a variety of reasons. In the first place, if the Prince and the Church people are conspiring to deprive us of our power and turn the Republic into a monarchy, they will of course take measures to prevent you from going if they know what your mission is, and they will do their best to spoil our ideas, and as yet we are not powerful enough to hold our own against such a combination of forces. In the second place, if the directorate were to hear of this, they would ask such extortionate prices for their land that the whole plan would come to nothing. In the third place . . ."

But I did not care to hear any further reasons. I already knew enough. My personal sympathies were entirely on the side of those two men who saw the ideals for which our fathers had fought so valiantly, go to ruin on the cliffs of selfishness, partisanship and religious bigotry. Of course they were business men and figured things out in terms of florins and daalders, more than I would have done who lived vaguely in that realm of science where money is rarely discussed because it is so seldom seen in sufficient quantities to attract people's attention. But on the whole, I did not doubt the integrity of their motives. Only I would need a little time to think things over. I told them so and they agreed most readily.

"Take as long as you like, Doctor," they urged me most cordially. "We have expressed ourselves quite openly to you and have placed ourselves in your hands. Go home now, for you must be tired after listening to this lecture, and let us know what you intend to do just as soon as you have made up your mind."

I bade my adieux and slowly walked home. When I crossed the bridge of the Saint Anthonie Lock, I noticed that there was still light burning in the upstairs windows of Rembrandt's house. I had not seen anything of him since the funeral of my brother and thought that I would drop in for a minute. I needed some one with whom to talk things over before I went to bed, for I was much too excited to be able to go to sleep right off.

I knocked on the door but got no answer.

I knocked again and a little louder.

I heard people stumbling about in the back part of the house.

Finally the door was opened a few inches. The nurse of little Titus was standing there. She was holding a candle in her hand and looked at me as if she were ready to kill me.

"The master has gone to bed and can't be disturbed," she snapped. "Please go away." And she locked the door in my face.

I went home.

I didn't quite like what I had just seen.

THE HOG (ETCHING)

THE RETURN OF THE PRODIGAL SON (ETCHING)

THE RETURN OF THE PRODIGAL SON (PAINTING)

Chapter 16

WHAT I HEARD FROM HOME DURING MY
PROLONGED STAY IN THE NEW WORLD

VIEW OF AMSTERDAM, DETAIL (ETCHING)

OF THOSE strange adventures which befell me in the New
Holland across the Ocean and which almost cost me my life,
I have given a detailed account in a number of letters which I wrote
to my son during my long period of convalescence. They had little
bearing upon my relations with Rembrandt and therefore I shall not
include them within these pages. Those interested can read them elsewhere. Suffice it to say that I learned many things useful to me in
my profession and that I discovered many things about my fellow
men, which until then I had not even suspected. When I was finally
able to travel (I had broken both my legs and had been most tenderly
nursed by those whom the people in our settlement regarded merely
as savages) and returned to Nieuw Amsterdam I discovered that my
prolonged absence had caused great consternation. Bernardo, who
was apparently still staying with his Mohawk friends, had written
to Captain de Vries to tell him of the rumors he had heard about me:
that I had reached the ultimate confines of the land belonging to the
Five Nations—that I had met with an accident—that I was being taken
care of in the house of an Indian chief near one of the smaller lakes

a few miles east of the Pacific Ocean—and that I had probably been killed during the famous raid of the Chickasaws against the Onondagas early in the winter of that year.

This strange hodge-podge of information and misinformation had made the excellent captain take a special trip to the capital to try and obtain some further details from the hunters and trappers who gathered together every spring to sell their beaver and bear skins to the traders of the Company. They had indeed heard of some commotion in the region of the small lakes, but some thought it had been a quarrel between the Oneidas and the Algonquins and others knew for certain that it had been merely a little border skirmish between the Cayugas and the Cherokees, who lived almost a thousand miles further toward the south and were then in open warfare with the English who had settled in Virginia, but no one seemed able to tell him just exactly what had happened.

He was delighted, therefore, when he heard that I had returned, and wrote me that he intended to visit Nieuw Amsterdam within a fortnight and hoped to see me. Meanwhile, after the years of comparative freedom, I had grown so accustomed to being my own master that I could no longer stand the restrictions imposed upon me by living in rented quarters. And as I had spent very little of My Lord Andries' money during the last two years (what I had with me when I met with my accident, Father Ambrosius had carefully packed in an old cassock of his and had put it underneath my pillow on the stretcher when he saved me from the massacre), I decided to invest a few hundred guilders in a little house of my own.

I bought a small piece of land from the bouwery which stood in the name of Wolfaert Gerritszoon. I got the land very cheap because it overlooked quite a large swamp, but this swamp which for the greater part of each year was very full of water, gave me the illusion of being near a lake. I found two Indians on Staten Eiland who said they could build me a wooden house such as were customary among the tribes of the Five Nations, and they proved to be excellent workmen and in less than a month's time my own house was ready for occupancy.

As soon as it had been finished, I sent word to Bernardo asking him to come and join me but he favored me with a rather cryptic reply. It was a small piece of parchment with a rough drawing of an Indian

on it, an Indian who bore a slight outer resemblance to Bernardo himself, and underneath it the cryptic words: "The Ten Lost Tribes have
been joined by one more."

I therefore gave up hope of seeing him until I should be able to
travel north once more, and meanwhile waited for Captain de Vries,
who had been delayed by some trouble that had recently occurred
in the settlement of Rensselaerwijk (the usual story of a greedy farmer
selling a plentiful supply of gin to some of the natives who thereupon had got very drunk, had run amuck amongst the villages and
had killed three women and two children before they themselves had
been shot), but who finally made his appearance early in the month
of August during a spell of such hot weather that my beloved swamp
ran almost entirely dry and reminded me by its appalling smell of
the happy days of my childhood spent among the mud flats of Veere.
Not only did he come but he brought me a package that was most
welcome to me as it contained nine letters which Jean-Louys had
sent me during the previous two years.

"I ought to have sent these to you when I first heard that you had
returned," he told me, "but people are so often careless with a small
package like this, and so I thought I would wait and bring them myself. I could have sent it to the Fort, but the Governor is in one of his
tempers. Some more trouble about that Board of Aldermen of the
late but not lamented Willem Kieft, and I would rather not meet
him when he is playing the rôles of Nero and Simon Maccabee all in
one, stamping around in his little room and complaining that everybody in the whole colony is a traitor and ought to be hung. I know
the old man means well, but when he gets in that mood, he is a hopeless bore."

"On the contrary," I answered, "I saw him only yesterday about
the final sale of this piece of land. I want to buy that swamp too,
otherwise some honest farmer will come here and drain it out of
sheer force of habit and I would love to keep my little lake. I found
him as soft as butter and as mild as a day in June. You never will guess
what he was doing."

"Reading you his last missive to the Board of Eight, calling these
worshipful gentlemen a gang of grasping rapscallions, low, lying,
thieving scoundrels?"

"By no means! He was writing a poem. A poem about a sunset

and a red sky and the happy husbandman slowly wending his way homeward."

"Was it as bad as all that?"

"It was worse. It was, I think, the most sentimental piece of poetry since the day of Tibullus, Tibullus with a wooden leg and a bald head. The whole thing was rather pathetic. For the old man no doubt is trying very hard to do his best and the directors at home as usual are succeeding in doing their worst. And some fine day all this will come to a sudden end and there will be a terrible disaster and the old man knows it and he can't do anything about it and so he spends his leisure hours writing sweet little elegies about pink sunsets and the virtues of the old Roman matrons. And now please let me have my letters."

The captain gave me a small bundle done up carefully in a leather bag. "Keep the bag," he said, "and read your letters. I hear that our grand duke is laying out a place of his own somewhere around here."

"So he is. The house has been begun. Go and have a look at it and be back at three and we will have dinner."

The captain left me and I spent the next four hours catching up with life on the other side of the ocean. There were nine letters in all. I had thought that they were all from Jean-Louys, but one proved to be from Selim. It was very short and sounded rather sad.

"This big city has grown very lonely," he wrote, "since you and Bernardo have left. Jean-Louys is a charming person, but he is mixing more and more mathematics into his omelettes and I do not like to sit down to a meal when I have first been invited to draw the cubic root from the soup and find the decimal points in the pudding.

"It may be true that God is merely an abstraction and a formula which M. Descartes will solve for us one of these days, but my brain is not strong enough to follow our friend there. And so I sit by myself much of the time.

"Of late I have been greatly diverted by the visits of the Reverend Simon Gallinovius, the son of honest Jan Kippenei, whom you will remember from our trip to the Diemermeer. The old fellow kept the third tavern on the left side of the road outside the Saint Anthonie Gate. His promising young offspring desires to make a name for himself and hopes to do so by converting the diplomatic representative of the Grand Padisha. Can't you see me going up for baptism in an enormous green turban and that long red robe of office that goes with my high rank? Well, I cannot, but he apparently can. He thinks it would be a fine feather in his dignified biretta.

"His mode of attack is rather unique and causes me a great deal of amusement. He has actually taken the trouble to read the Koran in a Spanish translation. He tells me that he has come to the conclusion that Mohammedanism and Calvinism are the same, as both creeds believe in the pre-ordination of every fact connected with human existence. This undoubtedly is a new point of view and it ought to be interesting to the sort of people who are able to take an interest in that sort of thing.

"But I am bored and the banks of the Bosphorus begin to look more and more attractive to this peace-loving exile. Three more visits from the long-winded Gallinovius and I shall set sail for the land of my fathers.

"What am I doing here anyway? What are any of us doing anywhere, anyway? When a man gets in that mood, you may be prepared for any sort of news.

"I embrace you and the excellent Bernardo. Mark my word, that boy will turn native if you do not look out. He is as much of a wanderer as I am. He is almost as lonely. Allah have mercy upon the likes of us. Farewell!"

Followed by a postscript: "Your good friend Rembrandt has been to see me once or twice. That man has a veritable passion for Turks. He wants me to pose for him. I asked him whether he was running short of models and he said, 'No, but my models are mostly Dutch vagabonds. I can dress them up in silks and satins and put a turban on their heads, but that does not make them Turks. They remain what they were before, Dutch vagabonds who happen to be dressed up in Moslem finery.' Perhaps I shall oblige him one of these days, if only the chicken-egged divine will leave me alone."

The letter was more or less what I might have expected. I turned to the forty or fifty pages covered with Jean-Louys' precise handwriting and I found that they contained a complete history of the last two years, as far as he and I were concerned.

The French often exasperate me. Not infrequently their actions fire me with disgust. They are unreliable and careless to a degree. They have no conception of neatness or order as these virtues are practiced at home. They are quarrelsome and vain. But when I have worked myself up into a complete and perfect detestation of the French nation and all its works, some individual Frenchman will do or say or write something that makes me forget all the manifold annoyances I have suffered at the hands of his race and makes me feel that the world without France would be as dull and uninteresting as a wedding party without music.

These letters of Jean-Louys had a beginning, a middle part (a core would be a better expression) and an end. They told me nothing too much and nothing too little. In their way they were as perfect as the meals he sometimes served us and which left one with a feeling of utter contentment without the unpleasant accompanying sensation of being too replete. I liked these epistles so much that I gave them to the Governor to read and he told me that they had given him more and better information about conditions at home than all the endless reports from his directors. He asked to be allowed to keep them a little longer and eventually forgot to return them when I unexpectedly sailed for home. He sent them after me on the *Drie Croonen*, but the ship went down on the coast of Virginia and was never heard of again. I therefore must rely upon my memory to reconstruct the most important items they contained.

Every letter began with the news that just before writing it Jean-Louys had visited my house on the Houtgracht and had found my son to be in perfect health. The child had completely forgotten me (as was of course to be expected), he was growing up to be a fine boy, had nice manners and went to see Master Rembrandt twice a week to be instructed in the art of drawing. He seemed to have a decided gift for that form of art and Rembrandt was devoting a great deal of his time to helping the boy along.

Then he talked of more serious matters. The long-expected had happened at last, peace had been declared between Spain and the Republic and the latter had been fully and most officially recognized as an independent and sovereign nation. The old Prince had not lived to see this final victory of the cause for which he had fought so long and so bravely. He had died a few months before. His end had been very sad, a complication of diseases as a result of the hard life he had led during his endless campaigns. His legs had been so swollen that he could no longer mount on horseback. Then he had had several attacks of lung trouble and finally his brain had given out and during the last two weeks of his earthly existence his nurses had been obliged to take care of him as if he had been a small child.

His son, the one who had married the Englishwoman, had succeeded him as commander-in-chief of the army and might cause considerable trouble. For he was a very ambitious young man who wanted to gain as great a reputation as a strategist as his father and uncle had enjoyed before him. It was generally known that the young Prince had used all his influence to avoid the conclusion of peace until he should at least have added Brussels and Antwerp to the territory of the Republic. But the Burgomasters of Amsterdam were dreadfully afraid of such a step. They feared the rivalry of Antwerp if it should ever be made a Dutch city. They had control of the Scheldt, and as long as Antwerp remained a city in the hands of their enemies, they were able to treat her as such, and by closing the Scheldt they could ruin their old rival. Amsterdam therefore had declared flatly in favor of an immediate conclusion of peace and, as usual, Amsterdam had won.

Their Lordships of the Town Hall and His Highness the Prince now regarded each other as open and avowed enemies, and it was feared that hot-headed young Willem was planning a coup against the city that had dealt such a blow to his pride. Thus far nothing had happened, but this friction between the two most powerful bodies within the State had caused a feeling of uneasiness which was doing a great deal of harm.

This came at a very inopportune moment, as business conditions were already very bad. As long as the Republic had been at war with Spain, it had been possible for us to organize a world-wide system of smuggling at the expense of our Spanish opponents. But now that Spain was a friendly nation and no longer a foe to be plundered at will, these smuggling concerns had lost millions of guilders.

Then there were the large number of industries that had been engaged, directly or indirectly, in building ships and making cannon and fabricating gunpowder and looking after the thousand and one needs of an army that was forever in the field and a navy that was rarely in port. Of course the ship-yards could now begin to work, for the commercial marine and sails and ropes would probably be needed as much as before, but there were many articles for which there was no longer any demand. That would mean a great deal of loss to the original investors and it would mean that thousands of people would be thrown out of employment and this was already becoming very noticeable to any one who ever walked in the direction of the harbor. Where formerly the shipping firms had been obliged to resort to crimps and soul-sellers to get their vessels manned, their offices were now beseiged by hordes of hungry men, often accompanied by equally hungry women and children who asked that they be given a chance to take a trip to the Baltic or the Indies.

Then there were the soldiers and the sailors of the navy, all of them out of a job and taking every day more and more to organized brigandage as a means of gaining an honest livelihood. All this of course was greatly affecting the money market, and the failure of two or three important houses which had speculated upon a continuation of the war and had filled their store-houses with enormous quantities of supplies which now went for a song, had shaken public confidence so severely that it would be years before the situation could possibly hope to return to normal.

And of course, as Jean-Louys remarked several times, the poor artists will be the first to notice this scarcity of ready money. Rembrandt had told him that he had not had an order for a new portrait for over six months, and the others seemed to fare no better. During the first moment of triumph there had been a slight demand for allegorical pictures to celebrate the manifold victories of the Dutch nation. But the two most important orders had gone to Flinck and to van der Helst, two of Rembrandt's pupils. The master himself had been passed. He had tried his hand at an imaginary historical picture representing the pacification of Holland and he had made a number of sketches for it. But no one wanted it and it was still standing in his studio at the time of writing. So were a great many of his other pictures. Nothing he touched seemed to be a success nowadays. He still had an occasional order for a portrait, but he was rapidly being forgotten for a number of younger men who not only charged less but were much more obliging when it came to giving their model his own way.

Indeed, throughout those eight letters there ran an undercurrent of deep and serious worry about the house in the Jodenbreestraat. The terrible nurse was still there, more noisily devoted to little Titus than ever before, but growing more and more unbearable as the years went on. Often, indeed, it seemed as if she were going out of her mind. Then she would buttonhole the unfortunate visitors who came to see her master and would not let them go until she had told them all her woes—how she slaved and worked for little Titus, how she had even made a will in his favor leaving him everything she had in this world, how she, through her own exertions, was keeping the household going because "he," pointing to the door of the master's work-room, was too lazy and too indifferent to attend to anything, but she was not going to stand for it much longer. She could tell a great many things about herself and the famous Rembrandt van Rijn that would astonish the world if it ever became known, a great many things, and had they ever seen the pearls he had given her and the golden ring? And so on and so forth, to the great embarrassment of the unsuspecting visitors who gradually began to avoid the house of the master rather than expose themselves to one of the whining parties of the wild-eyed nurse with her eternal wail that Rembrandt had not done right by her.

No one knew what this situation would lead to, but several friends had at last combined to go directly to Rembrandt and suggest that he have the woman examined by some medical man who was familiar with the subject of lunacy. Rembrandt had listened patiently, as he always did, and had thanked them for their kind interest. He had agreed that the woman ought to go, but he had hinted at several difficulties which made it impossible for him to be as drastic as he wanted to be.

What those mysterious "difficulties" were, Jean-Louys could not tell me. Some people thought that Rembrandt had borrowed money from Geertje which he was unable to pay back at that moment. The inheritance of Saskia had never yet been settled. Any lawsuit involving money would cause the court to examine the financial affairs of both parties, and the general opinion was that Rembrandt was not in a position where he could afford to have the magistrates pry a little closely into his business arrangements.

He was working harder than ever and was turning out a very large number of exceedingly beautiful and interesting etchings. But he had retired so completely from the company of his former friends that no one knew exactly how he stood in regard to those funds he was supposed to be administering for the benefit of his small son. No one even could say within five or ten thousand guilders how much there was left for the boy. Everything was all in a terrible muddle, and as Rembrandt himself never kept any accounts—invested his money in a most haphazard way—buying an interest in a shipping firm one day and a painting by Raphael the next—it was impossible to make any sort of a guess as to the funds that were at his disposal.

A few good friends had offered to arrange matters for him—to put some order into this chaos—but he had thanked them most kindly but also most determinedly. He himself would attend to this matter as soon as he had finished a new etching on which he had set great hope. It was a picture of Christ healing the sick and he meant to sell it for a hundred guilders, a record price for etchings. That print would once more bring him into the public eye. Then he would be able to enjoy a little leisure from the pot-boilers he had been obliged to make the last three or four years and he would call on some good and reliable notary to come and help him with his accounts and straighten everything out. Until then, he would just have to put up with the woman as best he could and meanwhile she was full of care for little Titus.

It was the same old story, but with a different refrain. And it made Jean-Louys fear that there was some other reason for his unwillingness or inability to send the nurse packing. Rembrandt had lived a very solitary life since Saskia's death. For all anybody could tell, he might have promised Geertje that he would marry her, or she might be in the family way, or she might pretend to be in the family way and blame the master. It was very difficult to get at the truth with an hysterical woman like that, and so there was nothing to do but wait until the situation had taken care of itself.

And as the weeks and months went by, it was more and more likely that some crisis would occur which would rid Rembrandt of his unpleasant companion. Meanwhile his friends hoped and prayed that this would happen before the situation developed into a public scandal. Already there had been a few veiled references from the pulpit about people who had better heal themselves before they made pictures of the Saviour healing others, and one reverend gentleman had gone so far as to hint that one of the figures in the supper at

Rembrandt van Rijn

Emmaus closely resembled the servant in the house of a certain famous artist who himself was in the habit of giving supper parties, but of a very different nature.

The problem therefore was to get the woman safely out of the house before this whispering campaign got a little too outspoken, but no one could foretell what would happen, as Rembrandt in all things, both good and bad, was known to be almost as obstinate as the gallant warrior who was then reported to be at the head of the government of the New Netherlands, and with this charming compliment at the address of My Lord Stuyvesant, the excellent Jean-Louys, who knew that letters were sometimes opened and read by the authorities, closed his account of affairs in the Jodenbreestraat.

He then told me a lot of gossip about European affairs, most of which I already knew: that the English were on the point of executing their king for a series of crimes which seemed to be rather vague, but that, as His Majesty had gained the reputation of being one of the most accomplished liars of his or any other time and had broken his word so repeatedly that no one could trust him for longer than two minutes at a time, he would probably be condemned to death, but whether he was going to be hanged or merely decapitated no one could as yet foretell; that the government probably would fall into the hands of some one called Cromwell, who was certain to proclaim himself king and would cause a great deal of trouble to the Republic, as he was known to be strongly in favor of a very drastic policy of protection for all British interests; that there was a rather amusing quarrel between the French crown and the nobility of that country, and that an Italian by the name of Mazarini, a former henchman of the infamous Cardinal Richelieu, had now got hold of the French government by making himself indispensable to the old king's wife, a Spanish lady with whiskers and not very bright, whom he flattered in the elegant Spanish manner which he had learned during the days of his youth when he was a flunkey in the suite of Prince Colonna and had accompanied that noble gentleman to the University of Alcala to inspect the original manuscript of the Polyglot Bible and place a wreath on the cradle of the great Don Miguel de Cervantes; that this shrewd Sicilian, a masterpiece of Jesuit educational skill, who looked like a Portuguese Jew and who stole money from the Public Treasury with the grace of a Neapolitan prostitute going through the pockets of an English lord, would soon break the resistance of the nobles and that it was extremely doubtful whether the French monarchy would go the way of its English counterpart, although many people in the Republic counted on such an outcome; that the "usual" trouble between Amsterdam and Denmark and Sweden about the tolls levied in the Sund was in the "usual" state of being almost settled by either war or a treaty; that, for the rest, nothing of any importance had happened except that the most eminent and learned Doctor Descartes had paid a brief visit to his native country, upon which occasion the Spanish-Italian-French cardinal had honored him with an annual pension of three thousand francs and the promise of a position at court, which seemed a strange ambition for the author of the "Discourse of Method" and the "Principles of Philosophy," but then, even very learned people must eat; and so on and so forth, forty-eight pages long.

I was reading these letters for the third time when Captain de Vries returned.

"A strange experience!" I told him. "The Old World suddenly making its presence felt in the New. I wonder what has happened to me. Those things used to interest me. They used to interest me most tremendously. They were part of my life. And now it is just as if some one were making music in a room in another part of the house. I try to listen, but it means nothing to me, except a little, vague noise—not very interesting and rather annoying and upsetting. What has happened to me?"

"It is the fresh air and the horizon. That strange horizon of ours. In Europe, a horizon means the end of something old and familiar. Here it means the beginning of something new and unknown. That horizon will get you as it has got most of us. Unless those old fools in Amsterdam who rule us without ever having seen us force me to go away (as well they may if they continue their present policy of acting as dry-nurses to ten thousand people at the other end of the ocean), I shall never return to the mother country. I would smother and die for lack of fresh air in one of our nice, respectable little cities. Another six months and you will feel the same way."

I confessed that I had already fallen a victim to the pleasant hallucination of space.

CHRIST PREACHING (ETCHING)

"Then send for your boy and set up as a surgeon right here. La Montagne won't mind. He is getting old and hates to go out nights. The others are quacks. Settle down here. Take you a wife and be happy!"

And I might have followed his advice if it had not been for the scrap of paper that reached me exactly two months later and that said nothing but: "I wish you would come home. I need your help and your friendship very badly," and that was signed with a large capital letter R.

CHRIST AT EMMAUS (ETCHING)

Chapter 17

I RECEIVE MORE BAD NEWS FROM AMSTERDAM AND
DECIDE TO RETURN HOME

VIEW OF AMSTERDAM (DRAWING)

AS FOR the other letter which somehow or other I managed to have kept all this time, it was of a very different nature and talked of matters a little nearer to our own home interests.

"A week ago to-day [Jean-Louys wrote] I decided to call on Rembrandt. But while going down the Oude Schans and by the merest chance, I ran across your old bookseller on the Rokin who also handles some of Rembrandt's etchings. He first of all asked me for news of you and then inquired whether I had heard of the latest troubles of Rembrandt. I said no, and as the old man has apparently retired from business and seemed glad of an opportunity to talk to some one, he gladly accepted my invitation to come home with me and help me eat my dinner, for I decided that my own business could wait. I had not been near the house on the Jodenbreestraat for almost half a year. The last time I had called there the situation had been so awkward that I had vowed to myself that I would never go there again as long as I lived. The nurse Geertje was still on the premises, and more violent and less accountable than ever. But shortly afterwards, so the bookseller told me, there had been an open break between herself and her employer and after that she had behaved so strangely that her relations had been called in and it had been decided to send her to an asylum for a few months' observation. But she managed to get away from them and then began a series of petty persecutions of Rembrandt—which still continue. For example, she went before a judge and swore that her former master had borrowed money from her and had never repaid her, and another time she complained that he had promised to marry her and had not kept his word, and still a third time she stated definitely that she and her old employer had had carnal intercourse and that he had turned her out as soon as he had done his will upon her. And so on and so forth. Until it had become clear to all concerned that she was stark raving mad and thereupon she had been taken away to the town of Gouda, whence she came from originally, and had been committed to the local lunatic asylum in that city.

"Lunatic asylum is perhaps a little too flattering a word. When you remember what our madhouses here in Amsterdam look like, you can imagine what they are in some small provincial hole like Gouda. They seem to consist of a few extra rooms in the local jail, and the turnkey feeds the poor devils whenever he happens to think of it. But anyway, the woman was at last out of harm's way and I rejoiced, for now there would be a chance to see something more of Rembrandt than I had done during the last year and a half, and I always liked the man though he has broken every law of nature in regard to those colors which God meant to be 'white' and 'black.'

"But that was only half of the story which the bookseller told me. For it appears that the lady in question is possessed of certain relatives who are not above a bit of blackmail, whenever it comes handy, and can be practiced without too much risk. And the risk in this case was very small, for Rembrandt, who is the world's most muddle-headed financier, has undoubtedly borrowed small sums of money from his son's nurse whenever he was in momentary need of a few guilders to pay the baker or butcher. Very foolish, no doubt, but you know how he is. When he is working, he just does not want to be disturbed and would take cash from the Devil himself. The whole thing, in the language of your esteemed country, is a mess, a 'rommeltje.' (I think that was the first Dutch word I ever learned.) It is a mess, a hopeless muddle. The 'disjecta membra' are all over the Breestraat and I have no idea what the outcome will be. I shall wait a few days and then I shall go forth and do some discreet reconnoitering and I shall let you know.

"After I had seen my guest out (intelligent booksellers are the salt of the earth and unfortunately as rare as a fine day in March), I decided that it was too late to go to work and too early to go to bed, and having the Breestraat still in my mind, I took my hat and coat and called on Rabbi Menasseh. I found him at home entertaining a number of people and I discovered that this curious old fellow had developed a new hobby. If Bernardo (from whom I have not heard for five or six years. He used to write in the beginning. Is he still alive?)—but if Bernardo actually finds the long lost tribes, and returns home with the good tidings, he will be a very much disappointed man. For Rabbi Menasseh won't even bother to listen to him; instead he will now tell him of a wonderful new scheme he has developed to bring the Jews back to England. He is completely obsessed by the idea. He allows his printing shop to go to ruin and forgets half of the time that he is supposed to teach the Talmud to little Jewish boys, so full is he of this marvelous project.

"As far as I could make out (for as usual everybody was talking at the same moment), he is firmly convinced that the Messiah is about to return and that the Jews, in order not to miss their opportunity this time, ought to settle in every part of the world and make ready to receive the long-expected no matter where he chooses to land on this pretty little planet. That is not exactly the way the good Rabbi expressed himself, but it will give you a fairly accurate idea of what is in his mind. He must have got his 'universal' idea from the East India Company, which has added so much territory to its former possessions that nowadays it is absolutely impossible for a penny's worth of profit to fall upon this earth without being caught by the pocket-book of some Dutch trader.

"After talking for about half an hour, when at last he came up for breath, I quickly asked him how he hoped to accomplish this purpose, as not a single Jew had been allowed in England since the end of the thirteenth century. But he answered that that was a mere detail. It was the English kings who had been responsible for keeping the Jews out of their realm. They had done so out of spite because the Jews were cleverer traders than their own dull-witted Saxon subjects. How they had hated and feared them, one could learn from that contemptible piece of the famous court hack, William Shakespeare. He had never seen a Jew in all his life. When he was born, there had not been a Jew in England for exactly two hundred and seventy-four years, but all the same he wrote his monstrous tragedy about Shylock to make the Jews unpopular and to please the Queen. God, however—God the righteous but wrathful—had heavily smitten the wicked rulers of that ungrateful land. The last one of them had been beheaded like a common criminal and now a new day was approaching. A man who truly walked in the footsteps of Jehovah had been called to lead his people out of the wilderness of superstition and intolerance and soon the Jews would be readmitted to all parts of the British Kingdom and to all of the British colonies, because Cromwell the Just not only respected the religious principles of the Jews but also recognized the debt of gratitude which Christianity owed the children of Abraham.

"At that moment, a dark-eyed youngster of about sixteen or seventeen years of age spoke up and rather dryly remarked: 'Undoubtedly he does, dear Master. He undoubtedly loves and respects us for the sake of our high-minded religious principles. But has it ever struck you that he may also have a certain admiration for certain commercial abilities which we as a race are supposed to possess?'

"Whereupon the excellent Menasseh flew into a violent rage. 'Baruch,' he thundered, 'are you going to be another Acosta and turn against your own race? Do you dare to come into my house and tell me to my face that this noble Englishman, this second Moses, this prophet and seer who has the power of a dozen kings, yet lives simpler than the simplest of his myriad subjects, is merely actuated by a vile lust for gold? I am truly ashamed of you!'

"But that young Baruch, whatever his last name was, remained perfectly calm and quietly answered, 'No, dear Master, I have not the slightest desire to follow in the footsteps of poor Uriel and I hold suicide to be a crime against the orderly arrangement of this world. I fully share your admiration for General Cromwell, but I hear that he is a man who takes everything very seriously and that sometime very soon the people are going to offer him the title of their Lord and Protector. Very likely, if he accepts this honor, he will not only try to protect their souls but also their purses. A few thousand Jewish commercial houses, moving from Amsterdam to London, would not come amiss at a moment like the present. It would be another feather in His Lordship's cap.'

"Here I interrupted him: 'I did not think so good a Puritan would ever condescend to wear feathers,' but the youngster merely looked at me for a moment (he had the blackest eyes I ever saw) and then went on: 'I meant his figurative cap, sir. In this house we are always speaking figuratively whenever the Master does not approve of us,' and he explained that that very afternoon he had been called upon to translate a Latin document which one of his father's neighbors had received from London and in which he was offered all sorts of commercial advantages and opportunities if he (his father) agreed to pack up his business and move from Amsterdam to London.

"As this subject of conversation did not particularly appeal to me, I soon afterwards bade them all a good evening and went home. But this true and accurate report of the proceedings in Menasseh's house will show you which way the wind is blowing in this part of the world. The people live under a cloud. They have fought for three generations to gain their liberty. Now they are free and there is a rival across the North Sea who is trying to cut their throats and they are beginning to realize that this was only the beginning and not the end of their difficulties. They will have to sail their newly built craft very carefully if they want to avoid being shipwrecked before they are more than a dozen miles out of port.

"As I said, they are beginning to realize this and then they look anxiously at the poop deck, where the captain and the mate are supposed to dwell in peace and amity that they may give all their thoughts and attention to the difficult business of navigation, and they see those worthies engaged in a disreputable quarrel that may develop into a regular fist fight at almost any moment. The whole thing is very disheartening. The young Prince, if he is not very careful, will end by making a fool of himself. The Amsterdam magistrates, if they continue to insinuate that they and they alone rule the Republic and that both the Prince and the Estates General exist merely for the sake of outward ornament, will find themselves one fine morning in one of the dungeons of Loevenstein with a pleasant-spoken but fierce princely guard on the other side of their doors.

"What will happen to this country unless the people learn to look a little distance beyond the exceedingly narrow limits of their own towns and villages, the good Lord only can foretell. Without quite knowing

CANAL WITH A LARGE BOAT AND BRIDGE (ETCHING)

how they did it, they have acquired such tremendous colonial possessions that they have become the masters of one of the largest empires that has ever existed. But they are trying to rule this empire with the same system of laws that was originally devised for half a hundred hamlets that belonged to some medieval chieftain of the Middle Ages. When told that now they are a big nation and should behave as such, they blush violently and in great embarrassment they answer, 'Oh, sir!' and run as fast as their legs will carry them to the nearest safe spot behind the familiar moat of some ancestral burgh and hastily pass a bill regulating the hours of the civic garbage collectors or stipulating the fee which wet-nurses may charge for their useful and pleasant services. All I can hope for at the present is that you and Bernardo will be safely back here before there is a war. Otherwise you will have to stay in your jungle forever, and we need you here.

"As for our mutual friend, about a week ago I desired a fish for dinner (I still obey the dietary laws my father's confessor taught me as a child) and behold! whom should I meet in the fish-market but the good painter from the Jodenbreestraat himself! I thought that he would try to avoid me, for our last meeting had not been exactly a happy one, but he came right up to me and shook me by the hand and said, 'You have heard, of course, what has happened?' And I answered 'Yes,' and he smiled rather sheepishly and then looked at me and said, 'Phew!' and I replied, 'Yes, indeed, phew!' and then we both roared with laughter and it was the first time I had heard him laugh for several years and so I decided that the obsession of that terrible female had come to an end.

"Then I asked him whether he had joined our Holy Church and was buying shrimps for his Friday dinner, but he said, 'No danger there! They have got hold of old Vondel and ought to be satisfied for the moment. I had a visit the other day from a young Italian nobleman who asked me whether I would be willing to paint him a Madonna in the manner of Raphael. I told him that I had painted any number of Holy Families in the manner of Rembrandt van Rijn. He was a very suave and pleasant young man and said that was exactly what he wanted. There was a patron of the arts in Rome (unfortunately he was not allowed to tell me his name) who had a tremendous respect for my work and who thought I was the greatest painter then alive. Of course my subjects were influenced a little by the surroundings in which I lived, but if I were willing to make just a few changes, such as providing my Virgin and the Holy Child with a halo—just a very small change, as I would undoubtedly see myself—then he on his side would not haggle about the price. I told him that I was deeply touched and flattered but

ABRAHAM ENTERTAINING THE ANGELS (ETCHING)

that I painted the way I painted because that happened to be the way I painted and that I could not change my way of painting any more than I could change the shape of my head. He then asked to be allowed to see what I had been doing recently, and I showed him the sketches I had been making for a large picture of the Good Samaritan and some other sketches for a large piece of Christ and Mary of Magdala which I have to finish next year and a half-finished picture of Abraham entertaining the angels, and he expressed himself as delighted with everything and told me that he would write to his employer and would let me know as soon as possible. And so you see I may be a rich man again, if I will buy enough yellow ocher for half a dozen haloes.'

" 'Which, of course, you won't do!' I said.

" 'Which, of course, I won't do,' he answered, and then he turned to a woman who was standing behind him with a large household basket and quite casually remarked, 'You had better buy another turbot, for if I am not mistaken, our friend here will share our dinner to-night.' And it was said so pleasantly that I forgot all my previous feelings of irritation at his extraordinary conduct and that night I dined with him and I never saw such a change in any human being before. The house was scrupulously clean and it looked quite cheerful, although the carpets were beginning to give evidence of wear and tear and the door and the floors would suffer nothing from a new coat of paint.

"Little Titus, now quite a handsome boy with long blond curls like his mother, was allowed to stand at the table and he had lost that look of a hunted creature which he had had ever since I first knew him. The meal was well cooked and the food was not thrown at us as in the olden days. I asked him where he had found this jewel, and he told me that she was a peasant girl from a small village near the German border, but she had come to Amsterdam to find employment as a general maid, and that a friend had sent him to her because he knew that he was looking for some one after the Dircx woman had been sent to the madhouse.

" 'I know nothing about her,' he confessed, 'except that she seems to have no other relatives than a sister who lives in a village called Breevoort, about a week's distance from here, something that suits me exceedingly well, as I have had enough of servants with brothers and sisters just around the corner, ready to perjure themselves at a moment's notice. For the rest, she is an excellent cook, keeps our rooms in order, is as nice to little Titus as if she were his own mother, and has a pleasant shrewdness when it comes to spending money, a quality which is perhaps not out of place in this particular household.'

" 'She is also a very handsome woman,' I ventured to remark.

186

Rembrandt van Rijn

"'Yes,' he answered, 'she will suit me wonderfully well as a model. I was thinking of using her for quite a large picture I mean to make some time—a picture of Bathsheba.'

"I looked at Rembrandt and I looked at the maid who had then turned nurse and was telling little Titus that it was time for him to say good night and go to bed.

"'Remember David!' I warned him.

"'I have thought of that,' he answered, 'but there is really very little danger of such a thing. I am only too happy that I have found a servant like that. The type is scarce nowadays. They all want to work in a shop

BATHSHEBA AT HER TOILET (PAINTING)

187

KING DAVID (PAINTING)

doing some dull job like curing tobacco or making paper boxes rather than cook for an old widow man.' And he got up to kiss his son good night and went to the door to open it for the servant, who was of a type that was scarce nowadays, and I noticed that he bade her farewell as if she were a very grand lady and then it suddenly struck me: she is a grand lady, even if she cannot read and write.

"And then Rembrandt took me up to the print room and we looked at his etchings and he showed me how he wanted to change the plate of the hundred-guilder print for the sixteenth or seventeenth time and when I went home shortly after midnight, it was as if nothing had ever happened between us. We were better friends than ever before, and when you return you will witness a miracle—the man is positively showing signs of becoming a normal and civilized human being. He also seems very hard up. But who cares? He is doing better work than ever before, so what is the difference? And fare ye well and come back to us soon. We miss you."

This letter removed the last vestige of doubt that still existed in my mind whether I ought to return or not. After all, this had not been entirely a pleasure trip. I had been sent out to do a very definite piece of work and I had accomplished my task as far as was possible. I had grown very fond of this new country. I had been happy there. But if My Lord Andries and his brother, who had financed the voyage, were in difficulties at the moment or likely to get in difficulties through their quarrel with the Prince, it was up to me to return home and give them that information which might be of the greatest possible value to them at the present moment. I sent word of my plans to Bernardo. The oldest of my two Mohegan servants offered to take the message personally. Two weeks later he returned.

"Your brother only shook his head," he told me.

That was all?

That was all.

I decided not to sell my house. I had become too much attached to that spot to give it up entirely. I went over my accounts and found that I still had more than one thousand guilders left. I gave each of my two servants one hundred guilders in gold and I sent them back to their own country. The ducats would make them rich for the rest of their days and they had well deserved such a reward. I would explain this expenditure to my employers and they would no doubt approve. As for the little house, I had stout doors and window blinds made for it and asked leave to deposit the key at the Fort. My Lord Stuyvesant graciously promised that he would send one of his men every other week to inspect the premises.

I don't believe in lengthy farewells. To say good-by to a dear friend is too much like a minor amputation and it is not good for either the body or the soul. All herbs that I had collected during these many years (with the exception of those I had gathered with Father Ambrosius and which had been destroyed by the Eries when they burned down our Cayuga village) were safely packed in heavy wooden boxes. I had made quite a collection of living plants and these were placed in rough wooden troughs on the poop-deck near the wheel-house, where they would suffer as little as possible from the sea.

I then paid an official call on My Lord Stuyvesant and was touched by the emotion he showed in bidding me God-speed.

"It will be the last time we see each other," he said, and stamping the floor impatiently with his wooden leg he repeated those words I had heard him use before: "A century hence this land will be of infinitely greater value than Java and all the Moluccas put together. But they won't believe me at home. They won't believe me. They won't believe me until it is too late."

And he actually wept, but whether it was from anger or grief, I could not say, though I am inclined to think it was from the former.

One afternoon, late in June, I had my last glimpse of the city of the hills. I had gone on board early in the morning and for several hours we had drifted down the harbor with the tide. On our right was the Staten Eiland, on the left the farms of Breukelen and Nieuw Utrecht. We passed through the narrow funnel that leads from the inner bay to the open sea. In the distance the white beach of the Konijnen Eiland was basking in the sun. Three or four Indian canoes had followed our ship. They were fishermen on their way back to Heemstede. They came very close to the vessel. One of the men in the nearest boat waved his hand at us and called out something. I thought that he was speaking in his own language and I leaned over the railing and cupped my hand to my ear to understand him better. Then I caught his words. They were in Dutch. "Goede reis!"

The Indian was wishing his white brother a safe crossing.

Then all the sails were hoisted and we turned eastward.

An hour later I had seen my last of the New World.

And seven weeks later I was back in my own country.

Chapter 18

I MEET MY COLLEAGUE, DR. EPHRAIM BUENO, WHO
HAD TAKEN CARE OF REMBRANDT'S FAMILY WHILE
I WAS IN AMERICA

OLD MAN WITH FLOWING BEARD
(ETCHING)

A DOZEN or so years before, ere I had started upon my American adventure, Jean-Louys, Bernardo, Selim and I used to meet each other nearly every Sunday morning to spend the day in some tavern at not too great a distance from town.

Now Selim had departed to partake of the quiet pleasures offered by the hospitable shores of the Bosphorus, Bernardo had become a Mohegan chieftain and Jean-Louys and I remained alone, and since even the best of friends will tire of each other if they have to listen to each other's everlasting monologues, it was quite natural that instead of going on long Sabbatical walks, we should drift into the habit of spending at least part of the day with our painter friend of the Breestraat.

Only extreme youth can be hilarious and full of good spirits early in the morning. We, however, were fast approaching an age when one likes to be alone for at least part of every twenty-four hours, and we used to improve the time when other people went to church, puttering around the house until, a little after eleven, Jean-Louys would drop in on me and then the faithful Jantje would invariably remark:

"I suppose His Highness will stay for dinner." (He was the only baron she had ever met and she meant to make the most of her opportunity.) And Jean-Louys would slap his hands in surprise and would say, "Ah, my beautiful Antoinette, but that would cause too much trouble." To which she would reply, "No trouble whatsoever. I have already counted on your being here." And they both would laugh right heartily, and we men would retire to my working room, where we talked of this and that until Jantje came to tell us that "the food was on the table." I had tried to teach her for many years to say, "Monsieur le Baron est servi," but at the last moment she always lost courage and the much less elegant but rather more direct announcement was the only compromise she would accept, although even this form of invitation to partake of her culinary efforts appeared to her as a direct manifestation of that French effeminacy which according to her innermost conviction would some day destroy the whole fabric of our noble northern civilization.

After dinner, during which we had been joined by my son, who had a seat and a knife and a spoon of his own (I never approved of the prevailing habit of keeping children standing at the table and letting them eat only with their fingers), we went back to the workroom to smoke a pipe of tobacco, and as soon as the chimes of the South Church had announced the third hour of the afternoon, we took our hats and capes and walked around the corner to the house on the Jodenbreestraat, which by this time had acquired a look of pleasant familiarity and no longer made the impression that it had been finished only day before yesterday. And inside too there had been many changes. The ground floor still looked like the storeroom of a dealer in antiques—statues and bits of old armament and a most heterogeneous collection of pictures gathered from all the four corners of the European continent; on the top of a large oaken cupboard, two large globes and a foreign-looking helmet which a few weeks previously had adorned the head of Rembrandt's brother Adriaen.

The staircase which led to the second story was half hidden by a bit of tapestry that had once been the pride of a small Flemish castle in the neighborhood of Antwerp which had gone up in flames during the siege of 1585. On the table in the center of the hall, a large marble wine-cooler and a couple of daggers of Italian provenance. Over the door that led to the side room was a Venetian mirror in an ebony frame. I only mention the things one remembered seeing when one entered. The others would fill a small catalogue, and as all of them were sold at auction long before the death of their owner, it would indicate a serious lack of piety were I to try to enumerate them.

But the old disorder had somehow undergone a change. During the last days of Saskia's life and immediately after her death, one felt that there was something wrong in this house. Tables and chairs and pictures and globes were all thickly covered with dust. Milk pitchers were standing in doorways where they did not belong. An occasional pail of forgotten garbage would strike an unpleasant note next to the green velvet covering of an ornamental Spanish chair.

Now everything was neat and clean and spick and span. People were living in this house, not just camping out like the mutilated soldiers and their wild women in the wooden shacks just outside the Haarlem gate.

But it was in the big living room in the back of the building, in the so-called hall, that the "vita nuova," the "new life," upon which Rembrandt seemed to have embarked, made itself most thoroughly felt. It still served as sitting-room, dining-room and reception-room to the whole of the family, and Rembrandt continued to sleep in the large bed built in the wall in which Saskia had died. Some day I suppose people will learn not to sleep in beds in which patients with pulmonary trouble have died. From my own experience I would say that it is a very bad thing to do. But I have never been able to convince any one else. Even Rembrandt, who by nature was a man of good sound common sense, would not hear of it when I told him that he must never let little Titus come near anything his mother had worn. He laughed at the idea and said that we doctors were always trying to scare the poor laity merely to show the world how learned we were, and he pointed to Titus and asked me whether I had ever seen a boy that looked as strong and healthy as he did.

I was thinking of that when I first met Titus again after almost eight years of absence. He must have been ten years old, going on eleven. A handsome and pleasant-looking youngster endowed with his mother's fine profile with that same agreeable smile that Saskia must have had in the days Rembrandt drew the little picture of her in a large straw hat—the only drawing we found among his

SASKIA, WITH THE STRAW HAT (DRAWING)

belongings when we cleaned out his room on the Roozengracht. But the child did not give one the impression of being very robust. His cheeks were a little too thin for his age, and his large, wondering eyes shone with that strange brilliancy one so often finds in those whom the gods love so well that they deem them worthy of an early death.

My first impulse was to talk to Rembrandt about my suspicions—suggest that the boy be kept outdoors a great deal of the time and not be allowed to spend the greater part of his days in the etching-room where the acid vapors caused even a healthy man to gasp for breath. But I felt a certain hesitancy about taking such a step on account of Doctor Bueno, who had taken care of Rembrandt's household after I left for America.

Bueno was a Jew. His full name was Ephraim Bueno, after his father, from whom he had learned his profession. He was a pleasant and modest little man and from all I had ever heard about him an excellent physician. But of course his position in the community had always been a little difficult.

In the first place, it had not been until just before the war with Cromwell (I think it was in the year 1652 but it may have been a few months later) that the Portuguese immigrants of Jewish extraction had been given full civil rights. Up to that time, from a strictly legal point of view, they had been merely tolerated. And this had made it impossible for them to join one of the guilds. Even when they opened a shop or started a business of their own, they had been technically guilty of a breach of law. Quite frequently the guilds had sent delegations to the Town Hall to ask the Magistrates to interfere and forbid these unwelcome competitors from exercising their trade at all. But Their Lordships had too great a respect for the commercial abilities of these profitable immigrants to take any such steps. They did not, of course, dare to treat the representatives of these ancient and honorable corporations as curtly as they sometimes treated the clerical powers who came to them for redress from some threatened heresy. The town militia was entirely composed of members of the different guilds and only the officers belonged to the class of the rich merchants. The Magistrates therefore were very polite and sometimes almost obsequious in the way in which they listened to such complaints as came to them from the united bakers or butchers or carpenters or cartwrights or soap manufacturers. But

EPHRAIM BUENO (ETCHING)

no sooner had these worthy guild members left the premises, highly flattered by their reception and quite convinced that very soon something was going to be done about it, than the petitions and requests wandered into the aldermanic stove and the matter was referred to the Kalends of the Greeks.

For our town, first and last and all the time, was a business estab-

PORTRAIT OF THE JEWISH PHYSICIAN EPHRAIM BUENO (PAINTING)

REMBRANDT'S BROTHER WITH A HELMET (PAINTING)

lishment. Since the average Portuguese Jew had proved himself an excellent and most industrious citizen, he was considered a good business asset and all attempts to oust him or turn him into a pariah failed as systematically and as efficiently as the efforts on the part of the established Church to turn Amsterdam into a new Zion on the basis of Doctor Calvin's shorter catechism.

But until the Jews finally were accorded full civic rights, their position was always a trifle difficult. Their surgeons, no matter what degrees and titles they could offer as a token of their competence and ability, really had had no right to practice until the year 1651, and if one of the Burgomasters had ever been foolish enough to enforce the strict letter of the law, he could have ordered all Jewish doctors to be driven out of the town by the hangman on the ground that they were mountebanks and quacksalvers and had no right within the jurisdiction of the city.

I therefore was very careful in the way in which I treated Ephraim Bueno. I had a great respect for his learning and did not want to hurt his feelings. Sometimes if I happened to be within hailing distance and some slight accident took place (once, one of the pupils burned himself heating a copper plate and once Titus had an attack of coughing which frightened Rembrandt almost out of his wits), I would be called in and then I did whatever was necessary (in the case of Titus it was only necessary to tell him not to eat so many green nuts), but as soon as the emergency was over I invariably sent a hasty note to Doctor Bueno asking him to proceed to the Breestraat as soon as would be convenient. It was Bueno himself who put a stop to my somewhat exaggerated civility.

"My dear colleague," he said one day, as we were returning from the hospital together, "we Jews are sometimes said to be very thin-skinned, and perhaps we are a little too suspicious about the intentions of our neighbors. But my people have lived here now for half a century. We shall probably live here as long as this town lasts. Suppose we cease insulting each other by being so frightfully polite and become friends." And he added as an afterthought, "I am a Jew, and that, as many of my neighbors never tire of reminding me, is pretty bad. But we both of us are leeches, and that is infinitely worse."

And in this he was quite right. For as soon as I had returned to

Rembrandt van Rijn

Amsterdam I had been struck once more by the anomaly of our position. In the New Netherlands there had been so few physicians that the people, depending upon our good will, had usually treated us with great respect. But the Republic was overrun by every form of charlatan and the public seemed either unable or unwilling to differentiate between serious practitioners who had studied at half a dozen universities and had spent seven or eight years walking the hospitals, and those jugglers and bone-setters and ointment venders who frequented the country fairs.

In the eyes of the "better classes of society" we still belonged to the guild of the "tonsorial artists" or "whisker-pluckers" of my childhood, and no amount of labor on our part seemed to be able to overcome that prejudice.

Indeed, I remember how, shortly after Rembrandt's death, I was requested one day to come to The Hague and pay a professional visit to My Lord Jan de Witt, who at that moment was the recognized leader of the Republic, and how His Lordship bade me stay for luncheon and introduced me to one of his youthful cousins (cousins of his wife, to be exact) whose name was Bicker and who curiously enough was an ensign in a regiment of the Scottish guards. I, trying to be pleasant to the young man, said something flattering about his relatives, whereupon the young man, affecting a strange English accent, said, "Oh, yes! I think I remember my uncle telling me that you used to shave him whenever he could not leave the council-chamber on account of the press of business."

This remark was not a success, for My Lord Jan slowly contemplated his cousin with two eyes that were as cordial as icicles and casually remarked, "I am sorry that your regimental duties will not allow you to sit down with us at table," and took my arm to show me the way to the dining-room without paying any further attention to the bewildered young man, who was left to the mercies of the maid, who in that simple household still fulfilled the rôle of a butler.

No, our own social position had never been a very happy one.

It was pretty bad. But, as Bueno said to me one day, it might have been infinitely worse. We might have been artists!

Chapter 19

CONCERNING THE POSITION OF ARTISTS IN A
COMMERCIAL COUNTRY

THE VILLAGE STREET (DRAWING)

E PHRAIM BUENO had meant his remark as a jest but there had
been considerable truth in what he had said. The position of
the artists in those early days of our independence was a very curious one indeed. I had heard from my colleagues who had studied
in Italy how the different princes and kings and grand dukes who
ruled that country considered themselves deeply honored if a painter
or a sculptor or a poet of renown deigned to honor their courts
with a visit. From my grandmother I had learned how in Flanders
in the days of her youth a whole city would go forth to meet the
man who was to provide their church with a new picture or statue
of the Madonna. I had not quite believed her when she told me that
famous artists were often requested to accompany the king or even
the emperor on his peregrinations through his realm. But during my

own lifetime (it must have been in the early thirties, for I had just moved to Amsterdam) we were much surprised to hear that Rubens, the Antwerp painter, had just been sent to London to act as ambassador of the King of Spain at the court of Charles Stuart, and I remember that I heard many people say that they thought such a step a very dangerous precedent, for painters ought to remain painters and diplomats ought to be gentlemen, and I am sorry to say that this was the general attitude of pretty nearly all classes of society.

There may be those who can explain this curious attitude toward the arts, but I cannot. Doctor Bueno's bitter remark that a first-rate salesman was of some practical use in a commercial community, but that a sculptor was not, was probably more or less true, but if it were wholly true, then how about Venice and Genoa and such towns as Florence or Bruges? All of those cities had been mere political counting-houses, like our own Republic. They had been ruled by bankers and cloth manufacturers and salt-merchants, plain, practical business men who loved a soldo just as dearly as our own little potentates loved their golden doubloons. I have seen pictures of these worthies and they looked for all the world like the older brothers and cousins of our Burgomasters. I have read a few stories about them and they were every inch as mean and as generous and as shrewd and as corrupt as Their Lordships of the Town Hall. But they apparently felt flattered whenever a painter or a musician was willing to come to one of their parties or dropped in for dinner, whereas our artists are forced to stand with their hat in their hand and listen very obediently when one of our great whale-oil magnates or some half-literate buccaneer who has recently returned home rich with the plunder of a dozen spice islands demeans himself sufficiently to address a few words to one of those "paint-spillers."

I am not exaggerating. I was present not so long ago when an unbearably patronizing young man (he bore my own name, but was no relation) asked old Ruisdael why his son, instead of taking up painting, had not joined his cousin in the frame-making business.

There is a man by the name of Hobbema living in an attic on the Roozengracht not far away from the house where Rembrandt died. I am told that he is the best landscape painter we have ever had, but the other day, in the boat to Haarlem, I overheard two young business men cursing him roundly as an impostor because one of them had bought a landscape from him for two hundred guilders and had been told by his father that he could have had the thing for one quarter the price if he had only jewed the poor devil down a little harder.

Not to mention poor Hals of Haarlem, who died only a few years ago, who was undoubtedly as great a man as Rembrandt, who was forced into bankruptcy by his baker (can one man eat quite so much bread?), whose belongings at the time of his death, amounting to three mattresses, one cupboard and a table, were sold at public auction for the benefit of the poor-house in which he had found refuge.

No, I have never quite understood why it should be that way in our country and so very different everywhere else. But if I sometimes wondered and worried, my anxiety was certainly not shared by the victims of this deplorable public negligence.

After I returned from America I spent a great deal of my time in the company of painterfolk but almost without exception they accepted their fate as something that was too self-evident to be a subject for public discussion or commiseration. Whenever they were together, they talked shop. They talked of different methods of grinding paint or of a new combination of acids with which to treat their copper plates or a better method of laying on a coat of varnish. Only upon some very rare occasions did they curse their poverty and declare Rembrandt to be an outrageously lucky fellow to be able to live in a house of two stories and to have been allowed to marry the daughter of a burgomaster.

But taking them by and large and as a group, they were a singularly contented body of men. A few of them of course got despondent and gave up in sheer despair and drank themselves into oblivion and an early grave by spending twenty-four hours of each day in the gin-shops with which our town was so richly blessed. But the vast majority lived like masons or plumbers—like unsuccessful masons and plumbers, I ought to say, and not to be compared in any way with the genuine masons and plumbers who were employed on Jacob van Campen's new town hall on the Dam.

Without exception they were very hard workers. The world accused them of keeping irregular hours, of being seen about the streets at all hours of the day and night. There was some truth in this. They did indeed lead very irregular lives. As a rule they were too poor to be able to pay much rent, and as they needed at least one large room for a studio, they were apt to go to the outskirts of the city and look for an old barn which they then converted into a more or less suitable workshop. For our painters, unlike those in Italy, don't seem to be able to work out of doors. They will sometimes make a hasty sketch of a landscape or a tree or a few boats out in the open, but then they run home as fast as they can and spend the next three weeks finishing the picture for which the sketch serves them merely as a reminder but not as an inspiration.

But since they spend the greater part of the day right there in the studio which also serves them as dining-room and sitting-room and bedroom and kitchen and nursery (for they rarely can afford more than one room), the whole place is almost always in a state of extreme disorder.

THE OMVAL (ETCHING)

Rembrandt van Rijn · ·

Then their rich neighbors, who live in a house with five or six different apartments, see the poor painterman sitting at his easel between a pile of yesterday's dishes and day-before-yesterday's cutlery—see the baby's laundry hanging from a rope stretched along the ceiling—observe his wife busily engaged making the weekly supply of pea-soup over a little charcoal fire in the corner, shake their heads and say, "Oh, my! oh, my! what a careless fellow! No wonder he is always hard up." But they entirely overlook the fact that poverty is more apt to provoke slovenliness than vice versa.

People, however, will cling to their preconceived notions as tenaciously as they will cling to the tables and chests and drawers which they have inherited from their parents. And I have long since given up trying to convince them of the error of this view. For even after I had brought them to the point where they were forced to agree with me and told me, "Well, perhaps there is something in what you say," they would find other reasons why the artist should not be regarded as a respectable member of society. And one of these was the so-called clannishness of all those who made their living by their brush or their wits.

"Why don't they ever associate with us?" I have heard respectable merchants ask. "Why do they spend endless hours in each other's studios? Why do they marry each other's daughters?"

To which I would make answer as follows:

"Why do you who are in the export business or grain trade always marry each other's daughters? Why do you who sell whalebones or distill gin know all other whalebone dealers and gin-distillers and rarely see any one outside your own profession?"

But then of course I was shouted down by a tumult of protests. 'Oh, but that is different! We have got to know each other to get along in business, we marry our competitors' daughters because we know fairly accurately how much the father will be able to give her. We are practical men of business and at the same time we like to sit down with people with whom we can talk about our own work."

"Very well," I would then continue my line of reasoning, "why shouldn't painters also like to meet men and women with whom they can talk their sort of shop?"

It was no use. I butted my head against a granite wall of prejudice and accomplished nothing. The artist was an amiable loafer, not able

or willing to do an honest day's work and therefore deserving all
he got in the way of poverty and neglect. One could of course be
an artist and at the same time a respectable member of society. But
such a combination was an exception almost as rare as that of Doctor Tulp, who was a gentleman and a member of the town government, although he had started life as a physician, or Gerard ter
Borch, who painted portraits in Deventer and was said to have
served one term as Burgomaster of that city.

Yes, ours was a strange country.

But there was one consolation. With the exception of two or
three rather weak brethren, I never knew a member of the Guild
of Saint Luke who cared a tinker's dam for the opinions of any
one who did not belong to his own profession. Not because he
thought himself superior to his surroundings but because he was by
far too busy to bother about such unimportant little details as the
respect of his community. Life was short and at the very best one
had only ten hours a day during which one could paint. That was
the answer to the second riddle of the artist's far-famed "queer-
ness." The fellow was never idle and, what was infinitely more important, he was interested in his work.

I wish that his neighbors could have said as much.

SKETCH (DRAWING)

Chapter 20

THE ARTIST IN A FLAT CAP WITH A
SHAWL (ETCHING)

BUT to return to Amsterdam, life at first was rather dull and we missed our old friends. Selim had become a man of vast importance in the land of his birth (returning sea-captains told wonderful stories about the luxury displayed at his palace and of the two hundred women who were said to be guarded by no less than three hundred eunuchs) and Bernardo had disappeared in the American wilderness without leaving a trace. Jean-Louys and I tried to continue our Sunday walks but we soon discovered that peripatetic duologues were very apt to degenerate into sedentary monologues, accompanied by too much beer.

For a while we did our best to make Rembrandt join us, but I never knew a man who had such a thorough-going aversion to exercise of every sort. I used to scold him, and Doctor Bueno used to back me with great cordiality whenever I told him that no human being could lead the sort of life he did without digging his own grave with his easel and his chair. I delivered endless lectures on elementary physiology, quoting a great deal of wisdom which I had borrowed from Jean-Louys, who in turn had culled his information from the writings of Monsieur Descartes. I used to explain how the human body was a sort of machine and just as windmills could not do their work without wind or water-mills without water, so the human body needed fresh air and exercise to keep in good condition.

I drew graphic pictures on the back of some of his sketches, showing him that the lungs were in reality nothing but a pair of bellows that had to be kept going all the time by moderate exercise, for otherwise (the metaphor was slightly mixed) the organ would give forth no sound whatsoever. From organs I would jump back to sailing vessels that were useless and deteriorated without wind, which is merely fresh air in motion. But I might as well have talked to the skeletons that were hanging from the municipal gallows near the harbor for all the impression I made.

Rembrandt never lost his temper and I admired his patience until I discovered one evening that he did not even listen. He just went on painting and let me talk. Only the week before he had complained to me that his heart caused him trouble—that he would wake up in the middle of the night with his heart beating like fury, and a severe pain in both shoulder-blades. I told him to ask Doctor Bueno to examine his heart and then I said: "When do you notice this trouble most?" He could not quite remember but he thought that it came when he had spent the whole day at his etching-press. "You see," he remarked casually, "those boys of mine mean well, they do their best, but if I want a really good copy, I have got to do it myself. I have not had many orders for portraits of late—you know how it is when there is a war. Everybody is scared. Everybody saves all the money he can. And portraits, after all, are a luxury. But people will buy etchings. They are good investments and I had orders for several hundred. So in the evening when those children had gone to bed, I used to strike off a few copies myself."

"At what time did you begin?"

"About seven."

"And when did you stop?"

"Oh, sometimes quite early. Other evenings I worked until four or five."

"Without stopping?"

"Yes. Sometimes I stopped for a quarter of an hour or so and had a glass of beer. One gets thirsty. It is hard work."

Rembrandt van Rijn

Seven until four or five—that meant nine hours of standing on his feet in a small room that was suffocatingly hot, pulling the wheel of a press that was almost too heavy for a cart-horse.

"Man alive!" I answered him. "No human being can stand that sort of exertion. How long have you been doing this?"

"Oh, not so very long. Since January last year when orders came in for those plates."

January of last year—that meant fifteen whole months of a sort of labor that would have killed a hod-carrier in less than six.

"But of course," I said, "when you do that sort of thing, you don't paint?"

"Yes, I paint the greater part of the day in my studio, as long as there is any light. Then I take the candles and go to the press-room."

"How many candles?"

"One as a rule. Sometimes when my eyes begin to bother me, I light a second one."

"When your eyes begin to bother you? Do they bother you much?"

"Not very much. We all of us have good eyes. We got them from our father. Bad lungs from our mother and good eyes from our father. No, there is nothing the matter with my eyes, I still can do a dry-point without using any glasses. But after five or six hours, I find myself weeping big tears as if I were walking in the wind and after ten hours, I get funny pains."

"What sort of pains?"

"As if some one were sticking a pin into my eye-balls. Not the pain on the side of my head of which I just spoke to you. That only comes when my heart does its funny tricks. But irritating little pin-pricks, and sometimes I have to stop for a few minutes until they disappear again."

Truly, the man was hopeless.

"Has it ever dawned upon you," I asked him, "that if you go on working that way you may end by losing your eyesight completely? A fine painter you would be with your eyes gone!" And I made ready to leave. At once he changed his tone. "Don't be angry with me, Doctor," he begged me, "you are probably right and I am undoubtedly wrong, but what will you? I can't stop. I have to go on."

"Why?" I interrupted him.

Rembrandt van Rijn

Rembrandt wiped both his hands on his blue painter's smock, a habit which made some of his enemies of the popular Italian school say that he carried his best works on his belly—took a bottle of acid from a low chair that stood in a corner of the room—reached down—picked up the bottle—took out the cork—looked at it and smelled it, and said, "That is the sixth cork in two weeks. That stuff is too strong. I told them they had made it too strong. I must get a glass stopper." And then added, "I will be good for this once and obey orders. My whole head aches and I might as well call it a day. You ask me why I work like a madman? Very well, I will tell you. Because I am really a little crazy."

"Professionally speaking," I interrupted him, "I never noticed it."

"Of course not. I am not crazy in the sense the Dircx woman was crazy. You need not lock me up. But I know that I am not an ordinary, well-balanced and respectable member of society and I know that no matter how hard I try, I never shall be. That is what is the matter with my work. So far I have kept out of the poor-house. But only because I happen to have inherited all that money from Saskia. The inheritance is a little slow in collecting, but anyway it gives me credit, which is almost as good as having money. You can buy whatever you want and people ask no questions. Are glad to sell to you.

"But if I did not have that money, I don't know what would have happened to me long ago. My work does not sell.

"In the beginning, the first ten years after I came here from Leyden, I was a sort of curiosity. I was the fashion. In those days many people were still alive who remembered the Rebellion. Of course you and I, theoretically speaking, lived through it too. But what did we ever see of it? Nothing! We paid our taxes and once in a while some former soldier with his arms or his legs gone would ask us for something to eat in the street and if he was very much of a bother, we called the guards and had him arrested.

"The people—I mean all the people like that grandfather of yours of whom you have so often told me, or my own father, or my own grandmother—men and women who had escaped with their lives but whose brothers and sisters and sons had been hanged and burned and broken on the wheel—that generation seems to have understood

more or less what I was trying to do. They had all of them started from very simple beginnings. So had I.

"There was a time when I used to pretend that I was a great nobleman. That was just after I married. I liked to dress up. Saskia was a lovely girl. I liked to dress her up. I liked to imagine that we were really fine folks. She was, but I am the son of a miller and my brother is a shoemaker and all the satins and silks in the whole world and all the feathers and frills will never make me anything else.

"That is why that older generation liked my work. That is why the younger generation is afraid of me. I think they realize that I am a fairly good artisan. I can paint, if I say so myself, and they know it. But I can't paint the way they want me to paint and they know that too.

"Of course you will say that I ought to be practical and ought to try and paint the way they want me to paint. Well, I will tell you a secret. I have tried and I have tried very hard, but I can't do it. I just can't do it! And that is why I am just a little crazy.

"An ordinary person who sells raisins or herring or cheese or who makes pictures for a living carefully studies his market, which after all is his bread and butter. When the taste of his customers changes, he speedily changes the nature of the goods he is trying to sell them. If they want their herring dried instead of pickled, he buys a couple of acres of land and hangs his fish up in the sun until it is as hard as a rock. If they want their cheeses painted red instead of yellow, he paints them red instead of yellow. If the fashion of the moment prescribes Italian landscapes with Italian skies and Italian beggars eating—what is the name of that stuff? macaroni?—he will paint them Italian landscapes with Italian skies and Italian beggars dropping handfuls of noodles into their gaping mouths.

"Personally I don't blame those people, as I have heard it said sometimes, when I am accused of being too proud or too haughty to paint differently from the way I paint. It isn't that I am too proud or too haughty. I just can't do differently—that is all. And so I stick to my own line and I suppose I shall stick to it until I go to the poorhouse or the cemetery and you may put a stone on my grave, saying: 'Here lies a fool' and you will never have been so right in all your life as on the day you ordered that inscription."

Chapter 21

REMBRANDT BECOMES TALKATIVE AND FAVORS ME WITH A FEW OF HIS VIEWS UPON ART

LION EATING (DRAWING)

THIS was one of the longest speeches I ever heard Rembrandt make. And contrary to his habit, he used it to mention a few of his theories on art.

Notwithstanding the war, which continued with uneven success, there was a good deal of money abroad at that time. Thousands of people were losing all they had; but a few hundred, who had been shrewd enough to speculate in grain and wood and gunpowder and all the other supplies of which the fleet was in such great need, made vast sums of money. Not knowing what to do with their newly found riches, they were buying luxuries right and left.

One day pictures would be all the rage. The next day it would be china. The little Japanese cups that had sold for three florins apiece had gone up to three thousand. The china craze switched over to pearls, and when all the wives of all the profiteers had been provided with ear-rings as large as carrots, pearls became vulgar almost overnight and the Nuremberg watch-makers reaped a fortune with queer and extraordinary timepieces that showed not only the minutes but also the seconds and that played a little tune when the hour was struck, just like the bells of the new town hall.

As they had heard that there lived a painter in the Jewish quarter whose house was a museum of everything that one could possibly hope to collect, a good many of them found their way to the Bree-straat.

In the beginning, Rembrandt felt rather flattered, and thought that this meant a renewed interest in his own work. But very soon he discovered that those noisy visitors with their even more noisy wives did not care in the least for his own art—very often were ignorant of his name—called him Ronnebrandt or Remscheidt—patronized him in most outrageous fashion—gave Titus sweetmeats and patted his head and said he was a nice little Jewish boy and then asked the master how much he would take for an enameled Turkish sword or a piece of ivory carving from the Indies. Then he would grow angry at such an indignity (for he well knew the value of his own work) and instead of making these miserable war profiteers pay an outrageous sum for some article which he himself had bought in a moment of weakness and for which his visitors were willing to pay ten times the original price, he would show them the door in a most abrupt fashion (he still could speak the vernacular of the Weddesteeg in Leyden with great fluency) and then these amazing guests would depart and would spread it among all their friends that this man Rompot, that so-called artist, who gave himself such airs, was an ill-natured ruffian and that one ought to give him a wide berth and have nothing to do with him.

Until the rumor had gone all over town that the painter of the Jodenbreestraat, you remember, the one who had done that queer picture of Banning Cocq, was a sullen and crabbed barbarian—a morose and splenetic fellow—whose swinish ill-temper had turned him into an involuntary recluse, shunned by all his neighbors for his violence and irascibility.

This was of course entirely beside the truth. Rembrandt was by nature an easy-going and friendly person, perfectly willing to meet his neighbors with a smile and only asking to be let alone. But that was just it! Our newly rich did not like people of an independent character. They had touched their caps to their betters for so long

Rembrandt van Rijn

that now they rejoiced to be in a position where (through their purse and their financial influence) they could oblige others to raise their hats to them. And any one who stood squarely on his own feet, went his own way, asked for no favors and (infinitely worse) accepted none, was something so utterly baffling to their sort of mentality that they could explain his attitude in only one way, by accusing him of a haughtiness of spirit that was as foreign to his nature as malice, envy or the very suspicion that such things existed in this world.

Here I am conscious of a doubt. If this diary of mine should ever fall into the hands of one of my descendants (if my son is to survive) and should be read by them two or three hundred years hence, wouldn't they instinctively feel that I have exaggerated my friend's character? Wouldn't they say, "This mysterious grandfather of ours seems to have had a sober enough eye when he contemplated the rest of his contemporaries, but when it came to Rembrandt (of whom we have heard very different stories) he feels compelled to indulge in the most noble-sounding terms, as if his friend were a paragon of all the virtues. Yet, when we contemplate his life, as it is revealed to us by the records of the Bankruptcy Court and the Public Guardians of the Amsterdam orphans, we meet with an irresponsible fellow who bears very little resemblance to the glorious picture revealed by our great-great-great-grandfather."

And when I say that I never met a man so little given to petty jealousy or so indifferent to malice, I do not mean to imply that Rembrandt was a saint who after a lifetime of seclusion and meditation had finally attained such a degree of spiritual perfection that he had become immune against the temptation (forever present in all of us) to regard every man as his possible rival and therefore as his potential enemy.

Nothing could have been less true than that. Rembrandt was of this earth earthy. He was fashioned out of the common clay of our land, and our land, lest we forget, lies fifteen feet below sea-level. But he had one enormous advantage over the majority of his neighbors. Like most other artists he had a purpose in life and he was too busy with his own problems to enjoy that leisure which is the breeding ground of gossip and spite.

This devotion to a single ideal sometimes manifested itself in very unpleasant ways. I never knew him to read a book. He owned quite a library—the hall was full of them, but every one of them had to do with the arts, wood-cuts by Lucas of Leyden, copper-plates after etchings by Raphael, the world's best pictures done in copper-plate reproductions, wood-cuts of Lucas Cranach, copper print reproductions of Guido Reni of Bologna and dozens more of the same sort. All of the best painters of the last two centuries were represented— Rubens and Titian and Jordaens and Michelangelo and Miereveld, Carracci, van Dijk and dozens of others, not to forget Albrecht Dürer's famous handbook on perspective.

But when it came to the so-called "belles-lettres," to literature as such, almost any ordinary household in Amsterdam, however humble, could have boasted of a better selection than this luxurious museum of the Breestraat.

I have spent all my life among books. When I am called in for a consultation in a house where I have never been before, I try if possible to cast a glance at the book-closet. One minute's examination of the different titles will tell me more about my future patient, his habits and tastes and even the probable nature of his ailment than hours devoted to a mere physical examination. But if I had tried this method with Rembrandt, my diagnosis would have been completely wrong.

For I don't think that I ever found more than five or six ordinary books in his house during all the many years I knew him intimately. One of these was a tragedy in blank verse, called "Medea," wished on him by the author, Jan Six, the linen merchant (afterwards one of the Burgomasters) by whom Rembrandt was befriended for a while and from whom, to his own great detriment, he borrowed a small sum of money. The others were devotional books, Josephus' "History of the Jews," Bibles and collections of sermons. And all of them, including some interesting products of the calligrapher's art by his friend Coppenol, had been presents, for with the single exception of a German treatise on military strategy which for some reason had caught his fancy, I don't think that Rembrandt during the whole of his life ever spent a single penny on books. I don't believe he even felt the need of them. If he had done so, he would have bought them by the cartload, for he had no sense of the value of money and bought whatever he wanted with the same sublime

COPPENOL, WRITING MASTER (ETCHING)

unconcern as that which is manifested by a very small child which pulls its mother's most beautiful glass vase off the table and lets it fall on the floor and break into a thousand pieces, and will feel itself completely justified by the smiling excuse, "I wanted it."

Whatever he "wanted" Rembrandt got, and our more or less veiled hints that life just simply wasn't that way, that one had to trim one's sails according to the wind and other bits of proverbial wisdom did not make the slightest impression upon him and never evoked any further comment than an admiring "But isn't it beautiful?"—it being almost anything from a painting by Giorgione to an ebony chest for little Titus's diapers.

Being fearsome of the ultimate results of this indiscriminate buying, I sometimes hinted at books as a substitute for the infinitely more expensive objects of art with which he filled his room. At one moment he got greatly interested in a certain Adriaen Brouwer, a pupil of the incomparable Frans Hals of Haarlem. This young man, of phenomenal ability, had died in the poor-ward of an Antwerp hospital at the early age of thirty-two. His works therefore were rather rare and in the dozen or so years after his death (he died in the early forties) they had greatly increased in price.

One evening I found the whole of the front room filled with Brouwers, a most heterogeneous collection, a woman and a child and a pastry cook and a couple of gamblers and a cook busy with a very greasy dish, all of them done with the most beautiful economy of line and color.

"Aren't they wonderful?" Rembrandt asked me, who had kissed Titus good night and was coming down the stairs with a candle in his hand.

I said yes, that they were very interesting but that they must have cost him a small fortune, and I pointed to one which probably represented my household expenses for more than half a year. Then I congratulated him on his success and said that I was glad he had done so well recently.

"Done well recently?" he asked and lifted his candle so that I should better be able to see the picture of a small studio (also done by Brouwer) which up to that moment I had not noticed. "Done well recently? Good God! I have not sold a thing for over two years."

"Then your Indian venture must have turned out prosperously." (For though he had tried to keep it a secret from me, I knew that he had been speculating in the shares of a rather doubtful Indian Company.)

He was a little surprised. "Oh, you mean those three ships. You heard of those?" (Who had not heard of them?) "No, they were not exactly what one would call a success. There was some trouble with the crew of one of them and the others suffered so badly from scurvy, they only got as far as the Cape. No, the money I put into that affair is lost, I am afraid."

"But I suppose they wanted cash for these Brouwers?"

"They did. I borrowed it. Aren't they marvelous?"

And then he took me into the side room, lit a fire, got me a bottle of ale and spent at least two hours explaining his conception of the uses of money and the duties of artists towards themselves, and he defended his point of view so plausibly and so reasonably that I went home convinced that he was right and that I was a hopelessly prejudiced miser who would never be able to look beyond the rock-ribbed system of "never spend more than you can afford." Which (if we were to believe our elders) was the foundation stone of the Republic's prosperity and greatness.

"You have been telling me to be careful," he began. "Everybody I ever knew has been telling me to be careful. You are a man of tact (that is why I like you) and rather than tell me outright not to buy pictures and helmets and all those things in this room and in the others" (he made a gesture that was meant to include the whole house) "you have encouraged me to buy books—and read. 'If he is kept busy reading,' you probably said to yourself, 'he won't spend so much time among the Jews, inspecting their antiques.' But what good has the reading of other people's books ever done an artist?

"You remind me of those people who have been coming to me ever since I was fourteen years old and had smeared some paint (very badly I am afraid) on a couple of pieces of canvas. 'My dear boy,' they used to say, 'this is all very nice and very pretty but it will never lead to anything. You can't learn your trade here. We in the North are all of us barbarians when it comes to the arts. Italy, the South, that is the country for you.'

"And then they would recite long lists of names of boys from Amsterdam and Haarlem and Leyden and Dordrecht, from every village and hamlet in the Republic who had gone to Rome and Florence and Venice to learn 'painting.'

"I used to make them very angry with my attitude. 'Painting,' I used to say, 'is nothing but seeing. You see something that impresses you and then you paint it, or if you have a gift for something else, then you draw it or hack it out of a piece of marble, as the

Greeks used to do, or you make a tune out of it and play it on the organ as old Sweelinck used to do when we were children and he got so excited one day about a thunderstorm he had just heard that he turned the 116th prelude into an imitation thunderstorm and seven people in the congregation fainted in their pews and had to be carried out.'

"And then I would add that it did not depend so much upon what you saw as how you saw it and that a good artist could get more inspiration out of a dead bullock hanging from a ladder in some mean village butcher-shop, than a bad one out of half a dozen beautiful churches in the village where Raphael himself was born.

"All this sounded like terrible heresies to the good people among whom I grew up. They took me aside and whispered into my ear that if I knew what was good for me I would not be quite so plain-spoken and express such open contempt for those marvelous Italian artists whom all the world held to be the greatest craftsmen after the sculptors of ancient Greece. In those days I was a great deal more impatient than I am to-day and I would lose my temper and would waste my time on foolish arguments—trying to prove that I had never said that the Italian painters were not among the greatest that had ever lived—that all I meant was that the Italians living in Italy should get their emotion (the word inspiration is good enough for theologians and for amateur artists) from Italian subjects, but that we people living in Holland should get our emotion from the subjects with which we were familiar in our own country and not from something a thousand miles away.

"But no, I was all wrong and even such a broad-minded man as My Lord Constantin, who has been a kind and steadfast friend to me all my life, could not see it that way and broadly scolded me because I refused to take the opportunities that were offered me to go to Italy. When I told him that his beloved Italians cared so little for their own great men that they were willing to let all of their best pictures be sold abroad, so that one could get a better idea of the work of Raphael and Giorgione and Titian right here in Amsterdam than in Florence and Rome (except of course the things they have painted on the walls of churches and monasteries that can't be pried loose), he did not quite know what to say and replied that anyway the trip would be good for me, that I was too young to spend my entire time working in a stuffy studio, that it was bad for my health never to take any exercise and sit or stand everlastingly in front of an easel, that I would die young if I overdid it as much as I was doing . . ." ("In which he was quite right," I interrupted him, but got no answer) . . . "and ended up by telling me of the wonderful landscapes he had seen on his way to Venice and that landscapes were only possible in a region where the sun was a brilliant ball of golden fire and not a greasy speck made by the nose of an inquisitive child on a pane of window-glass as it is in our own muddy country.

"But I would not be convinced and answered him that a rainstorm, if seen and felt by some one with the ability to see and feel rainstorms as intensely as some of the Italians were able to see and feel the sunsets over their native lagoons, would make just as good a subject for a picture as his dearly beloved Forum by moonlight, and a dozen years later (it was in '43 if I remember rightly) I sent him a copy of my etching of those three trees with the rainstorms in the distance, and I wrote him:

" 'My Lord, do you remember a talk we had when I was twenty-five years old and was just on the point of moving to Amsterdam? And will you graciously accept this poor etching as a token of my extreme gratitude and tell me whether I was right when I said that rainstorms could be made just as interesting as sunsets?'

"And he answered me with his usual courtesy that he was beginning to understand that, after all, perhaps I had been right and in '50, when he was here a few days incognito, after the Prince had attacked the town, I showed him that picture of a windmill that was afterwards sold to some one in England and I asked him once more: 'My Lord, isn't that mill as good in its own way as the little house that Giorgione painted in the background of his Concert?' (a picture which is in Paris but of which I have seen some very fine copies), and he looked at it for quite a while as if he were thinking of something that had happened long, long ago and, as if he were speaking to himself, he said:

" 'Of course, that pretty young woman would hardly be playing the flute the way she does at the foot of your mill,' and I answered, 'Your Lordship is right, but neither would the Graces of Botticelli bombard each other with snowballs.' And then he said yes, that I might be right after all, but, like poor Jan Asselijn, whom we buried

JAN ASSELIJN, PAINTER (ETCHING)

last year, I might have done both, and I asked His Lordship point-blank: 'Do you think his work was so much better than mine?' and he answered: 'No, of course not, and besides, he was really a Frenchman, so the comparison was not quite fair. I happened to be looking at the etching you made of him. That is probably why I happened to mention him.'

"And then, abruptly changing the subject, he said: 'I want to ask you something. It has always puzzled me and I have always wanted to ask it, but I never had the opportunity, but what are you really trying to do?'

"And I told him as best I could (just as I told you a moment ago), how when I was very young I had thought that painting was merely

Rembrandt van Rijn

a matter of seeing, of feeling, of sensing some particular object or idea and translating what you saw and felt into lines or bits of color.

"And then one day I was working in my father's mill and something happened to me. I don't mean that I was painting in my father's mill. In those early days I was not encouraged very much to become an artist. My people were simple folk and very pious. They had the usual prejudice against the arts and especially against the artists. When one mentioned the word painter, they thought of Babylon and Sodom at once, and when I first told them that I wanted to be a great painter, like Lucas van Leyden, who was the first man whose works I had ever seen, they shook their heads and said 'No,' they wanted me to be a good Christian and get ahead in the world.

"I seemed to have a fairly good brain—I was much cleverer than my brothers. One of them could succeed father in the mill and the others would be taught a trade that they might spend their days as God-fearing members in good standing of some honorable guild of artisans. But as for me, I was to go to the University and get a degree so that my parents could say, 'Our son, the Doctor of Laws,' and have something to console themselves for the hard labor which had been their share all during the time they were bringing us up.

"That plan never came to anything. I actually went to the University but I was a dreadful failure as a student. I never went to a single lecture. I wrote my name in a big book and got a piece of paper informing me most solemnly that Rembrandus Hermanius Leydensis or some such thing was now, at the age of fourteen, if you please, a duly enrolled stud-litt—whatever that meant—in the glorious University of Leyden, and entitled to all the rights and privileges connected with this distinguished rank.

"But it was no use, I never went near a professor or a book (I cared as little about books then as I do now) but instead I went to Jaap Swanenburch, who was a famous man in our town—he was one of those who had learned their trade in Italy—he had done the job so thoroughly, he even came home with an Italian wife who used to throw plates and knives at him every time we had a pretty model, to the great joy and delectation of his pupils—and when Swanenburch came to the Weddesteeg one day and told my parents that I had it in me to become a most successful and fashionable portrait painter, but would they please pay my tuition, they forgave me for having played hookey from my scholarly duties and as Swanenburch's charges were less than the tuition fee of the University, they decided that they might as well let me stay where I was and work out my own salvation according to the best of my own abilities.

"But before that time, I could only draw when no one was looking my way and every afternoon after school time, my brother Cornelis and I used to go to the mill on the wall and help father with his work.

"Have you ever been in a mill? You have. Ever been in a mill on a bright, sunshiny sort of a day? Well, then you have missed something. For the wings do curious things to the interior on a day like that. The windows of a mill are usually very small, but when the sun is shining brightly, especially in the spring when the air has just been cleaned by three weeks of wind or rain, the whole inside of the mill is flooded with a curious and very brilliant sort of light—a strange light that is like nothing else I have ever seen—though I must add that I have not traveled very far and that I may be all wrong when I say that it is only to be found here on this floating pancake of ours, where the sun and the fog are apt to do all sorts of queer things to the light, both inside our houses and out of them.

"Well, it was just such a day in April—I remember the date, for the experience made a great impression upon me. It was the fourteenth of April and Cornelis and I had been told to go and count a number of sacks that lay on the first floor and carry them up to the second floor where the grinding was done and stack them up neatly in a corner. We counted our sacks and carried them to the second floor and my father inspected them and found that one or two needed repairing and told us to get a needle and thread and attend to the job then and there. I got a needle and thread and sat down in a corner to repair the sacks, while Cornelis was sent away on an errand. It did not take me long to finish that task, but I was afraid that if I told my father that I was through, he would give me something else to do and so I said nothing, but sat very quietly in my little corner and pretended to be very busy. There was a brisk eastern wind blowing outside and the wings went past the window, g'chuck—g'chuck—g'chuck, just a sort of guttural sound like the snapping of a musket and then the sudden swish of those enormous wooden arms, cleaving the air. And every time one of those wings passed by one of the windows, the light was cut off for perhaps a hundredth part of a second—just a flash—too short to measure by the clock—but visible, just the same—very visible indeed, for every time it happened, the room became pitch-dark.

"Now you may remember that when we were young, the country was suffering from a plague of rats—perhaps as a result of the siege and the large number of people who had died—but anyway, our houses and our cellars were all of them full of rats. And there were people who did nothing all their lives long except catch rats—professional rat-catchers. They were usually old soldiers and very dirty and very picturesque and I have drawn them quite a lot, for they were interesting-looking scoundrels.

"That morning one of them had been at work in our mill. There were so many rats in that mill, we sometimes were afraid they would carry the old building back to Noordwijk where it came from. The rat-catcher, who liked to work in the dark, would not be back before evening, and one enormous wire cage full of rats was hanging by a strong chain from a rafter of the mill. Those rats—great big fellows —would have eaten through any kind of rope but though all of them seemed to be sitting on their hindsides, gnawing at the steel chain that held their cage, they hadn't a chance in the world. But through the scurrying and pattering of all these excited little bodies, with their bright beady eyes and their long, disgusting tails, the cage was slowly beginning to swing from left to right and it was making a curious shadow upon the wall. And all the time, the wings of the mill kept swishing past the window and every time they swished past, the room would be pitch-dark, and then for just one, two, three seconds, it would be filled once more with brilliant sunlight.

"But I had seen that sort of thing hundreds of times before and it had never struck me as anything very remarkable. And then suddenly—it really came to me just like the revelation that came to Saul—I noticed that that cage was not merely hanging in the light or in the air, as I had always taken for granted, but that it was an object surrounded by a whole lot of different sorts of air—all of which were of a different texture. In the beginning it was not at all clear to me and I can't expect to tell you what I mean in two words, but you know of course that there are a number of colors, like yellow and blue and red and combinations of colors and we painters are supposed to know all about those colors and their combinations and that is how we paint our pictures. We tell stories in daubs of color, just as others tell stories in lines or with the help of words or notes. At least, that is what I had always taken for granted and I had done my best to learn how to use those colors.

"But that morning in the mill, there weren't any colors, at least, none of the colors with which I had been familiar from my earliest childhood, when some one gave me my first box of paints. The light in front of that rat cage was different from the light behind it, which was different again from the light on the left of it and all these different sorts of light did not remain the same, but changed every moment. Of course, when I say 'light' I mean air and when I say 'air' I mean light. What I really mean is the space which fills all our rooms and all our houses and the whole world—the stuff we breathe, and through which the birds fly. And then the idea suddenly struck me (and that was the moment when I turned from Saul to Paul), does all this space—this air—really have a color in our sense of the word and is it possible to translate that color into terms of paint?

"Let me show you" (here he picked up a pewter mug that was standing on the table)—"let me show you. You see that mug. It is about three feet away from you. And now" (moving it towards himself) "it is only two feet away. Suppose I want to paint this. I can get the illusion of distance by applying the rules of perspective which Master Dürer of Nuremberg laid down in that little book of his. That would be enough when I use a pencil or pen and ink. But when I use color, I ought to be able to create that impression of distance in some other way—in the way nature does it, or rather, in the way I suspect that nature does it. For I have now spent the greater part of every day during the last forty years—Sundays included, to the horror of my good parents—trying to solve the problem and I know just as little about it to-day as I did when I first began.

"Your French friend, the Baron, told me the other day that those famous mathematicians of whom he sometimes talks work quite differently from the way we would expect. When a mason builds a house, he first digs the basement and then builds the first floor and next the second floor and so on until he gets to the roof. But mathematicians, so it seems, first make the roof and fit in the rest afterwards. 'They have suspicions,' the Frenchman remarked. They 'suspect' that two times two is four and accept their 'suspicion' as an established fact and then work backwards and by working backwards, they finally 'prove' that two times two is indeed four. I may have got this a bit mixed, but I think that is the way he reasoned it out. They first 'suspect' and 'surmise' and then they 'prove.' Of course, those are not the sort of ideas with which to entertain my own relatives nor those of Saskia either. They would either giggle sheepishly or run to their dominie and suggest that I be locked up in the asylum. And I am not quite certain that I am making myself clear even to you.

"But from that moment on, from the moment I saw those excited rats in their wire cage, hanging from the rafter of my father's mill, until to-day I have been convinced that every object in the world is surrounded by a substance (call it light or air or space or whatever you like) which somehow or other it must be possible to express in the terms of light and shade and half a dozen primary colors.

"Sometimes I even think that at least in a few of my pictures I have solved that problem pretty well. But I confess that I have been working backwards, painting the picture first and trying to discover afterwards why I had done what I had done. People, always looking for the outlandish and the unusual, whisper that I have a secret. Secret fiddlesticks! I am a mathematician who works in vegetable matter and who started out with a formula and who is now trying to prove that it works and is correct."

It sounded very plausible but I warned him that I had once heard of a mathematician who had hit upon a new formula that appeared to be perfect and who had died just before he had succeeded in proving his point.

"Yes," he answered, "that is the risk I run. I too may die before I have been able to find out exactly how this problem should be solved. But I am content. A few times when painting people, I have caught certain effects that seem to bear out my theory. What I would like to know, however, before I die is this—how did I happen to get those effects? Why are people able to say, when they look at one of my pictures, 'That man is actually sitting on a chair in a room, not leaning up against a mere background of chair and room'; or, 'That angel is really floating through space, not falling or resting on a cloud, but floating!'?

"I probably would have been more of a success in my work if I had not been told by my father to repair sacks in his mill on that particular morning. Now I waste half of my time or more on a problem that no one has ever solved before me—that no one, as far as I can find out, has even thought of. Rubens is a great man, but he does not even suspect that there is such a thing as I have been trying to put into paint for the last thirty years. Hals comes much nearer to it. That man Brouwer (you scolded me because I bought so many of his pictures) has done marvels in that field. They tell me there is a man in Spain, working for the King (his name is Velásquez or Velázquez, I don't quite know), who seems to be working on that basis. I have never seen any of his paintings and it is always difficult to imagine what a picture looks like merely from hearing some one else describe it.

"Of course, the public has no notion of what I am trying to do. Perhaps four hundred years from now, if any of my pictures are left, they will say to each other: 'This fellow van Rijn at least was on the right way and was going in the right direction.' But my neighbors— they see that one picture is very good, and how in the next one I tried a new method to prove that two times two actually makes four and have failed pretty completely, and they sneer, 'This man is a mere amateur. He does not take his art seriously. He does not paint things the way we ourselves see them.'

"Heaven forbid that I should ever see things the way they do! They may (and very likely they will) let me starve, but they can't rob me of the conviction that I am right and that they are wrong. Any one can learn to paint the things that are there. But to paint the things that one merely suspects to be there while one can't possibly prove that they are there—that, my good Doctor, that is the sort of task that makes life interesting. And that is the sort of thing that makes other people afraid of me. And now let us go to the back room."

"For a game of chess?" I asked.

"No, no more chess. Life is too short. At least for me. Too short for books and for chess—too short for anything except one single problem and one that I shall never solve. But if you will come with me, I will show you something. You remember the etching I made of Doctor Faustus, one or two years ago? Well, it wasn't right. I have worked a lot of dry-point into it since then and now at last I think that I know what is necessary to make it right. I will let you see it and then you will understand how it is possible (even in black and white) to make different sorts of light that flow into each other like wine that is poured into a glass of water. Speaking of which, Hendrickje shall make us a kettle of bischop, but please don't scold me any more

DOCTOR FAUSTUS WATCHING A MAGIC DISC (ETCHING)

if I continue to buy pictures instead of books. In the first place, it won't do you any good. I shall buy them anyway. And in the second place, I need them. There is always a chance that they will teach me something new. I am almost fifty. More than two-thirds of my days are gone and there is still so much to do. So terribly much."

We went to the back room. Rembrandt lit two candles and got the plate of Doctor Faustus. Titus was fast asleep in one of the two beds built in the wall. Hendrickje went to get the wine and the spices that were necessary for our drink. The kettle was standing on the floor in front of the fire. She leaned over to pick it up just as I looked her way. And suddenly my professional eye registered an unmistakable professional fact. She was pregnant and in her seventh or eighth month.

That too was a problem in space but one which Rembrandt seemed to have overlooked.

A WOMAN BATHING, DETAIL (PAINTING)

HENDRICKJE STOFFELS (PAINTING)

HENDRICKJE STOFFELS AS VENUS (PAINTING)

Chapter 22

I BEGIN TO UNDERSTAND THAT ALL IS NOT WELL IN THE BIG HOUSE ON THE JODENBREESTRAAT

STUDIES: HEAD OF REMBRANDT, A BEG- GAR, WOMAN AND CHILD (ETCHING)

IT IS very strange, but there are certain things which one man just can't possibly tell to another. He may, under certain circumstances, draw his friend's polite attention to the fact that he is a scoundrel or a thief, but he can never, and under no pretext whatsoever and however discreetly, inform him that his cuffs are badly in need of the laundry—that his collar needs starching nor that his coat after all these many years and many meals of spinach and soft-boiled eggs, would fill the heart of a dozen Josephs with envy and desire. Nor can he go up to even the most intimate of his friends and say, "Pardon me, but isn't that housekeeper of yours on the point of giving birth to twins?"

But for once Fate intervened in a very welcome and discreet fashion. Hendrickje suffered an accident, and as Rembrandt's regular doctor was out of town for the day (he had left by boat that morning to go to Ouderkerk for a funeral) they sent for me who lived just around the corner. When I arrived, I found Rembrandt painting in the large back room while Hendrickje was lying panting and gasping for breath in the same bed in which, almost a dozen years before, Saskia had died. I thought of course that her apparent lack of air had to do with her physical condition, but Rembrandt at once told me what had happened and then I understood the cause of her ailment to be much simpler.

The Life of

She had gone upstairs to clean the studio as usual that morning. The evening before, two of the pupils had been biting a plate in a new mixture that was supposed to be more effective than the usual "eau forte." It consisted of nitric acid and blue vitriol and a few other ingredients but nitric acid was the chief substance used in this particular compound. Those bright boys had become so deeply engrossed in their task that they had forgotten to close the bottle containing the acid. The faithful Hendrickje had paid no attention to the strange odors in the room—had carefully swept and cleaned and brushed—had breathed the poisoned air—had felt how her chest was gradually beginning to ache and how her eyes were beginning to smart—and how she was weeping bitter tears—and in great panic she finally had left the room, telling Rembrandt she was going to faint and would he please send at once for the surgeon.

It was not a very difficult case. I asked to be shown the room in which she had worked, for I thought that she might have tried to burn some old rags, which sometimes make a very dangerous smoke. As soon as we entered the studio, Rembrandt noticed what had happened, pushed open both windows, looked for the jar containing the acid, closed it and then called for the two pupils, whose ears he boxed with such an experienced hand that these young men probably remembered until the end of their days that a bottle of nitric acid was no child's toy and should be treated as circumspectly as a loaded and cocked gun.

We then took Hendrickje out of the badly ventilated back room and put her down on a couch in the garden and immediately she began to feel better. A few minutes later she fell asleep and as my morning had been spoiled more or less anyway, I decided to stay a while and reassure Rembrandt, who was in a great state of perturbation.

"I have lost one wife in this house through what was more or less my own carelessness," he said as soon as we had returned to the studio where the mild hurricane that was blowing in through the open windows had not only driven away the acid fumes but had also upset a picture of Hendrickje on which Rembrandt was working. It showed Hendrickje wearing the big pearl ear-rings of Saskia which he had bought about fifteen years before and which had figured so prominently in the famous libel suit which he had been forced to bring

Rembrandt van Rijn

against some of his wife's relatives who had accused him and his wife of being spendthrifts and ne'er-do-wells. That libel suit had come to nothing. The court had found Rembrandt to be technically right, but as he was only a painter and Saskia only the wife of a painter and both of them therefore "private persons" of no particular account, the amount of damage which they claimed had been reduced from 128 to eight golden florins and so in the end the case had cost Rembrandt infinitely more than he had got out of it. He still apparently retained the pearl ear-rings, for in the picture Hendrickje was wearing them and when Rembrandt had dusted it off with a piece of soft cloth, I noticed that it was a very fine piece of work. Perhaps he had made Hendrickje a little more of a "lady" than she actually was, but all the kindness and goodness of her beautiful eyes were there. I liked it and I told him so and he sat down in front of his easel and mixed some white with ocher to touch up the ear-rings (slightly damaged by the fall), and said, "I am glad if you think that all those things are there. I have worked on this very hard. She has been very good to Titus and to me. I would like to do something for her."

This was more or less my opportunity.

"I was obliged to examine her when I came in," I said, "for to tell you the truth, my first impression was that she was pregnant. And I discovered that she was. That isn't what you mean when you say that you wanted to do something for her?"

I knew that I had committed a terrible blunder. I had done one of those incredible, unbelievable things of which one is guilty once or twice in his life and which one never is able to forget—which come back to one at the most unexpected moments, during sleepless nights, and cause cold shivers to run down one's spine. And no sooner had I spoken these words than I regretted them with a thousand regrets, but it was too late.

Rembrandt, however, picked up the knife that was lying on his palette, put some raw umber on it, with which he lightly touched the background, stepped back, the better to look at what he had done, and then remarked in a most casual tone of voice: "No, that is not what I meant. I was thinking of this picture, for it is one of the best things I have ever done and people will look at it and will admire it— and her—long after we shall be dead. And as for the other little item you just mentioned, that I am sorry to say was an error on our part.

We are both of us glad it happened, now that it has happened, but it was a mistake. It happened once before, but you weren't in town at that time and the child died. Pity, for it was a girl and it would have been nice to have a girl. Perhaps we shall have better luck this time."

He made this announcement as if he were telling me of some new picture he was planning to paint and I really don't believe that it meant very much more to him than that. The picture was merely an incident in life, an interesting episode in which one pitted one's intelligence against the unwilling forces of nature. The child was an incident in life in which nature pitted its unreasoning forces against the intelligence of man. Sometimes man won. As a rule nature won. It made no difference. Everything that "was," was to Rembrandt a manifestation of the existing order of things. Some people tried to solve the problem by worrying. Others tried to solve it by working. Rembrandt worked—pictures, etchings—children. Everything was as it should be—no questions asked—no answers either expected or given —world without end. Amen.

"But," said I, who after all had been brought up in the atmosphere of profound middle-class righteousness (and can a person ever rid the garden of his memory of the weeds of inviolable respectability?), "but surely, now that Saskia is gone and you are a free man, you can marry Hendrickje, and I think" (what hideous spirit of mental bumptiousness possessed me that morning?) "that you ought to."

Rembrandt smeared some more ocher on his palette knife.

"I ought to, all right," he answered, falling into the vernacular of his childhood days. "Sure, and I know it. I ought to, even more than all right, but I can't."

"Why not? You are a free man."

"I am. I am absolutely free. I could marry anybody I pleased, provided she would have me, as soon as the banns had been read. I know all that. We have talked about it. But it can't be done."

"Why not?"

"The will."

"You mean Saskia's will?"

"Yes. Poor Saskia meant well. She loved me. She left me a will and all her earthly possessions."

"But that will is perfectly good."

"Of course it is. But the possessions are not. They looked very imposing on parchment. But they did not exist. Or if they did, my dear Frisian relatives got away with them. I don't know and to tell you the truth, I no longer care. It does not matter. I have too much to do. I think I have found a new way to handle a lighted candle in a picture I may be asked to do for the new Town Hall. I will show you the sketch. I think I now know how it ought to be done. The theme is Potiphar's wife. I tried something like that twenty years ago—a nude —but I didn't like it. I like to paint my figures clothed. The nude was a good thing for those old Greeks who made their statues that way— they were accustomed to see nude bodies. We are not. We never see more than three or four of them in all our lives and we can't paint what we do not see every day—what we do not know by heart. Yes, I want to do that again. Potiphar's wife, or something like that. And then I bought an old piece of armor—paid 300 guilders for it—rather expensive, but a fine piece of work. I am going to use that for all sorts of things, for I have never done brass the way it really looks when the sun shines on it, and I want to try my hand at some more landscapes and I have got at least two dozen etchings to do. You see, work enough for ten years!—if I live that long. If I wanted to get all those other problems straightened out, I never would be able to do anything else."

"Are they as bad as all that?" I interrupted him.

"Much worse. The only way I can go on is by forgetting that they exist. One of these days the public will come back to me. They will understand what I am trying to do. I am a fast worker. In less than a year I will be able to paint myself out of this financial hole. Then I can pay my creditors and marry Hendrickje. I am fond of her. Terribly fond. She is a nice girl. A good girl. She gives me everything I want. I would be a scoundrel not to marry her, but she will have to wait until then. And she does not mind. She says it makes very little difference to her and meanwhile it keeps this household out of trouble."

"But meanwhile will you be able to keep her out of the town gossip? Surely the neighbors will notice her condition and will talk?"

Rembrandt dropped his palette knife and looked at me with anger blazing in his eyes. "What of it?" he asked brusquely. "What of it? They talk anyway. They always have talked. They always will talk. That is what they are in this world for. To talk. They can't do anything else. They can—how does the Bible say it?—they can hew wood and draw water and talk scandal about their betters. The neighbors, indeed! Damn the neighbors! I am not thinking of them. Neither is Hendrickje. Let them go on carrying bricks and slopping around with pails of water. That is all they are good for. But this house is worth saving. Hendrickje likes it. Titus loves it. I have been happy in it. Some mighty fine pieces of work have been done right here in this house. We ought to save the house. That is what we are working for now."

I did not see the connection and told him so.

"Do you remember the will, Saskia's will?" he asked me.

I told him that I did so only in a very vague way, not having the sort of mind that easily retains official language.

"Well," Rembrandt said, "Saskia was not only very fond of me, bless her, but she also had great confidence in me—absolute confidence—and she wanted to show how she felt in her will. Her relatives had said rather nasty things about me—that I was a spendthrift and a wastrel—that I did not know the value of money—that money slipped through my fingers like water and that I would rather spend 500 guilders on some picture that interested me than use the money to pay my grocer. Perhaps they were right. I was never very good at figures and when I think what I am giving the world—what I have already given it—such little details don't matter.

"Anyway, Saskia left everything to me—absolutely and outright—no guardians to watch her son's interests—no notaries to poke their inquisitive noses into our affairs—no Chamber of Orphans to come and ask embarrassing questions. I was to handle everything but on certain conditions. I was to give Titus a first-rate education and establish him in some profession of his own as soon as he should become of age. In case, however, I died or married again, her fortune was to pass directly to Titus. Do you get the meaning of that? In case I married again, Titus was to have everything. If I married Hendrickje, then according to the terms of the will, I would have to go before the courts and fill out endless papers and swear a dozen oaths and turn everything over to Titus. And how am I to turn over 'everything' when there isn't anything—when there never was anything except promises and still more promises and lawsuits and family feuds, but no cash? Even when I wanted to buy this house, I had to

borrow. We ought to have been able to pay for it in full. But always
something was happening in Friesland and every cent we ever got
out of those people we had to take out with a block and tackle.

"Meanwhile the whole world has taken for granted that I am a rich
man. It was, 'Rembrandt, buy this!' or 'Rembrandt, I got a little
Italian picture. The moment you see it you will buy it.' Or, 'Rembrandt, my kids have not had a square meal for a fortnight and my
wife is expecting her seventh. You are a rich man. Let me have ten
guilders.' And I am a weak man where it comes to money. We never
had any when we were children. It was fun to be considered a Croesus.
Anyway, what did it matter? Some day that inheritance would be
paid out in full and I would have almost 50,000 guilders to pay all
my creditors.

"Meanwhile I painted, but since the Banning Cocq picture, the
public does not seem to like my work any more. What could I do?
Move away? Give up this house? The moment I whisper a word
about wanting to sell, I shall have all my creditors on my back. I
have got to keep up appearances if I want to keep up my credit. And
the moment my credit is gone, we shall all be in the poor-house.
Titus—Hendrickje—I. The kind friends who encouraged me to borrow when they thought everything was fine will fall upon me like a
pack of wolves. It would be the end. And so" (with a final dab at the
foreground of Hendrickje), "don't ask me, 'Why don't you marry
the girl?' for I can't and she knows it and she is very wonderful about
it. It won't be easy for her, but she says that she understands and so
I think that for the moment we had better let matters stand where
they are."

I agreed with him in the main but I am one of those persons who
like things done in an orderly fashion. I cannot work unless I am
neatly dressed, well shaved, my hair well brushed. The room in which
I work has to be neat. My desk has to be neat. Otherwise my brain
won't work. And being a man of such precise, almost meticulous,
habits, I like to have my business affairs in order. I know that I have
no talent for financial problems and I therefore leave them to some
one else who knows more about them than I do. But I don't think that
I could live if I were not sure that at any moment I could open a
drawer and undo a bit of red string and convince myself, within two
or three hundred guilders, just exactly what I had and what I owed

others and what others owed me. I know it is rather foolish to lay so much stress upon such things, homo est quod est and that is the way I am made. And so, though I did my best not to sound too much like a school-master, I could not help saying: "But, Rembrandt, my friend, you must know approximately where you stand!" But he smeared his hands on his smock in a most unconcerned fashion, smiled pleasantly at me and answered:

"I have not the faintest idea and that is the truth."

Then I tried to reason with him. I explained to him that he never would be able to get out of debt without first knowing approximately how much he was in debt—that fighting unknown debts was like trying to fight an invisible enemy in a dark cellar—that system and order was the only way in which one could ever hope to slay the monster of bankruptcy. But he was unable to consider the matter seriously and tried to distract my attention by conducting me into the press-room where three pupils were busy with a large etching of the Crucifixion, and presently he discovered a flaw in the shading of the figure of the bearded Pharisee in the foreground and called for one of the boys to sharpen him the steel needle he had bought that afternoon, for he would not bother to bite the plate again but would make his correction by dry-point and finally he forgot all about me and I watched him working by the light of a single candle (a terrible strain on his eyes and disastrous to anybody who has to make a living by one of the arts) and I stayed in the room for about an hour and then, realizing that I might sit there until four in the morning without being noticed, I went downstairs, found Hendrickje fast asleep and little the worse for her accident, and went home where I found a letter from My Lord Constantin written from his country place in which there was little mention of pictures but a great deal about politics.

"These are strange days," so the old gentleman wrote, "for those of us who like to contemplate the historical landscape from a more or less philosophical angle. History, as I have been told since childhood, does not repeat itself. But as certain human emotions are eternal and invariable, certain political conditions, arising directly from those human emotions, bear a very close resemblance to each other.

"Take this bugaboo of self-government, of democracy, or whatever you wish to call it. The average man feels feebly and vaguely that he ought to stand on his own legs—manage his own affairs—and he clamors

Rembrandt van Rijn

for a Republic—for a Res Publica—in which every free man shall have the right to express his own feelings in regard to the management of the state. As long as the country to which he belongs, or the city or the village of which he is an inhabitant continues to dwell in peace, he is perfectly at his ease and struts about in his gay colors, a sword at his side, and pats himself on the back and says, 'I am a pretty fine fellow, master of my own destiny, etc., etc.' But the moment he sniffs the first suspicious odors of danger—the moment he is brought face to face with a crisis—all his courage and all his high spirits leave him and he runs to the market-place and cries: 'A leader! Give me a leader! Give me some one who is stronger than I am myself. Give me a man whom I can follow when he leads. I am only a weak little creature—all these fine phrases were merely self-deception. Take me by the hand and tell me what to do.'

"As soon as we had got our liberty we felt that we had no longer any need for a man on horseback—a handsome young general on a prancing steed. And we got rid of the House of Orange. Henceforth our people were to rule themselves. The rabble of course were not consulted. They never had been and most likely they never will be. Our Burgomasters and Magistrates and our Aldermen and our merchants were to rule the Republic.

"Meanwhile, on the other side of the North Sea our English neighbors were doing the same thing. Being by nature more violent or more logical than we are, they cut their ruler's head off and declared themselves a Republic—just as we are—and Parliament, as representing the wish of the people, was to rule. This condition of affairs lasted exactly three years in both countries. Then they drifted into a war with each other, as they were bound to do, seeing that they both wanted the same thing at the same moment, and behold! England is still nominally a Republic, but it is ruled by a successful general who calls himself only a Lord Protector, but who is more powerful than the old Kings ever thought of being. For one thing, he has presented himself with a standing army of 30,000 men and every time a Stuart dared to ask for a corporal's guard of his own to keep order in the garden of St. James's Palace, there was an outcry of tyrant and murderer. Now an obscure country-squire from a county no one had ever heard of enjoys more power than any sovereign, duly anointed and booted and spurred by Holy Church, ever dreamed of exercising. And all the little people flock to his standard and shout: 'Long live our Chief!' and if he told them to throw themselves from the cliffs of Dover, they probably would do so because they have no confidence in their own weakness but full faith in his strength.

"And at the same moment we on this side of the North Sea are be-

ginning to repent of our courage of a few years ago. We are scared.
We don't know how this war with England will turn out. Just when we
had decided that we would rule ourselves and that it was folly for free
men to submit to the descendants of a little German robber-baron, we
seem to lose courage and the old, old story is about to repeat itself.

"Two years ago we got rid of King Log and to-day, amidst the en-
thusiastic plaudits of the multitude, we are trying to bring in King
Stork. Yesterday your old friend, Jan de Witt, was made Pensionary of
Holland. The title itself means nothing. The office in the hands of that
man means everything. It makes him Dictator of the entire Republic.
He can raise an army if he wants to and he can build himself such a fleet
as the world has never seen before. He can spend all the money he wants.
He is his own Minister of Foreign Affairs and his own Minister of Justice. He has a complete spy system at his disposal, to keep tab on his
neighbors. By formal resolution of the Estates (passed only a couple of
days ago) every private citizen is being urged to watch over his neighbor and to report him to the police the moment he suspects him of
disloyal sentiments—disloyal sentiments to My Lord Jan, of course.

"What the House of Orange never dared to do, this son of wine merchants (or were the de Witts in the wood business?) from a third-rate
little provincial town does and everybody says, 'How perfectly wonderful! how fine! how noble!' Because we are at war with a very dangerous
enemy—because we are afraid of our own shadows—because we know
that we can't ever hope to win without accepting the leadership of some
one whom we feel to be abler and stronger than we are ourselves.

"And behold! at once the country takes new courage. Stocks go up
which ever since the battle of Dover have been going down. The rate
of interest on the public debt has gone down from five percent to four
percent. We cannot quite undo the harm of the first year. Tromp is
dead. Van Galen is dead. We have lost more than sixteen hundred merchantmen, but Jan de Witt has taken hold of things and we are sure
that everything will come out all right and that we will yet win the war.

"I refrain from drawing any conclusions.

"But I have read my Plato.

"I think that I have read everything that was ever printed upon the
curious subject of a Res Publica and upon the even more extraordinary
subject of government by the average citizen rather than by the few exceptional men. It makes rather inspiring reading when one has nothing
else to do—when the day's chores are over and the motherland at peace
with everybody. But as soon as there is need of action, that sort of litera-

SELF-PORTRAIT (PAINTING)

ture becomes just so much trash—useless books of learning without the slightest practical value.

"It is all very puzzling, but as for myself, I have always served a prince and I shall be content to do so until the day of my death.

"Farewell.

"If you could see my late strawberries (my own invention, my own specialty, raised by the care of my own hand) you would rejoice. And I would rejoice too, for it would mean that you were here and I must confess that I miss your agreeable company."

I laid the letter aside and went to bed.

The next morning I got up early.

During the night I had evolved a little plan that seemed to promise good results.

It was impossible to let Rembrandt go on the way he was going.

It was time for some one to do something and I meant to be that some one.

I took my hat and coat and instead of turning to the left as I did every morning on my way to the hospital, I turned to the right and made for the quarters which Jean-Louys had occupied these last five and twenty years.

For although for once I meant to be a man of action, it would do no harm to proceed cautiously.

I knocked at the door and entered and behold! Jean-Louys was lying on the floor before a large flat bowl of water on which there floated a tiny ship made out of paper. By his side knelt a sort of red-bearded giant who was working a pair of bellows with which he was engaged in creating a mild hurricane in the vicinity of the paper vessel.

"Come in and join me," Jean-Louys shouted, without, however, moving an inch from his uncomfortable position. "Come in and join me. I am playing Jupiter and this is my Aeolus. I am at work on a new problem. I have discovered something new, infinitely more interesting than logarithms. And it will make us all rich. Come in and join me. Have you breakfasted? No? Then you will stay with me. This cut-throat here was for five years chief onion-soup-maker-in-extraordinary to the Dey of Algiers. Ten minutes more and you will know why the old Dey drowned three of his favorite wives rather than give up such a cook!"

Chapter 23

I VISIT MY BANKER AND LEARN SOMETHING ABOUT THE DEPLORABLE STATE OF REMBRANDT'S FINANCES

BEGGAR WITH A WOODEN LEG
(ETCHING)

WHEN I entered his office, I found Lodewijk busy cutting himself a new pen.

"What a day!" he shouted as soon as he saw me. "What a day! Was there ever such a climate in all the world? My sixth pen this morning. They melt in your hand—like fresh butter."

Then when he had fashioned the nib according to his desire: "Well, what can I do for you to-day? Want to know how your shares are doing? They are bearing up well under the bad news from the front. But you must not expect too much these days. We ought to be glad if we get through without losing more than ten or fifteen points. What is it you want?"

I told him.

He listened patiently, but did not seem surprised.

"I know all about that," he answered. "We all do. That man owes everybody money and is in debt way over his ears. It is a bad case. He will end in the bankruptcy courts."

"That is what I feared," I told him. "That is why I am here to-day. Exactly how bad is it?"

"Ah, there now! I can't give you a balance-sheet with all the details. When I said that I knew all about the case, I meant that I knew enough never to give the man a single penny, if he came here to ask me for a loan. Further than that, my interest did not go. But if you

241

want to have details, come back in a week's time and you shall have them all."

And then he dropped the subject and talked to me about certain of my own affairs which I shall mention in some later chapter, and he took me out to a small eating house in the Wolvenstraat where a greasy, bearded and squint-eyed Armenian kept what he called on his sign-board outside a truly kosher Jewish restaurant and he fed me a mixture of strange Turkish dishes which made me think of Selim's little brown beans which had made us all sick, and then I left him and went to the hospital, though I am sure none of my patients felt as miserable as I did that afternoon. And a week later I called again at the Singel and received a short report, writ by Lodewijk himself, and containing a number of facts which made me suspect that my worst fears were about to come true and that the position of Rembrandt indeed was hopeless.

"Don't expect too much," Lodewijk warned me. "This is not a stockholder's report. As a rule we disciples of Mercury know a great deal about our neighbors' private affairs. Or if we don't know, we can at least find out. But this is hopeless. Hopeless, I tell you! The man himself does not know how badly off he is. He is one of those chain-borrowers—the most disastrous form of all possible financial transactions. He will borrow one thousand guilders from one friend for the period of a year and at 5 percent interest. And at the same time he will borrow 1,500 from another friend for eight months and at 7 percent. Five months later he will borrow 900 guilders for thirteen months at 6¾ percent from another party. With half of that he will repay Friend No. 1, from whom he will immediately thereupon borrow another 2,000 florins for one year at 5½ percent and which he will use to repay Friend No. 2 one-third of what he owes him and Friend No. 3 two-sevenths of his debt, plus accumulated interest. As he seems to keep no accounts of any sort and carries all those complicated manipulations in the back of his head (which is already very full of other things which have nothing at all to do with finance), you will understand the hopeless muddle in which his affairs are after almost twenty years of chaos.

"To make matters still a little more complicated, he occasionally borrows money on pictures that have not yet been painted or on others that have already been promised to a third party. For good

Rembrandt van Rijn

measure he has hypothecated his house a couple of times and as to what he has done with his wife's inheritance, of which he was the trustee for his little son, nothing less than the day of the Last Judgment will ever solve that puzzle.

"But here you are, my friend. Here is the report as I pieced it together from two dozen different sources. Sit down in that corner and read it while I cut myself a fresh pen. It is raining again. It always rains in this damned country. Now sit down and read."

I did as he told me. I sat down and read and as I have kept that report I can copy it in full.

"CONFIDENTIAL

"For your own exclusive information. The subject of this investigation is the son of very simple folk, but his parents were not without means and possessed among other things one windmill, two small houses and a parcel of real estate in one of the poorer quarters of the town of Leyden. There were six children. Several of those seem to have died young. Those who are still alive have never done very well and are now actually in reduced circumstances. It is said that their brother (the subject of this investigation) supports them and keeps them out of the poor-house.

"As for the subject of this investigation, who hereafter will be designated as N. N., he was the brightest of the family and destined by his parents to follow a legal career. As such he was inscribed in the University of Leyden in the year 1620 at the age of fourteen. It does not appear that he ever actually followed any courses of lectures, having in the meantime made up his mind to become a painter. In 1630 his father died. The oldest son, having suffered an accident to his hand which made it impossible for him to work, remained behind, as a charge on the other brothers and sisters, but they each received a small amount in cash. N. N. took his share and left Leyden and moved to Amsterdam and took a studio on the Bloemgracht, afterwards moving to the Anthonie Breestraat, also known as the Jodenbreestraat, where he lived for upward of six years.

"At first he was a great success in his own field of work. He had developed a new style of painting which for a dozen years was very fashionable. He had customers among the richest and noblest families of our city and was even commissioned to work for the Prince, though in that case it appears that he had considerable trouble in getting his money. Meanwhile he had become engaged to a girl from Leeuwarden, the

243

daughter of a former burgomaster and well-known political leader, called Rombertus van Uylenburgh. The girl was an orphan and said to be wealthy. After the death of her parents she had first lived with two of her sisters in her native province and had then moved to Amsterdam and first came to live with a female cousin, the wife of Dominie Jan Corneliszoon Sylvius, who had been called to this town in 1610 and was considered a very powerful and eloquent preacher.

"N. N. met the girl through another cousin of hers, one Hendrick van Uylenburgh, who at that time was a dealer in antiques and who also acted as 'entrepreneur' for fashionable painters—that is to say, he acted as go-between for rich people and poor artists and then charged the artist twenty or thirty percent for his services if a sale was made and a picture ordered. N. N. married the girl in June of the year 1634 and went to live with her in his house on the Breestraat which even at that time he had already begun to convert into a museum, spending the greater part of his considerable earnings on old paintings, bits of statuary and fine silks and brocades.

"After his wedding he added pearls and diamonds and other bits of jewelry to his collection. He is still said to have those. As for his annual revenue during that period, we can find no details, but during the first ten years of his residence in Amsterdam he seems to have received an average of about 500 guilders for his portraits. In addition to his own pictures he had the right to sell the work of his pupils which must have netted him between 2,000 and 2,500 guilders a year. As we were unable to find out how much profit he derived from his etchings during this period, it is impossible to state the sum total of his annual income during this period, though it probably exceeded the sum of ten thousand guilders.

"But already in the year 1638 he seems to have been in financial difficulties. That was the year in which he bought himself the house in the Breestraat which he occupies at the present moment. The house belonged to one P. Beltens. It was the second one from the bridge. N. N. is still living in it to-day. The original price was 13,000 guilders. One-fourth was to be paid a year after taking possession and the rest at regular intervals within six years. Why he bought a house so entirely above his own position in life is not clear except that at that period he is said to have tried very hard to come up to the social standards of his wife's family, an attempt which also made itself evident in his art, for every time he painted either himself or his wife, he evidently tried to make the world believe that he was a member of the Medici family of Florence, rather than the son of a humble miller in the little town of

PORTRAIT OF DOMINIC JAN CORNELISZOON SYLVIUS (ETCHING)

Leyden. And even at that moment, when he was willing to spend any amount of money upon such old pictures or pieces of silver as had struck his fancy, he was unable to pay the installments on his house. Of those 40,000 guilders which according to local rumor his wife had inherited from her parents, he never seems to have received a penny, for he had to wait until his mother died in 1640, when he received as his share of her inheritance a sum of 2,490 florins, before he was able to offer the former owner any money at all.

"Eventually, with an unexpected inheritance from an aunt of his wife (who was also her godmother), and with a part of his own savings, he was able to pay off one-half of the 13,000 guilders he owed the heirs of the aforementioned P. Beltens. Thereafter he seems to have forgotten about the house, for he did not even attempt to keep up with the accumulated interest, which has been growing larger and larger every year, until to-day it represents the sum of 8,470.06 guilders, which is entirely beyond his present financial means. For in the meantime he appears to have contracted debts on all sides. As all of them have been made with private persons, it is impossible for us to discover the actual amount for which he is involved. Besides the eight thousand odd guilders for the house there is an I.O.U. for 4,180 guilders made out to the order of Cornelis Witsen, the well-known city councilor. Another I.O.U. for a similar amount (4,200 guilders, to be exact) is in the possession of Isaac van Hertsbeeck or Hartsbeeck, a local merchant. These curious amounts N. N. appears to have borrowed to placate the former owner of his house in the Breestraat, who for the last eight years has been obliged to pay the taxes on this piece of property and who has at last threatened to sue him unless he sees some money coming his way.

"Meanwhile, although the house does not really belong to him unless he shall have paid the full contract price, plus the accumulated interest and plus the accumulated back taxes, he is said to be contemplating making both the house and the adjoining yard over to his son Titus as half his share in his mother's inheritance of 40,000 guilders. This, however, is merely a bit of gossip. For in order to do such a thing, he would be obliged to make a public declaration of his affairs to the Board of Orphans and as he himself never seems to have received a penny from that Uylenburgh estate (which appears to have existed only on paper), it is not very likely that he will take such a step. For the Board of Orphans is well known for its very strict methods of accounting, and a father who is suspected of having made away with part of his son's inheritance, even if he could prove that it was a fictitious inheritance, would run the risk of doing several months at hard labor in the city jail. I therefore return to those debts and transactions which can be more or less identified. From his friend Jan Six, the linen-weaver of the well-known family, he borrowed a thousand guilders which My Lord Jan, however, seems to consider such a risky investment that he has recently offered the I.O.U. for sale and according to rumor on the Exchange, he is willing to accept anything at all. Then he seems to have borrowed or to be in the midst of negotiating a loan of about 3,000 guilders with a surgeon by the name of Daniel Franssen, and finally there are countless small items to different persons all over town. These consist either of unpaid grocery bills and baker's bills and doctor's bills and for money he owes to frame-makers and dealers in brushes and paints and oils and manufacturers of copper plates and printer's ink or of small amounts from fifty guilders upward of tiny sums borrowed under one pretext or another from those unfortunate tradespeople.

"In the meantime N. N. has lost favor with the public. He ruined his reputation with a picture of the company of Captain Banning Cocq which he painted in the year his wife died, in 1642. The members of that company were so outraged with the arrangement of the figures (but upon which he himself had insisted) that several refused to pay him and he is said to have received only 1,600 guilders instead of the 5,250 for which he had contracted.

"If said N. N. owes you any money, I would, as your banker, advise you to get hold of it as soon as possible. You had better take a few of his valuable antiquities if he is willing to give you those in settlement of his debt, but don't count on ever getting a stiver in cash. N. N. is hopelessly involved. His reputation of having married a rich wife will perhaps carry him a little longer. But sooner or later the day must come when his credit has reached its end and then there will be quite a scandal, for N. N. has nothing and he owes everybody. The conclusion of our investigation is as follows:

"Assets: Heavily mortgaged house full of objects of art on which, however, it will be very difficult to realize at the present moment owing to the unfavorable economic conditions which are the result of the present war with England; very little good will and no cash or securities whatsoever.

"Liabilities: The total amount is unknown but they must be well over 30,000 guilders.

"Credit standing of the person under discussion—o."

I slowly folded the paper and made ready to put it in my pocket. "I suppose I can keep this?" I asked Lodewijk.

"You can keep it, my friend. But please don't let it fall into the wrong hands. It is bad enough as it is. I am very deeply afraid that poor painter's goose is about cooked."

Then he dropped the pen with which he had been busy figuring all that time and rubbed his hand across his bald head.

"Too bad," he said, as if he were speaking to himself. "Too bad. Poor devil! I suppose he sees certain things we don't happen to see and so he fails to notice certain other things quite as important and which we ordinary human beings must have before our eyes all the time."

I stared at him hard.

"Lodewijk," I remarked, "did I hear you mumble 'quite as important'?"

"No," he answered. "I was wrong there. I suppose they are less important. As a matter of fact, I know that they are less important, but what will you? We all must keep alive. And there is but one way to keep alive—hunt with the pack and stick to the well-known tracks."

"But suppose you are so constituted that you simply must leave the beaten track and look for a path of your own or die?"

Once again Lodewijk rubbed his hand across his head.

"Then," he slowly replied, "you are just out of luck." But more than that he would not say.

SKETCH (DRAWING)

Chapter 24

THE MINISTERS TAKE A HAND IN REMBRANDT'S
AFFAIRS

SIX'S BRIDGE (ETCHING)

IT WAS a far cry from a broken-down old Portuguese doctor on
the banks of the Hudson River and a little peasant girl from
nowhere in particular who happened to be in the family way, to a
public riot in the streets of Amsterdam and the loss of that sum of
money with which I would have been able to save Rembrandt from
his disgrace. But the world has seen stranger coincidences than that,
and the episode attracted the attention of many who otherwise would
never have heard of me or the work I was doing.

Hendrickje was pregnant. I had noticed it that time she hurt herself and Rembrandt sent for me. Soon afterwards, others had noticed it too and then the trouble had begun. Not among Rembrandt's
friends. They understood the situation and knew why he could not
marry the girl. Even the exceedingly respectable family of My Lord
Jan Six (is there anything in this world more careful of its dignity

than one of our linen-weaving or beer-brewing dynasties trying to break into the slightly superior class of the hereditary magistrates?) did not appear to be censorious of a conduct which must have shocked them quite as much as the bankruptcy of one of their nearest relatives.

I never quite understood the friendship that had sprung up between Rembrandt and the rich linen merchant. But then, I never even met the young man. Rembrandt had repeatedly suggested that I accompany him when he called upon Jan Six and had accused me of being supersensitive and of being a snob, and had assured me time and again that I would find naught but the simplest of manners within the Six household. To which I invariably repeated that I had no doubt about the perfect graciousness that reigned within this charming home on the Kloveniersburgwal, and that I had no doubt but his friends would receive me with the utmost cordiality. Unfortunately their ways were not my ways and my ways were not their ways and what the habits and customs and prejudices of many generations had put asunder, we had better not try and put together.

And in the end it was shown that I had been right. For when the great financial crisis came in Rembrandt's life Jan Six sold the note which Rembrandt had given him to a professional pawnbroker and all that Rembrandt saved out of those years of intimacy and friendship was a presentation copy of a very mediocre Greek play in very mediocre verse. Whereas the Six family was left in possession of a number of paintings and etchings which will keep its name alive long after the last of their descendants shall have returned to dust.

Verily, as we say in our language, it is bad policy to eat cherries with the mighty. They get the cherries and you get the stones—if you are very lucky.

Upon this unfortunate occasion, however, both My Lord Jan and his relatives showed themselves rather more broad-minded than I had had reason to expect. Of course they had never met Hendrickje and had made no move which showed that they recognized her existence. But at least they continued to be on cordial terms with her husband (for as such she now invariably referred to Rembrandt), and that was more than could be said of most people.

They were shocked.

They disapproved.

THE DESCENT FROM THE CROSS (ETCHING)

If this sort of thing were tolerated once, where would the world end?

And since most people are in the habit of considering their own prejudices as part of the divinely inspired laws which underlie the structure of a well-ordered universe, it was quite unavoidable that the scandal on the Jodenbreestraat should become the most popular subject for family discussions and tea-party gossip. For although it was still considered good form among the higher classes of society to have a few bastards (all the children of the late Prince Maurice, although born out of wedlock, had been baptized by the court preacher of the House of Orange and had received high honors and dignities in the service of the Republic), the prospective arrival of an illegitimate infant in the household of a painter was still considered an event of such enormity that it could not be allowed to pass unnoticed by the reverend clergy who were supposed to be watching day and night over the morals of our New Zion on the Zuyder Zee.

And fortunately on this occasion at least the dominies had luck with them, as I shall now have to relate.

"Misfortunes never come alone," says an old Zeeland proverb, and during the days that followed I was often reminded of this bit of ancestral wisdom. And whereas under ordinary circumstances the birth of the little van Rijn child might have caused only a temporary storm in our domestic tea-cup, a most unfortunate combination of regrettable little incidents caused it to assume the shape of a national scandal.

It all started in a little village in Friesland. I have forgotten the name of the place. It was one of those terrible villages where the people looked like cows and the cows looked like people and where nothing ever happened until from sheer boredom and exasperation the inhabitants were willing to believe any bit of news that would bring them a little excitement.

In this miserable village, where half of the people had been dead for years but had never become aware of the fact because no one had taken the trouble to tell them so—in this far-off hamlet it had been necessary to repair one of the walls, and these alterations had in turn caused the temporary removal of several graves. As the last occupant of these tombs had died more than thirty years before, it was not expected that the architects would find anything beyond a few skulls and skeletons. But imagine the surprise of the grave-diggers when they suddenly came upon a corpse that was as good as the day it had been interred!

"A miracle," shouted the people who saw it. "This man was a saint. He was too holy to be returned to dust."

"On the contrary," a young and eager candidate of theology, who was preparing here for his final examinations, whispered. "On the contrary! This man was a sinner of such magnitude that even the worms refused to eat him."

As it was of course much pleasanter to believe evil than good of a departed neighbor, the populace heartily shouted amen, and immediately they began to delve into the past of this poor fellow to discover what crimes he might have committed to deserve such a fate.

This proved to be rather difficult, as the man had been dead for at least thirty-five years. During his days on this earth he had been a very humble shoemaker who had distinguished himself by nothing except his somewhat exaggerated respect for the wise precepts of his Lord and Master, Jesus Christ. He had been charitable to a fault and had not contented himself with surrendering one-tenth of all his possessions to the poor, but had often gone hungry himself that others, who were even more miserable than he himself, might be fed.

An old farmer in a neighboring village remembered him well and spoke of him in the highest terms. The deacon of the church he had attended (now well in the eighties) stated emphatically that so good and pious a man had rarely trod the unworthy soil of this planet.

Indeed, at first it seemed as if those who had proclaimed him a saint had been right, but the theological candidate refused to be convinced. "All this," he argued, "only proves that the man was also a very clever prevaricator and was able to hide the traces of his wickedness in such a way that he finally died without ever having been found out." And of course the quest into the fellow's past continued as merrily as before.

Now it happened that the widow of the mysterious corpse was still alive. She was a woman of about seventy and no one knew anything against her that was not highly favorable. She had only one child, a daughter who was married (and very respectably) to a master carpenter in Haarlem. Surely all these family details were commonplace enough to discourage even the most hardened scandal-mongers. But the young cleric kept on snuffling. The old woman was in her dotage and spent most of her days sitting in her little home—tending half a dozen cats and telling those who were willing to listen (and they were very few) what a fine man her husband had been. She was also very superstitious and terribly afraid to die. By playing upon her fear of the Hereafter, and by colorful description of the horrors of Hell, the unscrupulous parson finally got the whole story out of her and no Castilian explorer crossing the parched wastes of the great Mexican desert could have experienced greater happiness at the sight of his first lump of gold than this man of mercy when the trembling old crone at last revealed unto him the well-tended secret of her husband's one and only transgression.

She had never been married to him. They had never been united in holy wedlock. They had lived in sin, but it had all been done with the best of intentions, and then she had related the story which soon afterwards was to become known to everybody in the Republic, for it was a sad tale and our ballad-singers made the most of it.

It had really been her fault and she was willing to take all the blame upon herself. She had been a wayward girl and had got into trouble with a man who had deserted her. Her father, when he suspected her condition, had thrown her out of the house. She was wandering from village to village (she herself hailed from the neighboring province of Groningen) until she had reached that little town in Friesland. It was very late when she arrived and she was half starved and she had knocked at his door because he was still working and looked friendly as he sat there hammering at his bench. He had taken her in and had fed her. The next day she had been very sick. He had kept her there and had sent for an old woman who lived next door to nurse her. She had been sick for almost two whole months. When she got better, her condition had become noticeable. She then had told her benefactor the truth. He said that he wanted to marry her. But he could not do so as he was already married. Only his wife had lost her reason shortly after the birth of a child that had died in infancy. She had developed a case of religious mania and finally had escaped with the help of one of the many priests who still infested the country, notwithstanding the severe edicts promulgated against them. This man had taken her to Trier, where she had joined the Catholic Church and had entered a nunnery. All efforts on the husband's part to bring her back had been unsuccessful. The Archbishop of Trier had openly boasted of his victory over Antichrist, and even the Estates General, to whom the matter finally had been referred, had been powerless.

That had happened twenty years before and all that time the husband had heard nothing of his wife. Attempts to find out whether she was still alive had brought no answer. The prioress of the cloister where she was supposed to dwell had answered that those entrusted to her care were dead, as far as the world was concerned, the moment they set foot across the sacred threshold, and all further communications addressed to her had been returned unopened. The shoemaker had left his native village where all this had happened and had moved to that forgotten little town in northern Friesland, so as to avoid meeting his former friends. In his new home no one ever suspected that he had ever been married. In his compassion for the poor girl whom God had conducted to his doorstep, he had then decided upon a desperate plan. He had spread the news that he meant to marry her but that she wished to have the ceremony performed among her own people in Groningen. They had actually gone to the town of Groningen for a fortnight and had then come back as husband and wife. The child had been born shortly afterwards and the village elders had smirked pleasantly about their old shoemaker who apparently had not been such a saint as they had always held him to be. But as no couples among our peasants ever marry until they absolutely have to, the matter had soon been forgotten.

No one could have been more devoted to a child of his own than this humble shoemaker to that of another man, and as for herself, why, the woman had never had an unhappy day in all her life until the day her "husband" had died from old age and hard work, when she had buried him with all decency and had settled down to spend the rest of her remaining years honoring his memory and tending her cats.

The story struck me as rather marvelous when I first heard it. But in the hands of that miserable zealot up there in the Frisian hamlet, it became a monstrous tale of seduction and deception which filled the hearts of all good Christians with the utmost delight and satisfaction. God's hand became plainly visible in that pathetic, shriveled corpse which had been so unceremoniously brought back to life and literally thousands of sermons were devoted to the gruesome sufferings of that soul which had been refused admittance to both Heaven and Hell, as too vile for even the lowest dungeons of Satan's abode.

Hysterical outbursts of this sort have one advantage: they never last long. But just when the details of the case were beginning to be known in Amsterdam and when every self-respecting disciple of John Calvin was ransacking his Old Testament for suitable texts with which to bolster up the case of God vs. the Shoemaker, the fact that the painter Rembrandt van Rijn was living openly with his housekeeper was brought to the attention of a certain dominie by the name of Zebediah Hazewindus, and what then happened was something of which the people of our country may well be ashamed till the end of their days.

It is unnecessary for me to go into the details of the affair. They are only too well known.

On the twenty-fifth of June of the year '54 the members of the Amsterdam council of churches, gathered together in a plenary session, decided that "since a certain Hendrickje, also known as Hendrickje Jaghers, had now for a considerable space of time been living in open concubinage with a painter called Rembrandt van Rijn at the latter's house in the Breestraat, she therefore was to be ordered to appear before the consistory within eight days of the issuance of this summons and explain to the consistory what excuse she could offer for such scandalous conduct."

This message was delivered at Rembrandt's house one evening about six o'clock when he and Hendrickje were just enjoying a little respite from the efforts of the day's work on the stoop of their house. It was brought to them by the sexton of the West Church, who also acted as beadle. The sexton was well known to the neighbors. The message was not known, but they could guess at its nature. And soon all through the street and then through the next street and through the next street, the news had spread: "The painter and his woman will have to appear before the dominies. Serves them right!

Rembrandt van Rijn

SKETCH FOR THE PORTRAIT OF ANSLO (DRAWING)

We always told you so. Nothing good can come from that sort of goings-on."

And although no one dared to "say" anything, a great many people "looked" things and that was hardly desirable for a woman in Hendrickje's position. But in one small detail these good neighbors were mistaken. The neatly folded piece of paper bearing the seal of Amsterdam's church council did not mention the name of Rembrandt. When I called later in the evening and was shown the document and asked why he had not been summoned, together with Hendrickje, he could at first not give me any reason. Then it dawned upon him. "I am not a member of the church," he said. "That is probably why they left me out. Years ago, I forget just when, I withdrew or resigned or whatever one does when one bids farewell to the church. I let the ministers know that I would not attend divine service any longer and would refuse to pay my church-taxes in the future and would they please take my name off their register, and they answered me that I could not do this unless I could offer proof that I had joined some other denomination. I hardly knew what to do and so I talked it over with old Anslo, whom I had known for years. I asked him whether there would be any objections if I joined his own church, that I was not a very regular church-goer and perhaps not even a very good Christian. He said no, that the Mennonites did not believe in bothering people about their beliefs, that they would be glad to have me join them whenever I cared to come but would not worry me or bother me if for one reason or another I decided to stay away.

"So I joined the Mennonites and I have never been sorry. Anslo was a nice man. I liked to hear him preach. He never told me how wicked I was, but did his best to show me how good I might be if only I tried just a little harder. Yes, he was a good man. I am glad now I went to him. I would be doubly glad if it were not for Hendrickje."

The girl who had been studying the paper in her hand now looked up at us. "Yes," she said, rather dryly, "I have no doubt of that. But meanwhile, what shall I do?"

Without a word Rembrandt took the summons out of her hand and tore it up into a thousand bits.

"Do nothing," he answered. "Do nothing and forget about it. The dominies can of course make themselves very disagreeable to us, but that is about all. But they can't send a company of town guards to come and fetch you to make a public confession. You are safe— perfectly safe—and so that is that."

And he threw the little bits of paper into the air so that two little Jewish boys who were playing on the sidewalk shouted: "Oi, oi! lookit! lookit! it is snowing!" and then started fighting for the "snow" until nothing remained of the clerical document but a mess of dirty scraps which lay spread all over the Breestraat.

But although Rembrandt was entirely right when he proclaimed so bravely that the dominies could not send a company of town guards to drag Hendrickje to their solemn conclave, it was soon proved that those worthies were not entirely defenseless. They had other means at their disposal to make their displeasure felt and they were not slow to avail themselves of these convenient instruments of spiritual torture.

Rembrandt van Rijn

A great Parisian lady might of course have snapped her fingers at such a manifestation of clerical meddlesomeness but Hendrickje was not a great Parisian lady, but a simple little Dutch peasant girl from a simple little Dutch peasant village with all of the peasant's traditional regard for those standards of respectability which she had learned as a child. To be publicly cited to appear before the consistory of the big town of Amsterdam, accused of the dreadful sins of "lechery and adultery" (strange what delight pious people take in dirty words. If there are nine decent ways of expressing a certain thought and one indecent one, they will invariably choose the latter), was as terrible an experience to her as if she had been condemned to undress right in the middle of the municipal market-place. And I noticed the effects of this ordeal when a week later she was presented with a second summons which did not even reach her hands, as Rembrandt jerked it from the fingers of the beadle and threw it in the gutter without even bothering to open the seal.

Upon such occasions, the spirit of his old grandfather, who had been a notable fighter in the early days of the rebellion, would suddenly break through that decorous exterior which he had retained from the days of his marriage with Saskia.

"Get away from here, you damned black crow!" he shouted at the poor fellow who had delivered the message, and who was beating a hasty retreat. "Get away and stay away and don't bother my wife any more. If your masters have aught to tell me, let them come themselves and I shall throw them in the Anthonie Sluys. You dastardly, meddling old fool! Mind your own damn business and let me paint my pictures."

All of which was no doubt quite natural and more or less to be expected (there is nothing quite so wholesome to the physical well-being of the human race as an occasional outburst of first-class cursing), but a little beside the point. After all, the consistory had not told Rembrandt that he must not paint pictures. It had told his housekeeper that she must not live with him in sin. And it continued to do so until poor Hendrickje, in her great distress and misery, saw no other course than to obey their solemn command and present herself that she might confess her guilt and ask for their solemn forgiveness.

Exactly when she made her appearance before the consistory, I never found out, for she kept the fact hidden from Rembrandt. One afternoon she quietly slipped out of the house and when she returned, it was all over. She went right up to her room and to bed. In the middle of the night, Rembrandt sent Titus to ask me whether I would please come at once. Hendrickje seemed to have a fever. Her mind was wandering. She talked of hell-fire and of Satan, who was chasing her with a torch made out of a burning sheaf of grain. Then she wept as if her heart would break, calling for her mother and saying that she would be a good girl and that she had only done it because the man had been so good to her. "He is good to me and you and father were bad to me," she kept on crying.

I gave her some hot milk to drink and put a cold poultice on her forehead, and after a short while she calmed down. In the morning she was happy and cheerful, as if nothing had happened.

The following Sunday when I called after dinner, as I was in the habit of doing, I asked her (really without thinking very much of what I was saying), "And well, Hendrickje, what was the sermon about this morning?"

But she looked crestfallen and answered, rather indifferently, "I don't know. I did not go."

Three days later, I discovered the reason why. As punishment for her sinful way of living, she had been forbidden to partake of the Lord's holy communion.

That may have been good church discipline. But it was not the best thing in the world for a woman who was eight months pregnant, as we were to find out soon afterwards.

THE ANATOMY LESSON OF PROFESSOR NICOLAES TULP (PAINTING)

HENDRICKJE STOFFELS (PAINTING)

Chapter 25

HENDRICKJE HAS A CHILD AND THE CLERGY OF AMSTERDAM EXPRESS THEIR OPINION UPON MY RESEARCHES IN THE DOMAIN OF PAINLESS SURGERY

SKETCH FOR THE "ANATOMY" (DRAWING)

IN SEPTEMBER of the year '54 the blow fell.

During the first week of that month I had suddenly lost two of my patients. They had died while I was administering the usual dose of hemp and the thing had been a great surprise to me as the operations for which they had been brought to the hospital were not of a serious sort and under ordinary circumstances their chance of recovery would have been very good. But they passed out after a few whiffs of the Cannabis fumes and all efforts made to bring them back to life were in vain. Both of them were middle-aged women and like most women in our country who have been forced to bear children ever since they were nineteen or twenty, they were not in good physical condition.

News of this disaster became soon known all over town and those who had always disapproved of my methods were delighted. They had always known that something like that would happen some day. If I were allowed to go on I would eventually kill the whole population of Amsterdam. The authorities ought to interfere and close that so-called hospital. As for me, I ought to be forced to resign from the Surgeons' Guild. I had defied the will of God and now see what had come of it!

Within less than twenty-four hours I received an official document bearing the signature of one of the Burgomasters. I was told not to administer any more hemp until the matter should have been officially investigated. Three physicians of good repute were delegated to perform an autopsy upon my unfortunate patients and report to Their Lordships. One of these three doctors was a good friend of mine. The other two belonged to the old school of medicine and regarded me secretly as an impostor and mountebank.

The bodies were taken to the dissecting room. Afterwards the doctors reported unanimously that death had probably been due to natural causes as both women seemed to have suffered from inflammation of the valves of the heart and under those circumstances any sudden shock to the system might be fatal. As they would have died with almost equal certainty if the operation had been performed without an anesthetic, the administration of a pain-relieving agency could not, under those circumstances, be held responsible for the unfortunate outcome of the case. This was very pleasant news for me but unfortunately Their Lordships did not deem it necessary to communicate the findings of their committee to the public, and all over town the murmurs continued about the surgeon who was in the habit of poisoning his patients in order to get hold of their bodies and then study them by cutting them up into little pieces which afterwards he fed to the rats.

That was trouble No. 1.

Trouble No. 2 happened immediately afterwards.

Now that I had come to know Hendrickje a little more intimately, she was no longer as shy with me as she had been in the beginning, and so she told me of her worries in connection with her coming confinement. She had had a baby before. It had been born a year after she had come to live with Rembrandt, but the baby had died immediately afterwards and she had had a most dreadful time and had almost died from pain. Even now, whenever she thought of it, she shuddered with the memory of so great an agony. She fully expected that this time the child would have to be taken by force and if that was the case, would I perform the operation? I examined her and realized that she might be right in her fears. She had an unusually narrow pelvis and the child was already very large. I promised her that I would do as she asked me and suggested that she come to my own place, where I had plenty of room and could work much better than in the stuffy, built-in beds of the ordinary house-

THE UNRULY CHILD (DRAWING)

hold. At first she hesitated. Simple people seem to think that there is something sacrilegious about children that are born outside their own homes. But Rembrandt was greatly in favor of this arrangement, and during the first half of the first week of October Hendrickje came to the hospital.

Five days later she had her first pains. Her labor lasted three whole days. In the end she suffered so terribly she asked that she be killed and even tried to climb out of her bed to throw herself out of the window. On the morning of the fourth day, when it looked as if I would have to perform a Caesarean operation (I was afraid the child would otherwise die), she told me that she could stand it no longer and asked me to give her some quick-working poison. Instead of that, I administered my hemp extract. She was so exhausted that it worked almost too well, for she was still unconscious long after the midwife had washed and cleaned the new-born infant (a girl it was, and in the end no operation had proved necessary) and wanted to bring it to her for its first meal. She recovered very rapidly and a fortnight later she was back in the old house on the Breestraat, looking very handsome and very happy and quite like her old cheerful self.

The child was baptized in the Old Church on one of the last days of October. The minister must have received a hint from the Town Hall that further censorious remarks on their part were considered out of place, for little Cornelia was duly registered as the daughter of Rembrandt van Rijn and Hendrickje Stoffels and no embarrassing questions were asked.

But for me it was only the beginning of my trouble.

Hendrickje had been deeply grateful. So grateful, indeed, that she told the dry-nurse who took care of her how good I had been to her and how I had saved her from any further pain when she thought that she could no longer stand the ordeal. The dry-nurse, a very competent and well-meaning woman, but like all the members of her guild, an incurable chatterbox, had told the neighbors.

"And you know, Doctor Jan gave her something at the last moment and then she never felt any pain at all. Isn't that wonderful? Though of course, it is not quite what we read in the Scriptures."

And then the fat was in the fire.

A week later, the Reverend Zebediah preached his famous sermon on "Childbearing without God's curse." And two weeks later the whole town knew about the scandalous and blasphemous proceedings that went on in the hospital of "this libertine and Arminian who pretended to be wiser than God." Once the rumor had started, it was utterly impossible to stop it.

Within a month, Hazewindus felt himself strong enough to lead a delegation of outraged citizens to the town council to ask for my immediate arrest and to suggest that my "place of business" be closed for all time. He went to see Their Lordships, followed by thousands of his parishioners.

I would rather not write about what followed, for in a way it was a very sincere tribute to the confidence which Their Lordships placed in me personally. They promised the young parson that they would hang him from the highest gallows at the disposal of the city of Amsterdam if he ever bothered them again in this matter, and had the bailiff kick him bodily out of the council-chamber.

I hoped that that would be the last of my difficulties and that now I would be left in peace to continue my experiments. But two days later, during the middle of the night, a mob of several hundred men and women, proceeding very quietly and very orderly, as if they obeyed a single will, suddenly broke into the hospital, carried the eighteen patients they found there out into the street (fortunately it was not a very cold night) and then set fire to the premises, disappearing in as quiet and orderly a fashion as they had arrived.

When I came upon the scene of the conflagration, the house was already doomed. It burned until the next afternoon. Of my invested capital which was to be used for the good of humanity, nothing remained but four charred walls and a pile of smoldering beams and red-hot bricks.

That was the end of my dream.

I petitioned the Magistrates and insisted upon an indemnity. My property had been destroyed as the result of a riot which they had failed to repress.

They told me that I was entirely right and that they would take the necessary steps to satisfy me. After deliberating this item on their calendar for seven whole years, they finally voted me about one-third of the sum for which I had asked. After another four years, they paid me half of what they had promised me. When I hinted at the unfairness of such an arrangement and suggested that I should at least receive five or six percent accumulated interest on my money, I was informed that Their Lordships had been exceptionally generous in dealing with me and that I should be contented with whatever I got, on pain of not getting anything at all.

And that is the reason why I could not move a finger to help my poor friend during those dreadful years of his bankruptcy.

Once more the shrewd Lodewijk had been right. I had tried to benefit mankind—whether wisely or not it is not for me to say. According to the best of my ability, I had tried to be of some service to those who were less fortunate than I. And they had risen in their wrath and had destroyed me because I had dared to deprive them of what was dearer to them than life itself—their own misery.

The Reverend Zebediah Hazewindus preached a triumphant sermon.

And I went back to general practice to make a living.

WOMAN CARRYING A CHILD
(DRAWING)

Chapter 26

OUR JEWISH NEIGHBORS, WHO HAVE COME TO US TO
ESCAPE FROM THE INTOLERANCE OF THEIR SPANISH
MASTERS, SHOW THAT RELIGIOUS BIGOTRY IS NOT
RESTRICTED TO ONE SECT OR RELIGION

JEWS IN SYNAGOGUE (ETCHING)

THE war with England came to an end. And as the ships returned
home, I met a great many of the captains (for I now spent
about half of my spare time at the admiralties) and I heard stories of
such surpassing heroism that I was obliged to revise most of my previous notions about the human race or at least that particular part of
it to which I myself happened to belong.

Quite often when I was visiting Jean-Louys in his tower near the
water front, I had been an unwilling witness of the departure of our
brave tars. Disorderly crowds of drunken, disheveled men and
drunken, disheveled women, with here and there a howling, bedrag-
gled child, pacified by an occasional raisin drenched in gin.

This mob would slowly come down the quay, pushed forward by

large numbers of town guards and looking and behaving exactly like a moaning herd of sheep that were being taken to the slaughter-house.

Now and then a drum and fife corps would try to start a patriotic air or even a hymn, but after a few bars of some well-known tune, shrill, ribald voices would interrupt the musicians with one of those blasphemous ditties that seem to have sprung straight from hell and at once the whole of the crowd would join in—improvising words as they went along and indulging in a wild orgy of dancing and bucking and skipping, accompanied by gestures of such utter vulgarity that even the town guards would blush and they would repeat this performance until after hours of jostling and shrieking, the embarking stations had been reached where the rum-soaked cattle were unceremoniously pushed into a large number of flat-bottomed barges and at once turned to the big vessels that lay at anchor just off the Rijzenhoofd Bulwark.

That was the last we saw of them until we heard our first vague reports of battles and encounters and victories and an occasional defeat.

But one day, years later, a number of high plenipotentiaries assembled around a green table in a large hall in the center of Westminster, affixed their names and seals to a yellow piece of parchment, and shortly afterwards the tired ships would painfully limp back into port—without sails, without masts, without a scrap of that paint that had made them look so spick and span when they had gone forth to war. Then anxious women would come once more around the ancient bulwark and numb-faced children would cling to the rotting wharves and every time a boatload of sailors approached the shore, they would all of them rush forward and scan the faces, many of which were still black from gunpowder or covered with bandages that clearly showed the untrained hands of the bungling nautical doctors.

Then there would be anxious questions: "Is that you, Piet?" or "Have you heard anything of Klaas, who was on the *Zilvere Ster?*" or "Jan! oh, Jan! are you there?" And sometimes the answer would be, "Yes, I am here, as fit as a fiddle," but more often there would be a gruff "Go home, woman, your Klaas is dead," or "They are bringing your Piet home on a stretcher. His legs are gone." And then there would be cursing or weeping (according to the nature of the woman who was told that she could now spend the rest of her days scrubbing other people's floors and hallways) and silent groups would mutely separate themselves from the main body of spectators and would move desolately toward that part of the town where lived those "gallant gentlemen" whose name only a fortnight before had been on everybody's tongue and who early the next morning must begin the endless round of those workshops and offices where the "No sailors need apply" signs told them how deeply a grateful country had really appreciated their self-sacrificing valor.

For that was the queerest part of it all—those drunken, disorderly and disheveled ruffians who had to be conducted to the arsenals between lines of heavily armed town guards, for fear that they would set fire to the city if they were left to themselves—those selfsame rowdies, once they were on board and realized that they were fighting for their own women and kids and that hovel they considered home—would perform deeds of such unheard-of courage and of such incredible loyalty, that each one of them, if personal heroism is really a safe-conduct to Heaven (as was held to be true by the ancient Greeks) had more than fully established his claims to at least ten square yards of the celestial domain.

They were not very communicative, these "common sailors," and even their sluggish brains revolted at the recollection of many of the sights they had seen—at the sickly sweet smell of blood that would be forever in their nostrils. But gradually little bits of narrative prose, far superior to any poetry ever composed by one of our peaceful, home-staying bards, would find their way into the ale-house gossip of our every-day lives and Homer himself in his most inspired moment could not have devised such deeds of valor and devotion. There were men who had continued to fight when only five or six of the entire ship's crew had been left alive and who, when nothing could save their floating charnel-house from sinking, had boldly jumped on board the enemy craft and with their bare fists almost had captured their former aggressor.

One sailor in the midst of an encounter had managed to swing himself on board the vessel that flew the admiral's flag, had reached the top of the mast and had removed the English colors, thereby causing a most useful panic among the other British men-of-war, who thought that their leader had been killed. Trying to jump back into the rigging of his own vessel, he had missed his footing and had dashed his brains out on the deck, forty feet below, but with the enemy's flag still tightly held between his dead teeth.

The son of Admiral Tromp, commanding a vessel in the harbor of Livorno where the reigning grand duke had forbidden him to take action against his English rivals, who were at that time in the same harbor, had waked up in the middle of the night to find his craft in the hands of the English, who had broken the truce. Rather than surrender, he had jumped overboard and after swimming for more than three hours, he had finally been picked up by a Dutch sloop. With that sloop he had rowed back to his own ship and had recaptured it.

Captain Jan van Galen, during the battle that had followed, had had one of his legs blown away by a cannon-ball. But rather than go to the sick-ward and have his wounds attended to, he had told his officers to carry him to the top of the poop-deck from where he could better watch the battle while he slowly bled to death.

On one occasion a small squadron which was convoying one hundred and fifty merchantmen, fought a much larger English force during the greater part of three days and three nights and then only gave up the fight because they were completely out of gunpowder. Nevertheless, they not only had saved all of the merchantmen but they succeeded in escaping themselves with the loss of only two of their ships.

Truly the men who could perform such acts of valor deserved a better treatment than they usually received and I was very grateful that with the unwavering support of the Pensionary I was able to do something for them.

Up to that time the operating room of those few vessels that had any operating room at all (on most of them the surgeons worked right among the guns) was located way down deep in the hold of the vessel and below the water-line. As a result these places were pitch-dark and absolutely devoid of fresh air. The surgeons were obliged to amputate arms and legs (the usual wounds) by the light of a candle and as they were not allowed to make a fire and heat their irons on account of the proximity of the powder-room, they had no adequate means of closing the arteries except by using large quantities of lint, a method which failed in ninety out of every hundred cases.

Besides, the transport down the narrow stairs of such desperately wounded men was a form of torture which one would not have meted out to one's own worst enemies. In order to change this and provide better facilities for the medical staff on board our men-of-war, I suggested that the admiralties offer a prize of 500 florins for the best plan that should remove the sick-ward from the bottom of the ship to one of the upper decks, without interfering too seriously with the manipulation of the heavy guns which filled the two top decks. As the sum was a very large one, practically all the nautical engineers of the entire Republic took part in the contest, and for several months my office resembled the draughting room of a ship-yard.

I remember one strange meeting I had during that period. One night the maid told me that a foreign-looking gentleman wanted to see me. "He carries a small ship's model under his arm," she added. "He is probably one of those funny people," and she pointed to the diagrams and specifications that were spread all over the walls and the floors.

The visitor proved to be what the maid had predicted. He had come to show me an invention of his own. Unfortunately it had nothing to do with the problem in which I was interested. It was a new device to raise the angle of gun-fire without the clumsy arrangement then in use. I told the mysterious stranger that he had come to the wrong place with his little model, that he ought to take it to the admiralty which undoubtedly would be greatly interested. He answered that he had already been to three of our admiralties but that none of them had shown the slightest desire to examine his invention any closer and that he was now thinking of selling it to the English or the French.

I replied that that did not seem a very patriotic thing to do and he readily agreed. "But," he added, "what am I to do? I am a poor school-master and have a daughter who is a cripple and I need the money and I thought that you perhaps could help me, as I have heard of you from one of my pupils," and then I discovered that he was the famous Dr. Franciscus van den Ende, of whom I had heard a good deal, but whom so far I had never met.

271

Rembrandt van Rijn

This van den Ende was a curious citizen who lived in a sphere of mystery. He had come to Amsterdam during the early forties and had opened a book-store which had not done any too well and which a few years afterwards he had been forced to close for lack of cash and customers. He had then started a Latin school of his own and had revealed himself as one of the most competent teachers we had ever had in our city. He had a veritable genius for making irregular verbs palatable and in his hands even the most refractory hexameters would behave with the docility of so many tame kittens. Within a very short time all the little boys of our best families were learning the fact that "all Gaul was divided into three parts" at the school of Monsieur van den Ende. For the doctor was a native of Antwerp and preferred that appellation to the more sober-minded Dutch "Meester."

He knew of course that his neighbors were slightly curious about his antecedents. But before any inquiries could be made in his native town, he had told us all about himself and about the reasons that had caused him to move northward.

He had, so it then appeared, started life as a Jesuit, but had lost his faith and had been forced to flee for his life. The story of course appealed to us and it had given him an excellent standing with the Magistrates who prided themselves (and rightly) upon the fact that Amsterdam was the most tolerant and liberal community of the entire world. But now I discovered that van den Ende was something more than a good classical scholar. He also appeared to have devoted several years to medical studies and showed by a few casual remarks (in answer to a few equally casual questions on my part) that he understood his subject thoroughly. And so I told him to forget all about his ship's model, which did not interest me anyway, as I was interested in saving people's lives and not in destroying them, and took him down to the dining-room and invited him to partake of some refreshments, for I have found that it always pays to be pleasant to a colleague, even if you never expect to see him again.

Thereupon we talked of many things—of the superior way of teaching as practiced by the Jesuit fathers, who shape the material in which they give instruction so as to suit the individual pupil, rather than making the pupil fit the material he is supposed to study (as we do in our country), and of several other subjects that were

HEAD OF A JEW (PAINTING)

of interest to both of us, and then quite unexpectedly the Belgian said: "But of course I already know all about you and your views." And when I asked him how that was possible, as this was the first time I had had the pleasure of meeting him, he answered: "No, but I have a pupil who has a great admiration for you, a Portuguese Jew by the name of Benito d'Espinoza," and then I recalled that this was the man of whom young Baruch Spinoza had been talking to me and of whom he had said that as a school-master he was worth at least five dozen ordinary rabbis and Talmudic pedagogues.

I repeated this observation to van den Ende (where is the man of ability who does not like an occasional bit of flattery?) and he was much amused by it.

"A marvelous brain, that Portuguese has," he told me, "but they are going to have a lot of trouble with him," and the conversation once having taken this particular form, we quite naturally drifted into the discussion of a topic that was beginning to assume rather alarming proportions—the problem of the Jews who in ever-increasing numbers were flocking to our town. For just about a week before Doctor van den Ende called on me with his little ship, one of those absurd things had occurred that, although utterly insignificant in and by itself, might easily have led to bloodshed if the town militia that week had not been commanded by an officer who was not only a strict disciplinarian but who was also possessed of a sense of humor and a delicately trained taste for the grotesque.

The Jews in our town were not obliged to live in ghettos as they had always done in Spain and in Poland and in Germany. They were free to settle down wherever they pleased but out of force of habit they invariably flocked to the same neighborhood. But of course the Portuguese immigrants stuck closely to the Sephardic Synagogue and the Polish and German Jews remained within a stone's throw of the Ashkenazic temple. They were both in my own part of the town and I often walked around the island of Vlooienburg or Fleaburg (as it was soon called by the people) and I was quite familiar with the habits and customs of these strangers who even now, after having been with us for almost a whole century, continued to address each other in the Portuguese and Yiddish tongues and who spoke our own language (which is supposed to be theirs) as if it were a foreign tongue not worthy of their attention. And so of course I knew all about the famous Doctor Alonzo ben Immanuele, commonly known as the Tongenkijker or Tongue-looker.

His real name was not Alonzo nor was he an Italian as he pretended to be, nor was he a direct descendant of the famous Jewish friend of Dante, as he claimed to be upon every possible occasion. He was the son of a Frankfort mohel and had studied to be a mohel himself until he fell in love with a Christian girl and in consequence thereof was disowned by his family. When he tried to communicate with the object of his affection, the parents of the girl had called the police, who amidst the plaudits of the Frankfort mob had thrown him into the river Main (it was the month of January if you please) and when he had scrambled onto an icefloe they had shot at him with their guns.

They had missed him but he had left Germany for all time. Eventually he had taken service with a French surgeon who had gone to Bologna to study anatomy with Malpighi. Being an exceedingly clever boy, he had picked up considerable medical information in the course of the two years he had spent at that famous Italian university, blacking his master's boots during the daytime and spending the midnight hours reading his textbooks on materia medica. And when the Frenchman returned to Paris, il Signore Dottore Alonzo ben Immanuele continued his peregrinations northward until he reached the city built upon the humble bones of a million defunct herring, where he felt himself so completely at home that he decided to stay there the rest of his days. But as the town seemed already well provided with doctors and apothecaries, Moritz Schmultz (for that was his real name, as I had the chance to find out) came to the conclusion that he must do something that would make him widely conspicuous if he did not want to die in the poor-house.

Among his scanty baggage he carried a discarded doctorial robe of his former master. To this he added the sort of peaked cap the rabbis had been obliged to wear in former times, and in this garb he now began to wander through the streets of Fleaburg announcing in a fine flow of Italian-Yiddish and German-Hebrew that he had discovered a new method of treating the sick. All they had to do to get cured was to show him their tongues from behind the window panes of their rooms. He would then make his diagnosis and send them the proper medicines. The consultation was free but a slight charge was made for the medicine to pay for the bottles and the corks and the labels, etc., etc.

The usual story and with the usual result. The man was soon rolling in money. Every morning at eight he would make his appearance on the famous island and would slowly proceed from the Amstel to the Uilenburgwal and back again.

He was accompanied by a coal-black negro whom he passed off as an Arab and a direct descendant of Ishmael, the unfortunate son of Hagar, a fable which would have given grave offense to the Christian part of the population if they had ever heard it, but as soon as the Professor had crossed the bridge of Saint Anthonie Lock and had entered the domain of the Goys, the honest blackamoor was re-baptized Sebaldus and became a Nubian slave who had been set free by Admiral de Ruyter during one of his campaigns against the Tunisian pirates and who had come to Amsterdam to receive instruction in the true faith according to the Heidelberg catechism.

It is hard to believe that this genial impostor had made such a deep impression upon the inhabitants of the Jewish quarter, that as soon as Sebaldus, alias Hagarson, had rung the big brass bell which he carried in his left hand (in his right hand he held the satchel which contained the doctor's nostrums) the windows of scores of houses would be opened and everywhere anxious mothers would appear with small children whom they would lift halfway out of the windows (upon one occasion a small boy was actually dropped into the street, but as he landed on a pile of rubbish, no great harm was done) and all those unfortunate infants would be obliged to stick out their tongues at the famous doctor, who would contemplate that organ for a few minutes with a profound frown upon his face and would then whisper a few words in an ununderstandable vernacular (it was supposed to be Arabic) to his black-faced familiar, who would thereupon rush into the house and leave a bottle of "Elixir Vitae Salamonialis" with the afflicted family in exchange for one guilder if it was for a boy and ten stivers if the patient happened to be a girl.

I once had an opportunity to examine two such bottles, a male and a female one. As far as I could make out, they contained nothing more harmful than a mixture of water and Tamarindus Indica and were worth exactly two cents wholesale. But when I told the man who had bought them for seventy times that amount (a dread-

SELF-PORTRAIT (PAINTING)

TITUS (PAINTING)

TITUS (PAINTING)

fully poor butcher who never made more than three guilders a week), he waxed very angry and hinted that I was trying to kill my colleague's trade because I was envious of his success.

For there could be no doubt about it. The Tongenkijker was an enormous success. Not only professionally, but also socially. From far and near people were flocking to Amsterdam either to consult him or merely to see and enjoy the free show which he put up right in the heart of a highly dignified and respectable Christian city. Why the Magistrates never interfered with him, I don't know. But they either considered it beneath their dignity to take any notice of him or they believed (as many other governments had done before) that a bit of ridicule would be good for the souls of these obstinate heathen who so tenaciously clung to their self-imposed ghetto and therefore (unless it was a case of murder or rape) they usually left the Jewish quarter severely alone and told the police to do likewise.

But the Portuguese Jews, much better educated and infinitely more polished than their Polish and German neighbors, regarded this absurd comedy with profound abhorrence and did all they could to bring about the arrest of this saltimbanque and if possible his expulsion from the territory of the city of Amsterdam.

The Town Hall, however, remained deaf to all their petitions and supplications and in the end they took matters into their own hands and staged a regular riot during which the unfortunate Inspector of Tongues was almost drowned in the Amstel (he seemed to have a fatal tendency to get himself ducked) and in which several people would undoubtedly have been killed if it had not been for the tact of the officer of the guard, who had succeeded in restoring order without firing a single shot.

The affair, however, caused a good deal of discussion and no less alarm. For what was this world coming to when foreigners who had come to us in sackcloth and ashes to find a refuge from foreign persecution could so far forget their duties towards their hosts as to stage a pitched battle right in the heart of the city of their habitation? And for no better cause than that they failed to approve or disapprove of a silly old man who ought to have been left to the mercies of the police?

The more enlightened among the Jews (regardless of the party to which they belonged by birth) tried to pacify Their Lordships of the

Town Hall by promising that they would do all they could to prevent a repetition of such an unseemly outbreak. But the rabbis, especially those of the Ashkenazic fold, would not listen to any compromise and exhorted their followers to further violence. In the end it became necessary to have the entire Jewish quarter patrolled by armed guards for more than six weeks, and the militia who were called upon to perform this extra duty felt very bitter about it and even talked of burning down the whole of the Fleaburg Island.

The plague, which had been very severe in Leyden the year before and which was beginning to make itself felt in Amsterdam with increasing severity, may have helped to quiet the mob. Dr. Alonzo ben Immanuele received a gentle hint to go and practice his beneficent arts elsewhere and peace and order were gradually restored but many people began to ask themselves what the end would be.

"Only a short while ago," so they reasoned, "those people came to us on their knees, begging us to give them shelter and protect them against their enemies, all of which we did. More than that, we allowed them to worship as they pleased, though their faith is anathema to most of our own citizens. Then they asked to be given permission to have butcher-stores of their own and to have a Sunday of their own and they insisted upon wearing a garb that was quite different from the clothes which we ourselves wore at the time and they continued to speak the Spanish or Portuguese or Polish or German tongues of the countries that were such cruel taskmasters to them, so that there is hardly one among every hundred of these foreigners who can write an ordinary business note in Dutch. And now, after having shown in every possible way that they wish to keep themselves apart from the nation which has offered them a home, they are beginning to take the law into their own hands and they try to settle their private quarrels as if they owned the city and as if there were no magistrates whom God has placed over us that they might rule us all with diligence and wisdom, and that will never do!

"No, it will never do, and if they continue to behave in this fashion, they had better return to Lisbon and to Madrid and to Warsaw, for while we don't particularly want them to say 'Thank you' to us for our kindness, neither do we care to have our community ruled by these upstarts who came here after we had purged the land of those enemies that were theirs as well as ours and who now want to reap the benefits which they did not help us sow and, on top of that, try to tell us how we ought to run our own government."

There was a great deal of unreasonableness in this accusation, for the vast majority, both of the Portuguese and German Jews, were almost fanatically grateful to those whom they invariably addressed as Their Saviors and they were not only loyal to the country at large but most generously inclined toward the particular city in which they happened to have settled down. Their rabbis, however, were an unruly lot and they bore a close resemblance to the clergymen of our own official church. As a rule they belonged to the lower classes of society and seeing little opportunity in following a business career, they chose the clerical profession because it promised to give them an outlet for their ambitions. But as no upstart can ever hope to rule without first discovering a "grievance" around which he can rally his followers, the rabbis, exactly like our own beloved dominies, were forever detecting dangerous issues which they thereupon attacked with the utmost violence and a complete disregard for the truth.

These were sad days for Menasseh, who spent almost every evening at the home of Rembrandt, presumably to talk of the illustrations for his forthcoming book, but in reality because he did not care to stay in his study, where at any moment he might be disturbed by the visit of one of his fellow rabbis. Poor Menasseh! His first great dream of finding the descendants of the Lost Tribes among the inhabitants of the New World had come to nothing. Next, in order to forget his miseries he had thrown himself upon the study of the Old Testament and he had done that with such fury that soon he had begun to hear mysterious voices and then one day he appeared among us boldly announcing that he had stumbled upon a hitherto unrevealed bit of prophecy that would set clear everything that had been dark thus far.

Being profoundly bored by that sort of hocus-pocus, I never quite understood what he was actually trying to prove. But it had something to do with Nebuchadnezzar or rather with Nebuchadnezzar's dream, which was supposed to be a prophecy of the coming of the Messiah, not the false Messiah whom we worshiped but the real Messiah who had not yet put in an appearance, et cetera, et cetera.

Next he got that Babylonian dream associated with the stone with which David slew Goliath and the stone which served Jacob for a pillow when he had his famous dream and it was all very muddled, but Menasseh himself was so full of his new idea that he persuaded Rembrandt (much against his will, I am afraid) to make a number of illustrations for the book which was to explain these mysteries to an unsuspecting and indifferent world.

The book was written in Spanish and not in Dutch and that may have been one of the reasons why Rembrandt never quite realized what he was doing and made such a bad job of the pictures. As he himself was beset by a thousand troubles during all this period, his friends hesitated to tell him just how bad these illustrations were. But the publisher of the Nebuchadnezzarian dream, being a business man and looking upon the venture from the angle of profit and loss, was inspired by no such delicate sentiments and simply threw the Rembrandt pictures out and had some ordinary hack do another set of plates which proved much more satisfactory from a popular point of view.

But when this happened, Menasseh himself was no longer among us. His Messianic premonition had left him no rest. He had missed meeting the Lost Tribes but he meant to be present when the great prophecies went into fulfillment. His position in Amsterdam was no longer a very pleasant one. Doctor van den Ende had been right when he told me that young Espinoza would some day, very soon, be the cause of considerable difficulties among the Jews of our town and Menasseh was forced to agree with him. He was very dejected about it.

"Those rabbis," he complained, "seem to have forgotten all we ever learned during our many years of suffering and persecution in foreign lands. Here we can enjoy a new and happy home of our own and they are all of them on the look-out for trouble. First it was d'Acosta, but he was not very bright and a little bit crazy. But this Espinoza boy has more brains than all of us put together. Instead of letting him go his own way, they are going to try and turn him into an errand-boy of the synagogue, a nice little fellow with a little brown coat on who goes around to all the people on Friday night to see that they clean their cupboards neatly and that they don't eat a chicken that has not had its head cut off in the right way. It is terrible!

"This Baruch, he is proud. He won't submit. He will fight back and the Christians will say, 'See those Jews, they are always the same. Quarreling again among themselves, as they did even in the days of Nebuchadnezzar.' And speaking of Nebuchadnezzar—did I ever tell you of his dream . . . ?"

And the poor man would be off again to tell you about his great discovery.

Poor honest soul! He left us soon afterwards and went to England, where the Jews were once more being admitted for the first time, I believe, in four or five centuries. In London he fought valiantly and successfully for the good rights of his own people to be granted the right to live in the New Commonwealth. In the beginning he used to write to us—short letters in fluent Spanish and not such fluent Dutch. Then he complained that he was too busy to correspond, for the Lord Protector had granted him a pension and he was now able to devote all his time to the task of preparing the way for the coming of the Messiah, whose appearance might be expected at almost any moment. Then for a long time we had no news from him. But in the summer of the year 1657 I happened to be in Veere for a few days to see about the repair of the houses I had inherited from my grand-uncle and which were badly in need of new floors and stairs. One day, quite early in the morning, the Baptist minister from Middelburg was announced. He begged that he be excused for disturbing me at such an unseemly hour, but in the hospital at Middelburg there was a sick man—he seemed to be a Jewish divine— who had asked after me and as it was known that I was in Veere at that moment, he had thought it his duty to warn me. I thanked him most cordially and together we walked back to Middelburg, where we arrived at noon.

The sick man was Menasseh. He was suffering from a pulmonary ailment and was already unconscious when I reached his bed-side. I heard that he had arrived in Flushing two days before with the body of his son Samuel, who had died in England and whom he wanted to bury in Amsterdam. He had been sick when he reached Flushing and had fainted in the coach that carried him to the ferry to the next island. The coachman had therefore driven him to the God's House and the matron had warned one of the ministers that she had a patient who seemed on the point of dying. But when it appeared that the man was a Jew, and a rabbi at that, there had been little enthusiasm on the part of the official clerics to attend him in his final hours.

The Baptist preacher, having been informed of the good woman's predicament, had then offered his services and having heard how the patient in his feverish wanderings had repeatedly mentioned my name, he had taken the trouble to come all the way to Veere and warn me.

Together we watched over the patient and when evening came, he had a moment of consciousness. He recognized me. He smiled and whispered: "I love all my good friends in Amsterdam. Tell them so. And tell them to be prepared. The hour is at hand. The Messiah will come. Surely he will come!"

And thus Menasseh had died at peace with all the world, and two days later we had buried him, together with his son Samuel, and this had been the end of a good and righteous man and a true friend whom we could badly spare at the very moment when the little group of people who fought for a more intelligent and charitable world was so dreadfully in need of his patience and his humor and the satisfaction one derived from his oft-repeated meditation:

"Ja, am Ende, wenn wir nur wirklich wüssten—if only we knew— if only we knew!"

Chapter 27

MY SON BEGINS THE EDUCATION OF HIS FATHER

BEGGARS IN CONVERSATION (ETCHING)

MEANWHILE little Titus, Rembrandt's son, had grown up to be a boy of almost fifteen and my own offspring was also approaching that age when a father looks at his perambulating resemblance and asks himself: "What in the name of high Heaven am I going to do with that boy?"

Titus, I am sorry to say, was causing Rembrandt more worry than my own boy was causing me. In the first place, he was not at all robust. He had inherited his father's face but his mother's delicacy of nature—her beautiful hands—her slender bones but also her weak lungs, and general lack of resistance. Really, it was too bad. If only it had been the other way around! If he had inherited his father's frame, who had the physique of a cart-horse, but the face of a good, honest, hard-working blacksmith or carpenter, which lacked all the charm and vivaciousness that had belonged to his aristocratic wife.

Jean-Louys and I had often speculated whether on the whole it was better for one to have started out with good blood or with a good education and how much education could do for one who had been born under humble circumstances and whether one who was born of good blood could ever quite belie his origin. And we had both come to the conclusion that there were so many exceptions to whatever rules we felt tempted to establish that we had better drop the subject as beyond our power of solution.

283

In the course of these discussions, Jean-Louys had hit upon a very clever new definition of "education," as different from mere "ability," by laying down the rule that "ability" allowed one to get along without "education," whereas "education" allowed one to get along without "ability." But when I suddenly asked him, "Yes, but what has that got to do with the subject of which we were talking?" he had answered, "Nothing at all, but it is past two o'clock of the night and then one is no longer supposed to talk sense," and so we had gone to bed and the matter never had been decided, which was a pity, for in the case of little Titus I felt that I was face to face with a problem which I for one would have great difficulty in unraveling. The poor lad seemed to have inherited from both parents exactly those qualities which were bound to be of absolutely no help to him in making his way. His handsome looks were of very little use to him, because he was a boy, and the talent for painting which he undoubtedly possessed, was so slight and insignificant as to be almost negligible.

He gave one the impression of an amiable and rather tender boy with excellent manners (the work of Hendrickje, though where she had learned them herself I never was able to fathom) and the best of intentions but without any force or stamina. I asked his father what he intended to do with him afterwards and Rembrandt, in that vague way in which he dismissed all subjects that had not some direct bearing upon his work, answered:

"Oh, I suppose he will become an artist."

And when I continued: "But how will he live?" he said:

"Oh, well, I suppose he will live somehow or other."

And he peacefully continued with the portrait of Jan Lutma, the goldsmith, on which he had been working for quite a long time, and which needed a general overhauling.

But how was that poor innocent and rather incompetent child ever to survive in a world that had been turned completely upside down by the war?

His father had had a difficult time making both ends meet, but he at least had worked in a normal world. The peace of Westminster, however, had destroyed all the old values. Even a great many of those rich merchants who ruled our towns and our country for so long and who seemed so firmly entrenched that nothing could possibly happen to them, even they had suffered reverses from which they were never able to recover and were forced to go back to a much simpler way of living than that to which they had been accustomed for three or four generations. And among those just a trifle below them on the social ladder there was hardly a person who in one way or another had not felt the influence of that great upheaval. Either their ships had been destroyed by the English or they had speculated in wood or gunpowder when they should have concentrated all their forces upon cornering the market in hemp and meanwhile other younger or more ambitious and perhaps a little less conservative and undoubtedly much less scrupulous firms had grabbed all the right profits at the right moment and had made millions. They were now buying up the town houses and country houses of those who had guessed wrong, and they were buying themselves noble carriages and an occasional coat-of-arms to put upon the doors of those vehicles. But their taste in furniture and art and music was as bad as the manners they displayed both in public and in private and the pictures they bought came almost exclusively from Antwerp and Paris where regular picture-factories were now working for "le goût Hollandais."

How mild little Titus, with his mild little portraits (they were a very weak and therefore bad reflection of those of his father), would ever be able to sell one of his works to the barbarians of the new era of prosperity was something I could not quite see. But the boy was still very young and might decide to do something different when he reached the age of discretion.

As for my own son, he never caused me any trouble. He seemed to have inherited absolutely nothing from anybody, neither from his mother nor me, nor for that matter from his grandfather or grandmother. Instead, he jumped right back to his great-grandfather, my own beloved grandfather, and I rejoiced in this biological miracle. For nothing could have been more to my taste than to see all those qualities of independence and enthusiasm and efficiency return in that flesh and blood that was so very much my own.

The youngster had absolutely no interest in the work that had occupied me ever since the days of my childhood. He was very nice to sick people and in a mild and non-committal way he felt rather sorry for them too. But he did not like them. He was too sound himself to have much sympathy for those who were suffering from some ailment. Nor did his grandsire's characteristics manifest themselves in a tendency toward things military. He told me once that he would not mind fighting but that it seemed a silly thing to do. It was too destructive—too aimless to suit practical taste. He wanted to make things. And he wanted to make them not only with his brains but also with his hands, for he had fingers that were as strong as steel nippers and he liked to use them. And from childhood on (so I was told, for during the first ten years of his life I had been in America) he had been busy with windmills and toy carriages and miniature dredges. But when I returned from Nieuw Amsterdam he was no longer pottering around with tiny little mills made out of packing cases and pieces of sail which he had begged or stolen at the water front (a proceeding which seems to have shocked his faithful nurse more than anything else he ever did during a somewhat obstinate and turbulent career) but he had graduated from such futile pastimes and was beginning to revaluate his practical engineering experiments into terms of certain abstract mathematical formulae —formulae which meant nothing at all to me but which he explained to me as representing wind-velocities and the friction of wood upon wood and of stone upon stone and other intricate details of that mechanical world that will forever remain closed to me.

Where exactly he had learned all this I was never able to find out. I had first sent him to a school which was famous for the excellence of its Latin and Greek teaching. But there he was a complete failure. He went to sleep over his syntax, and his copy-books contained diagrams of new hoisting devices instead of those terrible Greek verbs, the knowledge of which was considered an indispensable part of a gentleman's education. But whenever I tried to make this clear to him, he merely looked pained and bored and upon one memorable occasion informed me that I was talking through my hat (he used an even less complimentary expression which I must refuse to repeat here)—that he had no desire to be a gentleman if I meant by this that he would be allowed to spend five years at some university drinking gin and running after the servant girls of the town and generally misbehaving himself in those ways that were then considered highly fashionable among the young men of leisure who deigned to patronize those institutions of erudition and that, anyway, he could learn more from ten minutes' talk with the owner of the "Cow" (a well-known mill just outside the Saint Anthonie Gate, where he was in the habit of spending a great many of those hours he should have been at his desk at school) than from four entire years aimlessly pawing the dreary pages of a Greek grammar.

I then spoke of the beauties of ancient poetry and he quietly looked at me and said: "But, father, have you ever heard the regular swish-swish of a mill that is running full speed? Could anything be more wonderful or more beautiful than that?"

I then began to discover for myself what must have been clear even to Adam, who certainly was no shining beacon of intelligence. (What a pity that our earliest ancestor should have been such a terrible bungler! Just suppose that he had been a bright fellow like Jacob or Joseph! Ten to one he would have beaten Jehovah at his own silly apple game, but it is too late now to waste vain regrets upon such a hopeless case of stupidity.) I was beginning to understand that we can't teach our children anything at all. We can expose them to education in the hope that they will catch some of it. But just how much or how little of it they catch depends upon certain mysterious elements in their make-up, the exact nature of which will probably remain hidden to us for all time.

But I know this much, that if a boy has a definite "tendency" towards certain subjects of learning, he will "catch" those subjects, in spite of every obstacle. But if, on the other hand, he has no such "tendency," he remains what we physicians call "immune" and we can expose him as much as we like, but he will never succeed in making that subject an integral part of his mental equipment.

I was not always as sane upon the subject as I am now after my son has been trying to educate me in this direction for almost twenty odd years. But on the whole I am happy to say I suspected the existence of this pedagogic axiom long before I had been able to prove it and as a result the boy has never given me any trouble and I have given him as little trouble as was possible, considering that I was his father and therefore more or less his natural-born enemy.

Poor Rembrandt! I was sorry for him when on Sundays, as sometimes happened, we took our boys out for a walk. Little Titus was usually bored, would want to go back home and color his pictures or look at a book. After half an hour he would complain that he was tired. After an hour he would sit down and weep, for he really was not strong and got exhausted very easily.

Meanwhile my own young barbarian would occupy himself with some mechanical contrivance he had put together during the previous week—would try it out on the waters of the Amstel where the winds blew ever fresh, would talk of the day when mills would not only pump water and grind flour and saw wood but would also peel rice and make oil and perform Heaven only knows what other miracles.

Then Titus would look at him and would say, "I hate mills. They are ugly. They make such a noise."

And the answer would be: "Pooh! Ugly! They are useful. Useful things are never ugly."

As for Rembrandt, he would listen to this childish conversation, but it never seemed to penetrate to him what they were saying.

"They are young," he used to comment, once in a while. "They will grow out of it, both of them."

But there I had my doubts.

Does any one ever really "grow out" of something that was put into him even before the day of his birth?

STUDY (DRAWING)

Chapter 28

WE BUILD A NEW TOWN HALL AND REMBRANDT
ALMOST PAINTS A PICTURE FOR IT

REMBRANDT DRAWING AT A WINDOW
(ETCHING)

DURING the fall of the year '55 it became more and more clear that the situation in the northern part of Europe must soon lead to a crisis. Our Baltic granaries were in danger and without those supplies half of our people would have starved to death.

I don't think that there were a hundred burghers in the entire Republic who cared a straw for the Poles, either as a nation or as individuals, while our relations with the Swedes had always been most cordial, and furthermore the Poles were Catholics of a most pronounced and bigoted sort and the Swedes belonged to our own church, although they took to Lutheranism, rather than to Calvinism. Nevertheless, when it was seen to be a question of guilders and stivers, all personal considerations were curtly set aside and as soon as Danzig had been taken by the forces of King Charles, a squadron of our ships was sent to that town—it was recaptured and was given back to the Polish king.

The situation was not entirely clear. Even after this event we were still supposed to be at peace with the Swedes and My Lord de Witt strongly urged a union between the two great Scandinavian powers, Sweden and Denmark, with the Republic of the United Netherlands as the "honest broker" keeping the peace between the two rivals and preventing them from flying at each other's throats.

But this plan failed as ignominiously as his project for that English-Dutch treaty which he had explained to me upon the occasion of our memorable interview. In both instances it was the town of Amsterdam that rudely upset his calculations. The great Pensionary was a "party man." He firmly believed in government by the "best people," and the "best people" of course were his own relations and their friends, the rich merchants of our big cities. But he was a man of such brilliant parts that, almost against his own will, he was sometimes obliged to look beyond the immediate interests of his party. Whereas Their Lordships, who ruled us from the big new building on the Dam, believed the world to end at the city boundaries and invariably put their own profits ahead of those of the country as a whole. They were wise and sagacious magistrates and I hasten to add that as a rule their policies coincided with those that were considered most favorable for the Republic as a whole. Nevertheless, it was a very unfortunate system of government, for it allowed a single community to override the clearly expressed will of all of its neighbors.

But it had been that way ever since the beginning of our independence and I suppose it will continue to be that way until the end, for I don't know of any man or party powerful enough to change it unless one of the princes of the House of Orange succeeds in making himself our king, something which seems hardly likely at the present moment when the only surviving member of that family (with the exception of a few negligible cousins in the northern part of the country) is a young boy who suffers dreadfully from headaches and who does not seem destined to live very long.

In this particular instance it fortunately was proved that Amsterdam had chosen the wiser course. Since the death of my old friends, the Bickers, the affairs of the town were managed by a member of the van Beuningen family. The first half century of our independence offered wonderful opportunities to young men. Jan de Witt was only twenty-eight when he was appointed to the highest office in the state. And Conrad van Beuningen, at the age of thirty-three, had more power than many of the dictators of ancient Greece about whom we read in our history books. He belonged to a family that was greatly interested not only in the Baltic grain trade but also in the spice trade of the Indies and he was supremely endowed both by nature and by years of serious study for the rôle he was to play during the next twenty years. He was good-looking and he could speak well in public—an accomplishment which I am sorry to say has been sadly neglected in our community, since we are rather apt to frown upon every form of rhetorical elegance except that extraordinary variety which is practiced in the pulpit.

But His Lordship was not given much to sermonizing. As a matter of fact, he was a person of very liberal ideas and it was said (though no one could offer any definite evidence) that he preferred the wisdom of Seneca and Marcus Aurelius to that of Calvin and Knox. But as he was enormously rich, such accusations were never uttered beyond a whisper and it is only in recent years, when it seems that he is afflicted with the family curse of insanity, that people are beginning to speak out a little more openly about his heretical tendencies.

But in the year 1656 of which I am writing at the present moment, no one in his senses would have even dared to hint at such a possibility. And His Lordship could devote all his time and all his tremendous energy towards a realization of those plans which should turn the Baltic into another Zuyder Zee, into a lake that should be dominated by Dutch interests. His friend, the Pensionary in The Hague, agreed with the views of Amsterdam in a general way but was inclined to proceed a little more cautiously. He had had more to do with navies than van Beuningen and knew how precarious a thing even a well-equipped fleet remains even under the most favorable circumstances and how little one can depend upon it in time of need. A sudden storm or an unexpected fog, and victory may suddenly be turned into defeat. Besides, ships cannot be constructed overnight. It takes fourteen months to build one of those gigantic modern men-of-war which measure six or seven hundred tons, but one unfortunate hit in the powder-magazine will send them to the bottom of the ocean in less than a minute's time.

Therefore while the Pensionary was just as anxious as the Burgomasters of Amsterdam to bridle the ambitions of the Swedish monarch and keep the old Baltic granaries open for the Dutch trade, he felt less inclined to risk the whole of the navy upon this one venture.

"How about England?" he asked his friend in Amsterdam. "Suppose that the Lord Protector avails himself of the opportunity which is offered by the absence of our ships in the north to stage a landing on the Dutch coast. What will happen then?"

Those of Amsterdam answered him that since the Republic was at peace with England and even had concluded a treaty of amity with that country, we need have no fears from that angle.

"What are official documents between nations?" the Pensionary replied. "Since when has a piece of paper prevented a people from attacking another when it seemed to their own interests to do so?"

And he cited a large number of instances in which empires and kingdoms and republics had treated the most sacred treaties as mere scraps of paper because it was to their advantage to do so. But Amsterdam refused to give in and since our town paid most of the taxes of the province of Holland and since Holland alone paid almost half of all the taxes of the entire Republic, Amsterdam had its own way and for five entire years our navy was kept busy in the north.

During this campaign some of the measures which I had been permitted to suggest were tried in practice, and on the whole I am grateful to say my fellow practitioners on board approved of them and gave me their hearty coöperation. I myself was present at the encounter in the Sound when the Swedes under Wrangel were defeated, although it cost us the life of one of our ablest commanders, the famous Witte de With, who was a wild-man-of-the-sea, who could swear almost as well as he could fight, and who had hacked his way through so many naval engagements that he seemed to be possessed of a charmed life. On this occasion the tide carried his vessel on a bank, but he turned it quickly into a castle and defended himself until almost all his men were dead and he himself lay dying, causing so much admiration by his conduct, even among his enemies, that the next day they sent us his corpse with full military honors.

I arrived just too late to be with de Ruyter when he bombarded Nyborg and entered Copenhagen. I was allowed, however, to visit that town during the winter our admiral spent there and found it of very pleasing aspect, reminding me in many ways of our own city of Amsterdam, though it struck me that the people were a great deal gayer than our own and much less inclined to rowdyism.

I found it hard to account for this difference in outward behavior of the two nations. I have heard it claimed that the bad weather of our lowland, the eternal fog and rain in which we are obliged to dwell from the day we are placed in a damp cradle until the hour

TITUS (PAINTING)

we are lowered into a water-soaked grave, is at the bottom of our depressed mood and depressing ways. But surely nothing could be viler than the climate of the Danish capital, which, like my own town of Veere, resembles a pancake afloat on a sea of mud. So it can't be that.

Others have told me that "It is the difference in religion. These people are Lutherans, whereas we are Calvinists."

I am willing to grant that I would rather have gone fishing with the Wittenberg reformer than with his Genevan colleague, but what I saw here of the Lutheran ministers did not exactly give me an impression of levity of spirit. Indeed, I found them to be very much like our own dominies—perhaps a trifle more human but not very much, and just as eager to force their own views upon the rest of the world as the best or worst of our Amsterdam clerics. The most likely solution was given me by a young man who was one of the aides of Admiral van Wassenaar.

The latter, a very rich man and lord of the village of Obdam, an hereditary member of the Estates of Holland and the owner of a vast country place near The Hague, had begun life as the colonel of a regiment of cavalry. But during the recent English war, he suddenly had been ordered to take command of the fleet and he had stepped on board his first vessel as ignorant of naval strategy as a baby is of playing the harpsichord.

He owed his sudden rise in the world to the fact that he was a staunch supporter of the party that opposed the House of Orange, whereas de Ruyter and Tromp and Evertsen and all the others were suspected of leanings toward the little Prince. However that may be, the admiral-on-horseback had proved himself a very able man and a person of tact who had gained the respect and affection of his subordinates by his pleasant manner and his willingness to listen to their advice.

At the time I was summoned to his flagship he was suffering badly from podagra. A draughty ship's cabin was no ideal place of residence for a man thus afflicted, but he bore his pains with great fortitude and spent most of his time playing backgammon with his aide, who had developed a technique of losing that was truly admirable. This young man, the son of a Frisian nobleman and a French mother, but who vowed that he would never again set foot in that part of the world where a square foot of air weighed ten million Flemish pounds, was an amateur student of politics of no mean ability and he had developed a social theory which greatly amused me, although I soon realized that in most of what he said, the wish was father to the thought.

"The trouble with our country," he used to say while we paced up and down the deck, waiting for the Admiral, who was a handsome man but rather vain and very particular about his outward appearance, to finish his toilet, "the trouble with our land is the lack of standards which is due to the lack of a court. In some ways that is our strength, but in many other ways it is one of our great weaknesses. It is true we can't just suddenly be lifted out of our beds and taken to a dungeon in some prison, as happened to the husband of one of my mother's cousins. It took the greater part of a year to discover where he was kept and next it took the combined efforts of the Estates of Holland and Friesland and five personal letters of the Grand Pensionary to get him out again. He had, so it appeared, laughed a little too loudly when one of the Mazarin girls was murdering the King's French a little more atrociously than usual. The Cardinal had observed that smile and His Majesty had obliged his faithful servant with a little slip of parchment, beginning, 'de par le Roi.'

"Good! I grant you that sort of thing is quite impossible here, and we will put that on the debit side. We have no sovereigns by the grace of God. As a result, we have fewer priests and not quite so many scaffolds. Whatever violence is committed is the work of the riffraff that has been preached into a frenzy of destructive holiness by the gentlemen of the cloth, but it is not the result of a sleepless night or indigestion on the part of one of the Lord's anointed.

"But now take the credit side. We are a circle without a center. As a result, politically speaking, we wobble, and socially speaking we are nowhere at all. We are supposed to be 'a country.' The poor innocents in Paris or London are still under the misapprehension that we are 'a country.' The day they discover that we are nothing of the sort, but merely an aggregation of squabbling, squealing, fighting, quarreling little provinces and cities and hamlets, each one with the pretension of being the equal of the grand duchy of Muscovy, they will fall upon us and divide us among themselves, as Philip of Macedon fell upon the so-called independent democracies of ancient Greece and took away their liberty.

"Being a race of merry pirates, the inhabitants of our seacoast, who are devils when it comes to discipline, but perfect angels when there is any fighting to be done, may be able to hold out a little longer than if we were some inland state like that curious kingdom of Poland where I spent six whole months or one hundred and eighty-five days this spring and where every truckman and stevedore is a count or duke in his own right and has the power to veto any law he does not like.

"But I was telling you what is wrong with our social system. Well, we have no rallying-point—we are without any standards whatsoever. Standards of conduct and standards of beauty and standards of customs or manners may not be necessary for such a genius as that painter friend of yours of whom you have told me so much, and who lives with his cook and has children by her and quietly goes on painting, but most of us are no geniuses, and without standards we are lost, like ships at sea without a compass.

"As a very young man I went to London and I was there again as a sort of secretary during the negotiations at Westminster. The difference between the London of the Stuarts and the London of the Roundheads was incredible. I was very young when His late Majesty was still possessed of his head, and when one is very young, everything looks fine. But the people still had manners—they still had a code which told them what to do on all occasions and it made the whole social machinery run smoothly and evenly and quite pleasantly for all concerned.

"But two years ago—Heavens above! what a difference! One heard the social machine creak and groan. Each one of the men and women one met in the streets seemed to have worked out some little system of behavior of his or her own, and as not two of these systems were alike, the result meant continual friction—a chaos of conflicting interests which made me feel as if I were being entertained by my uncle of Witmarsum, who is famous for his dog-kennels and whose chief pastime in life is to invite his friends and relatives to be present when the brutes are being fed.

"We had a few audiences with the Lord Protector and I have never met a more charming or a more urbane man in all my days.

But then, he was a landed nobleman of the old school and had been brought up under the monarchy.

"But take France or Italy, for I believe you told me that you had been there once. In each one of those countries there is a court with a king and that court is the bureau of standards for everything that has to do with a civilized existence. His Majesty decides that he must no longer dive into his goulash with his fingers, but use a fork, and the whole country, or at least that part of it that wants to be considered civilized (and the rest does not matter), hastens to go to the silversmith's shop and order a couple of forks for every member of their respective families.

"Or His Majesty wants to build himself a new palace. He knows nothing about bricks and mortar himself and therefore he sends for the best architects in the land and says: 'Messieurs, go to it.' I don't mean to say that you and I will invariably agree that they are the best architects according to our own tastes, but never mind, they are bound to be among the best, otherwise they would not have got the job.

"Or His Majesty becomes enamored of a beautiful damozel and wants to honor her by such a feast as this world has never seen. He sends for the best fiddlers and the best dancing masters and says: 'Gentlemen, it is up to you to show us what you can do, and please don't disappoint us, for our royal displeasure would be fatal to your reputation.' Do they work their poor brains overtime to please His Majesty? I assure you they do. And their music and their plays set a standard for all others.

"Or again His Majesty wants to enliven the dull walls of his castle. He asks who are considered the best painters within his realm and tells them to get out their palettes and their brushes and give him what is the best. I repeat, this 'best' may not be the 'best' according to your taste or according to my individual taste, because we happen to be people of profound discrimination, but at least it is a sort of norm for those hordes of patient subjects who have no more idea of taste than my dog Nero has of how to catch storks.

"And the result is a pleasant average of behavior and of comedies and tragedies and paintings and sculpture and of cookery and dancing and love-making.

"In our Republic we have a few people who are far above that average, for we are a nation that is by no means devoid of ability and talent—I might even say genius. But our 'average' is bad. We really have no average. We have whatever it pleases every man and every woman (and sometimes every child) in every street of every town and village to give us. It is good enough for them. It suits their needs. We don't like it? Very well, we know what we can do about it! And so while we have worked ourselves up to the rank of a God-fearing, prosperous and highly respectable nation, we have in everything that does not pertain to our fear of God, our prosperity or our incredible respectability, remained what we were four hundred years ago when my ancestors killed your ancestors with pitchforks and bludgeons. We have remained a rowdy mob of self-embarrassed and clumsy yokels who either giggle or moan and as a rule giggle when they ought to be moaning and moan when they ought to be laughing. . . ."

But at that moment the Admiral had finished his toilet and sent for me and I never quite heard the end of this diverting speech. But I think that I know what young Aitzema had meant. Denmark was a country dominated by a single big town and that town, ever since it had been founded, six hundred years before, had been a royal residence and school of manners which was attended by pupils from all over the land. Whereas we at home had been left to our own devices —every man for himself and the Devil take the hindmost! Which the Devil had not failed to do, as I discovered the moment I returned to Amsterdam.

For the last eight years we had been building a new Town Hall. As soon as the Peace of Westphalia had been signed and our independence had been recognized, Jacob van Campen had been ordered to draw up plans for a new civic center. The old Town Hall was considered a little too shabby for a city of quite such magnificence as ours. Besides, the building had grown much too small and no one felt very sorry when it burned down during that memorable Saturday night in July of '52 when a cousin of Rembrandt's friend, Burgomaster Six, saved the books of the city bank and gained the everlasting devotion of the grateful depositors.

For eight long years one part of the Dam, right behind the ruins of the old Town Hall, had been hidden from our view by a high wooden fence. Meanwhile we had heard stories of the wonderful things that were going on behind that fence, which by then had become an excellent advertisement for the thoroughness of our public school system, as the usual dirty words were written as low as a foot from the ground, showing that even the youngest of our children were able to write and spell correctly.

Every citizen knew exactly how many Norwegian pines had been sunk into the ground to give this building the necessary stability. (I was the only exception, having no brain for figures, but the number ran somewhere between twelve and fourteen thousand, which made a forest of respectable dimensions.) And every citizen knew the width of the basement and the height of the towers had been carefully recounted, together with the number of rooms (including, as I remember, three different and separate jails) and the number of chimneys and the water reservoirs on the top floor which were to protect the building against fire.

But what had interested us most of all had been the plans for the interior decorating of all these many stately mansions that were to be occupied by Their Lordships the Burgomasters and by the high court of justice and by the aldermen and sheriffs and by the tax-gatherers and by all the many other dignitaries that made up what we were pleased to call our "magistrates." There would be need of a great many pictures and who was better fitted for such a task than Rembrandt? He had shown them that he could handle the most complicated subjects in a superb way and that size and shape of the canvas meant nothing to him provided he was really interested in the subject. Accordingly ever since I returned from America I had made it a point to speak to every one who possibly might have some influence with the authorities to say a good word for the man who was the ideal candidate for this very important task. And many of those whom I approached had answered, "Yes, that is a good idea. A very good idea. He is the fellow who painted that large picture that now hangs in the Doelen?" And without exception they had promised that they would do their best to give my friend at least a few of the orders that were to be placed among the local painters.

But when I happened to meet them again, they were always full of excuses. "Yes, they had mentioned his name to His Lordship, the first Burgomaster, the last time they saw him." Or again, "The big reception room which is a hundred by a hundred and twenty feet is just the sort of room that man Rembrandt ought to do, but the roof was not quite ready yet and therefore it was impossible to judge of the light effects and until the roof had been finished, it would be impossible to make a decision."

Meanwhile I learned that Bol and Flinck and Jan Lievens and several others were busy in their studios on portraits and allegorical works that were to find a place in the new edifice, while Jan Bronchorst was about to submit elaborate plans for the ceilings of the new court-room.

The public at large did not take a great deal of interest in this whole matter. As long as Their Lordships had thought fit to place their orders with such and such painters, well, why talk about it? Their Lordships undoubtedly knew what they wanted and Their Lordships undoubtedly knew best.

When it became known that practically all the necessary bits of sculpture had been commissioned to a certain Aert Quellin, who was a native of Antwerp, a voice was heard here and there asking whether we had no artists of our own who could do that sort of work just as well as a foreigner, but since it was conceded by every one who laid claim to a genteel taste that the Belgian painters were far superior to our own—much less coarse in their subjects and infinitely more refined in their treatment of the nude (and as furthermore Quellin happened to be one of the ablest sculptors of our time), these murmurings were never taken very seriously, and on the whole the populace approved most heartily of the choice of their rulers.

I knew both Flinck and Bol from the days they had been Rembrandt's pupils and I went to see them. They were quite loyal to their former teacher and wished that they could be of assistance to him. But both of them agreed that it would be suicidal for them if they should try to agitate on his behalf in any way that might be constructed as a personal interference with the plans of Their Lordships.

"Even now," Bol told me frankly, "we may at any moment be replaced by some Fleming who paints more in the Rubens manner than we do. Rubens is the great man here. He and Jordaens are our heroes. Rembrandt? Why, he is either too dark or too muddy or too something to please our public. Both Flinck and I and practically all the men that studied with our old master have been obliged to change our technique, become a little more Flemish, a little more Rubenesque—if you understand me—to keep our customers. If we had not done that, we would now be starving to death. If you don't believe me, go to any of the art-dealers and ask them whether they will take a chance on Rembrandt. Yes, here and there a man who sells to the Italian trade. Perhaps because there is so much sunshine in Italy that they can stand something a little dull better than we. But the others? They won't touch him. They won't come near him. And if we went to Their Lordships and suggested the name of Rembrandt, they would show us the door, and ask us to mind our own business, which consists in being just as Flemish as we can be."

I knew that they were right, but refused to give up. The next time I was in The Hague, I mentioned the subject to My Lord de Witt.

"I don't know much about such matters," he confessed, "and the Lord have mercy on my soul if it ever should become known that I had dared to make a suggestion concerning anything that had to do with the purely domestic affairs of that very independent city. If it should be rumored that I was in favor of yellow curtains, Their Lordships would at once order every curtain in the whole place to be dyed a bright green. No, I dare not interfere in any way, but I will give you a letter to my uncle. He is a man of sense and a man of taste and not without influence in his own country."

This was expressing it very mildly, for every one knew that nothing could be accomplished in Amsterdam without the silent approbation of the famous Lord of Polsbroek.

This title was one which he had acquired in later life by buying himself the seigneurial rights to the village of Polsbroek. Why he did this, I do not know, for as simple Cornelis de Graef he was known far and wide as the uncrowned king of Amsterdam and as one of the strongest men in the Republic. He was not really an uncle of My Lord Jan but of his wife, the former Wendela Bicker. That, however, made little difference. If the two men had not been related at all, they would have appreciated each other just as genuinely. For they both were far above the average in intelligence and integrity and as neither of them coveted outward glory, or dignity (having enough of the latter not to be obliged to worry about the former), there was no danger of their ever getting into conflict about mere matters of policy.

Whether My Lord of Polsbroek was as staunch a party man as his famous nephew or had secret leanings towards the House of Orange, no one was ever able to discover. He never quite gave himself away, being perhaps too much of a philosopher to make a good politician. It was his business to see that Amsterdam remained the most prosperous city of the old continent and for that reason he wished to remain on cordial terms with the government of the Republic as represented by the Estates General who met in The Hague. His nephew by marriage happened to be the most influential person in the Estates General. It really was a most perfect arrangement. The uncle acted as general adviser to the nephew, while the nephew kept the uncle informed about everything that happened in his corner of the woods. From such partnership great things are born and as long as both men lived, the country enjoyed such affluence and such uninterrupted good fortune that the period of their coöperation will probably go down in history as the Golden Age of our Republic.

But in the matter of art, I found His Lordship was about as helpless as his nephew had pretended to be.

I found him in his house on the Heerengracht to which the family had moved when they ceased to be cloth-dealers and were promoted to the rank of merchant-princes. But nothing could have been more delightful or cordial than his reception. Like all men of big affairs, he seemed to have plenty of time for everything and bade me be seated and at once spoke most sympathetically about the loss I had suffered.

"An outrage," he said, "a perfect outrage and absolutely inexcusable. But what will you? The rabble needs a victim once in a while. I am sorry that this time the popular lightning (which is about as reasonable as that of the great god Zeus) has struck one for whom I feel such sincere personal regard. And you shall have full redress. You shall receive full compensation for everything you lost. Unfortunately such things proceed rather slowly. That is one of the most regrettable sides of our form of government. If we lived under a monarchy, such a wrong could be settled in one quarter of the time it takes to do such a thing here. One royal signature and the difficulty would be out of the way. Also if the royal signature for some reason were not granted, you would never see a cent of your money, and your children and grandchildren could die in the alms-house and His Majesty would not care. Here, under our system of government, you are at least reasonably certain that part of the funds will be in your hands before you die and that your son will get the rest. I wonder why governments always work so slowly. But an official exchequer is like those ingenious bow-nets with which, in the days of my youth, I used to catch eels. Everything can go in, but nothing can ever go out. However, in what way can I hope to be of service to you to-day?"

I told him. He threw his hands up in a gesture of despair.

"Ask me something else," he said. "Ask me something easy like declaring war upon the Emperor or making the East India Company publish a true account of their last year's budget. Ask me to have you appointed ambassador-in-extraordinary to the court of the Great Khan. Ask me to have the Amstel diverted into the North Sea instead of the Zuyder Zee. But don't ask me to risk my position and my prestige in a matter of this sort."

I looked at him and was dumbfounded. Here was My Lord of Polsbroek, without whose permission (as the people used to say) it could not even rain in Amsterdam, confessing to me, a poor leech, that he could not order a few pictures for his new Town Hall from the greatest painter alive, and for what reason—for what reason on earth? I asked him. I asked him humbly and politely, but nevertheless I asked him. What considerations of a political nature could oblige him to give me such a disappointing answer?

"What considerations of a political nature?" he burst forth. "Politics be damned. I will appoint any man to any place I please as long as it is a matter of politics, but that is just it! This is not a matter of politics. This is a matter of religion—of theology—of the one thing I have vowed I would keep clear of, all the rest of my live-long days."

"But surely," I answered, "Your Lordship need not ask Rembrandt to paint an allegorical picture that could possibly shock the pious. He is most excellent at portraits. You must need a great many portraits for the new Town Hall. Allegorical pictures never were his strong point anyway."

"My dear Doctor," he said, and looked at me the way I had noticed other people look before, when I had asked a particularly foolish question, "don't you see how it is? You may think that we are almighty at the Town Hall, that we can do as we please. We can to a certain extent but we have to proceed very carefully. After all, there are window-panes in our houses and it costs a lot to replace them. The clergy still has a hold upon the masses that we philosophers are a little too apt to overlook. And numbers count, especially in a city like this that has no court and therefore no life-guards. Some of our colleagues know this and make use of it to excellent purpose. I have one in mind, a certain Valckenier. His father made a lot of money in the East India Company. He is one of the most unpleasant people I have ever met and he has a temper that is as nasty as the bite of a sturgeon. But he is intelligent and he has a terrific amount of ambition. He wants to succeed van Beuningen if that poor man should ever be shipwrecked on one of his endless voyages. He has not a friend among the members of the city council. But he needs a party—some one to back him up. We watched him turn pious almost overnight. He has not one single quality of a true Christian and is a hateful and spiteful man. But every Sunday—three times every Sunday—you can see him in his pew in the New Church.

"The 'small people' worship him as one of their own. What would he say, or rather what would he not say, if I suggested that we give a commission for an official portrait to a man who lives in open sin with his maidservant? He would drop a hint and the dominies would pound their pulpits and would start their usual fulminations against the new Sodom and would preach sermons about the whore of Babylon and it might end in bloodshed.

"And now I don't even consider the possibility of his finding out that you, of all people, suggested this to me. You, a mere surgeon who tried to cheat Jehovah out of his allotted measure of pain—you, an iconoclast who tried to set woman free from one of her most disastrous burdens. Why, we would have to turn the whole city into an armed camp if I so much as suggested the name of this man van Rijn for a single piece of work.

"Ask me some other favor and it is granted before you even express the wish. But let me die in peace. Our day will soon be over. I have spent much of my time reading books of history. For every five years that the world has been ruled by Reason, the human race has insisted upon five hundred during which it should obey the dictates of its own passions and prejudices and follies and foibles. You see, I am quite eloquent upon the subject. Mankind has but one enemy, its own stupidity, but it loves that enemy as truly and as devotedly as many a poor simpleton who is married to a shrew loves and obeys the creature who has turned his existence into a living hell.

"I would like to oblige you. I will give orders that the new Town Hall be burned down if that pleases you. But as for giving an order to your friend van Rijn, no, that I won't do because I can't do it."

I saw his point and thanked him for his courtesy and took my leave.

The new Town Hall was inaugurated with many ceremonies. There was a service in the Old Church and a service in the New Church and a procession of all the dignitaries connected in any way with the government of the city and there were public performances on the Dam and there was music and a great deal of patriotism and a great deal of drunkenness, as is apt to occur on such occasions. I spent the day quietly at home and in the evening went to Rembrandt's house and helped him polish some plates, for he was in the midst of one of his attacks of etching when he was apt to work twenty hours a day.

But ere I finish this chapter, I must run ahead a few years and tell of something that happened much later.

In the month of February of the year 1660 Govaert Flinck, who was still working on the decoration of the big gallery in the Town Hall, died. He had been sick for quite a long time and it was known that he would not be able to finish the work he had begun. Just then my old friend and colleague, Doctor Tulp, was treasurer of the town of Amsterdam. He had achieved much greater honors in the world than I and was then one of the most respected burghers of our town. But we had always remained on a pleasant and cordial footing and besides I knew that he had a great admiration for Rembrandt, who had painted his picture some twenty odd years before when they were both still comparatively young men and at the beginning of their respective careers.

Since that time, Tulp never again met Rembrandt, and the last time he had had his portrait painted he had had it done by a foreign artist. Nevertheless I decided to say a good word for Rembrandt and as the Town Hall was no longer a novelty and no one paid much attention to it except those who went there on business and native Amsterdamers who had to entertain guests from abroad,

Rembrandt van Rijn

whom they dragged right from the boat to the Dam to behold the "eighth wonder of the world" and tell them that in the globe carried by the Hercules who guarded the entrance gates, there was room for at least three people enjoying a meal at a middle-sized table—as in short the Town Hall and its decorations were no longer in the public and in the clerical eyes, the excellent Tulp complied with my wishes and Rembrandt was told to continue the work which his own pupil had not been able to finish.

SKETCH FOR "THE CONSPIRACY OF CLAUDIUS CIVILIS" (DRAWING)

It was to be an historical picture representing the great Batavian hero, Claudius Civilis, who for a short period of years had set our country free from the rule of the Romans. All this of course had happened a long time ago and no one knew exactly where or under what circumstances, but every well-behaved child could reel off the date: "100 B.C. the Romans arrived in our country and 50 B.C. Claudius Civilis set our country free from the Roman yoke."

Rembrandt showed less enthusiasm than I had expected. This order was what he called "mustard that comes after the meal," and true enough, it was not very flattering for him to be called in only as a sort of stopgap. But once he had started, his enthusiasm grew by leaps and bounds. He decided that since this was a conspiracy, the scene must have been laid at night and in the dark, when the Romans were supposed to have gone to bed. He chose an enormous canvas, almost sixty feet square, the largest canvas he had ever handled, and he made the Batavian rebel the center of a festive meal, during which he explains to his friends and followers what his plans are for the coming uprising.

The problem of having the entire scene bathed in the light of a few small oil lamps fascinated him. He spent months on it and produced something so weird and mysterious that it made me feel queer to look at it. The figure of the one-eyed Claudius dominated the scene. The sword in his hand glistened ominously. I expected great things of this work of art and eagerly awaited the day when it should be hung in its place.

Rembrandt was to get only 1,000 florins for the whole picture (no more than Flinck would have received), but I was sure it would cause so much talk that he would be completely rehabilitated in the eyes of his neighbors and, what was even more important from a purely practical point of view, in the eyes of the art-dealers.

But the magistrates rejected it. They rejected it flatly and unceremoniously. Some said that Claudius Civilis looked too much like Hannibal. As the Carthaginian hero had also lost one eye in battle, they had some excuse for this complaint, but it really had very little to do with the value of the picture as a work of art.

Others said it was too dark. Still others complained that the light was all wrong, that no one ever had seen a lamp that threw such shadows. It was never hung in the big gallery. It was at once re-

CLAUDIUS CIVILIS, DETAIL (PAINTING)

moved to the garret to be stored away until some future date when Their Lordships should decide what else they could do with this monstrous canvas that was by far too large for any ordinary room and much too beautiful for ordinary people. To this day I do not know what became of it. I have heard that it was cut into four pieces and sold to a junk-dealer.

Just about a year ago I happened to have a patient who had been secretary to My Lord van Beuningen during his last voyage to Sweden. He told me that in Stockholm he had seen a picture that looked very much like a sketch that was hanging on my wall. The sketch in question was a small pen and ink study for the Claudius Civilis which years before I had fished out of Rembrandt's fireplace (fortunately it was summer), into which he had thrown it in a moment of despair. I asked the young man whether he was certain and he said yes. I asked him how large the picture was and he answered, "About half of the wall of your room."

Then I begged him to describe it to me a little more in detail and I recognized the central part of the Claudius Civilis picture.

But it may have been merely a copy. Or the young man was mistaken. For although I wrote to Stockholm and for years afterwards interviewed every one who returned from the Swedish capital, I never could discover another trace of this lost masterpiece.

The open space in the gallery left behind by the death of Flinck was filled in by some local talent whose name I have forgotten.

And Rembrandt was obliged to split his fee with this young man, as it did not seem fair to Their Lordships that a man should be paid for work he had not really done.

SKETCH (DRAWING)

Chapter 29

REMBRANDT RECEIVES A CALLER. HE PROVES TO BE
AN OFFICIAL FROM THE BANKRUPTCY COURT

THE GOLDSMITH (ETCHING)

IT IS curious how one loses track of time when one is at sea. Besides, my trips of inspection to our squadrons in the Baltic took place at such irregular periods that I have no very clear recollection of any of them. They have become one vast blur upon my memory—a blur composed of uncomfortable berths in uncomfortable cabins—of miserable hours of wetness and depression in some small boat that was being rowed to the flagship—of miserable hours of wetness and depression a short while later in the same little boat that was now being rowed back to shore—of quarrels with superannuated but obstinate ship's surgeons—of pleasant dinners with captains who had but one wish in life—to invite the Lords of all the Admiralties on board their ships and then make them stay on deck to take part in some major engagement, of long, placid sails along the flat coasts of northern Germany and Denmark and of sick and wounded people who hated to die and whom one could not possibly hope to save for lack of even the most primitive and elementary sanitary precautions.

Here and there in this blur there is a short breathing space caused by a week or perhaps a fortnight on shore. It was during one of these periods of respite that after a hard day's work preparing a report for the Pensionary I decided to take a walk, and a walk with me always led right around the corner to Rembrandt's house.

The house looked no different from other times, but as soon as I had entered, I knew that something was wrong. Two strange hats were lying on the table in the entrance and I heard the noise of unfamiliar voices coming from upstairs. I went into the living room, where I found Hendrickje busy putting little Cornelia to bed. She asked me to go into the little garden by the side of the house and wait for her. Shortly afterwards she joined me.

"We have had a terrible day," was the first thing she said. "I am very tired. If you don't mind, I will sit down with you for a moment." For though we all liked her sincerely and treated her in every way as if she were really Rembrandt's wife, she could not get over a certain shyness when she was in the company of those who belonged to what she still considered a higher class of society.

"What has happened?" I asked her.

"Oh, just the usual thing. People with bills. Grocers and bakers and the butcher. Then more people with bills. Paint dealers, money-lenders. I don't know them all by name but it was pretty awful."

Just then Rembrandt himself appeared in the doorway.

"I got rid of those two," he said. "I wonder how many more there will be to-day."

"Perhaps none," Hendrickje suggested.

"No, when they once begin to come, they go on the whole day. Can I have something to drink? Is there any gin left in the house? I shall have to work all night to make up for these interruptions."

Hendrickje got the gin. Rembrandt took two glasses.

"Such days are terrible," Rembrandt said. "I have just started two new pictures and those fools come and talk to me about money! Well, I have not got any. That is simple enough, isn't it?"

There was a knock on the door.

"Don't open," Rembrandt told Hendrickje, who had got up. "Don't let them in. They will go away soon enough."

"But then they will be back early to-morrow morning."

"In the meantime I shall have been able to do a whole night's work."

"What are you doing now?" I asked him.

"Mostly oil. I am doing one etching, a portrait of Jan Lutma, the goldsmith. His family ordered it. But for the rest, just pictures. Biblical subjects. There are not many portraits ordered these days. And those who order won't pay. Last year I did one for a Spaniard, a portrait of his daughter. He paid me seventy-five guilders in ad-

Rembrandt van Rijn

JAN LUTMA (ETCHING)

vance and then he said that he did not think the likeness was any good and wanted his money back. He is still after me with his lawyers. No, the war has killed the portrait business and besides, I am too old now to sit before my easel and be told what to do and how they want little Wimmie to hold a dead parrot and how little Susie must absolutely wear that dress of brown and pink. If there are any dead parrots to be put in the picture, I will put them where I like them myself. And so I paint Biblical pictures. When I do that my models can't talk back. If I want to put Joseph here and Potiphar there, they don't say, 'Ah, sir, but we would rather face the

311

JACOB BLESSES THE CHILDREN (PAINTING)

other way around.' They stay where I put them and when Jacob blesses the little children no one is going to tell me what color the counterpane of his bed should have. Meanwhile these people out there seem to have given up hope. At least, they have stopped knocking," and he poured himself another gin.

"A lovely day," I said, to say something.

But this merely angered him. "A lovely day? Good God! A lovely day indeed! Yes, the sun was shining, I believe, but if you had had had my sort of a day—"

"What has happened?"

"Oh, the old story."

"People who want money?"

"That is no longer a story. That is a legend. But it is about Titus."

"But the boy is perfectly well, isn't he?"

"Better than ever. But it is about his inheritance."

Rembrandt van Rijn

And then I understood what he was driving at. It was the question which I had found mentioned in the report Lodewijk had given me.

What I had dreaded for such a long time seemed at last to have happened. The uncles and aunts of young Titus had asked for an accounting and Rembrandt apparently had done nothing about it, had put their letters aside and had not even taken the trouble to answer them. Thereupon they had insisted upon a public inspection of his books (as if the poor man had ever heard of such a thing as book-keeping!) to see whether at least part of their nephew's non-existing fortune was still intact and present.

And now they had threatened him with court proceedings and had hinted that they would ask the Chamber of Orphans to attach the house in the Breestraat and sell its contents at public auction that Titus might receive his legal share of his mother's inheritance.

I wish that I had been in town when that had happened, for most likely he would have come to me and I would at least have been able to send him to a reliable advocate who could have advised him. But Rembrandt, confused and panic-stricken, had asked the first person who happened to come to his studio to give him the name of a lawyer —"any lawyer will do"—and that person happened to be an art-dealer of rather doubtful reputation who had called on him in the hope of selling him a spurious Michelangelo and he had answered, "Yes, so and so is an excellent man. Ranks as high as the best of them."

And he had sent Rembrandt to a shyster. This fellow probably knew that the situation was hopeless but, in order to keep his hands on at least part of his client's tangible assets, he suggested that Rembrandt have his house on the Breestraat transferred officially to Titus, as "part of the boy's maternal inheritance."

The meaning of this move should have been clear to any one not quite as inexperienced in such matters as Rembrandt. It was an attempt to placate the Uylenburgh relatives by swindling the other creditors. How this lawyer ever was able to persuade Rembrandt to accede to such a desperate plan I do not know, except that he probably did not pay the least attention to anything that was being said beyond a vague and pained "yes" or "no" and "Will this take long, or can I go back to work now?"

But of course in order to make this transfer "official" (and nothing less would be accepted by Titus' uncles and aunts), the deed of transfer had to be attested before the Chamber of Orphans, an institute that was known for its severity and its scrupulous honesty.

They, so it seemed, had asked no questions, well knowing that not a soul in the world would dare to appear before them and ask them blandly to register a house as "orphan's good" when said house was no longer in the possession of the donor but had belonged for years to a syndicate of creditors. But for the nonce, these worthy gentlemen were mistaken. Rembrandt, totally ignorant of business methods, had not even bothered to tell them that the house was heavily mortgaged. The transfer had been made and the next morning of course all the other creditors knew what had happened. To say that then the fat was in the fire was to express it mildly. The two hats I had seen in the hall belonged to two of the main creditors. They had insisted upon being received. They had called Rembrandt a swindler, and I could hardly blame them for being very angry. They had asked that the deed giving Titus his father's house as part of his mother's inheritance be revoked within twenty-four hours and they had threatened that unless he give them his written promise to this effect and give it to them then and there, they would serve papers in bankruptcy on him before the end of the day.

Rembrandt had listened to them vaguely and had then requested to be excused for a moment. He had wanted to ask Hendrickje what he should do. But the door of the studio had been open and it was still light. Just when he passed that open door he had noticed something he had for a long time wanted to change in the colored turban of Potiphar. He had picked up a brush to make this small correction. Then he had forgotten all about his visitors and he had continued to work until the loud slamming of the front door suddenly reminded him of the reason for which he had come upstairs.

At first he had felt rather ashamed of his rudeness, but in the evening when I saw him his annoyance had given place to merriment.

"Served them right," he said. "Served them right for disturbing me on a day like this. And now they will probably leave me alone."

But at that moment there was another knock at the front door, a knock that sounded official and refused to be denied.

"I will open," Hendrickje said.

"You had better," I added.

"Oh, very well," was all that Rembrandt remarked.

A moment later, Hendrickje returned. She was followed by a little man wearing a long brown cloak and looking for all the world like an undertaker's assistant.

"Have I the honor to address Mr. Rembrandt van Rijn?" the little man asked.

"Never mind the honor," Rembrandt answered roughly. "What do you want?"

"Nothing, except to give you this."

Rembrandt automatically picked up the large yellow envelope which the undertaker's assistant gave him.

"What is this?" he asked.

"An order in bankruptcy," the brown beadle answered.

"Oh," said Rembrandt. "So soon? Well, I suppose you can't help it."

"I most surely can't, sir!" the little man said. "It just happens to be my business."

"Then perhaps you will have a drink?"

"I would not mind at all."

Hendrickje got another glass. Rembrandt poured it full of gin, but took none himself.

"Your health," said the little man, as he poured the glass down his throat with one gulp and wiped his mouth with the back of his hand. Then he bowed low and wished us all a good evening. A moment later we heard him slam the door and all was quiet until the chimes of the South Church began to play the hour.

"What time is it?" Rembrandt asked. "It stays light so late these days."

"Ten o'clock," I answered, counting the strokes.

"Then I had better go back to my studio. I suppose I am in for a hard time. Well, I am young still. I painted myself into these difficulties. Now I will have to paint myself out of them again."

But he never did.

From that day on until the hour of his death, he remained an "undischarged bankrupt."

MOSES SHOWING THE TABLETS OF THE LAW (PAINTING)

Chapter 30

THE HOUSE ON THE JODENBREESTRAAT STANDS
STILL AND EMPTY

THE BLINDNESS OF TOBIT (ETCHING)

THE next day half a dozen of us, all good friends of Rembrandt, gathered at his house to see what we could do. We knew that all efforts to save this sinking ship would be useless. The question before us was how we could transfer the passengers of the doomed vessel to another one with as little delay as possible and without causing any more annoyance to any one than was absolutely unavoidable.

They could not remain in the house for they were not allowed to touch a thing and the officials of the Bankruptcy Court could now come in at any moment to make an inventory of all the furniture and the paintings. After that they would not even be allowed to sleep in their own beds. I offered Hendrickje and little Cornelia the hospitality of my own house. They could have my room and Titus could share the room of my son. The others agreed that this would be a good plan, as Cornelia was only two years old and still needed a lot of care, being by no means a very strong child.

That left Rembrandt on our hands. We had to find quarters for him, for if he were left to his own devices, God only knew what he would do. He must have seen this disaster coming upon him slowly for at least ten years. But he never apparently had realized how serious conditions were until that little undertaker-man in the brown cloak handed him the big yellow envelope. Ever since he had walked

317

aimlessly through the house—picking up one piece of his collection after another—holding it in both hands and looking at it for a long time as if he were saying good-by to it. We had to take care of him as if he were a small boy, whereas Titus, to whom no one among us had ever paid very much attention, now suddenly stepped forward as if he were a full-grown man, sent for the baker, the grocer, and the vegetable-man, explained the situation to them with as few words as possible, and made arrangements through which his father obtained at least a few days' further credit.

Then some one, I think it was Francen (the art-dealer, not his brother the surgeon), said: "There is quite a good place in the Kalverstraat, called the 'Keyserskroon.' It belongs to a fellow by the name of Schuurman and it is not too expensive. It is a large place. I think it used to be an orphan asylum. If all this has to be sold" (and he waved his hands around him), "the auction could be held right there, and meanwhile Rembrandt could live there."

I interrupted him. "Wouldn't it hurt him terribly to be present when all this is sold?"

But Francen was less sentimentally inclined than I.

"Undoubtedly it would," he answered, "but just now it is not so much a question of how to save his feelings as how to save his family. If he is present or if it is known that he is about, the dealers won't dare to offer as little as if they knew that he wasn't there. Don't you other gentlemen agree?"

The others agreed, and I too could see the reasonableness of Francen's point. And in order to prove that I was sincere in this, I offered to tell Rembrandt what plans we had made for him and his family.

I found him in his studio cleaning his palettes. "I don't suppose these belong to me any more," he said. "I don't suppose that, strictly speaking, I am even allowed to touch them. But I can hardly let them go to ruin. They have been very faithful servants so far."

I assured him that no one, not even the most strict-minded notary, could object to his keeping his tools in order, and then I told him what we had decided for him and his family. He listened, carefully scraping the paint off his large round palette, and merely nodded his head.

"When ought we to leave?" he asked.

Rembrandt van Rijn

"Oh, there is no immediate hurry. Sometime within a week or ten days."

"Then why not to-day? You know, it is rather hard on me to stay here any longer, now that all this is about to be taken away from me."

"Very well," I replied. "I will ask Hendrickje."

I found her in Cornelia's room packing. She was perfectly quiet and self-possessed.

"It really does not mean so much to me," she explained. "I have always been poor and to tell you the truth, all this luxury was just a little too much for me. But it will be terribly hard on him. His heart is in these things. I hope it won't kill him."

I told her that I did not think it would. He came of a strong race and could stand a blow better than most people. Then I went back to the meeting and reported what we had decided. The others thereupon went home, but Jeremias de Dekker, the poet, and I remained behind to see whether we could be of any further assistance. I sent Titus to the shop of a carpenter who lived on the Oude Schans, to ask him for the loan of one of his assistants and a cart and had the fellow take Hendrickje's belongings and Titus' small trunk and Cornelia's cradle to my home just around the corner. I told de Dekker to go with them to see them safely to their new place of residence. Then I went upstairs and helped Rembrandt put a few clothes and shoes and shirts and sheets and blankets in a small leather portmanteau.

When this had been done, he returned to the studio.

"I don't suppose I can take any of these things," he said.

I told him that I was afraid that could not be done.

He picked up a large surgeon's needle, which I had used for small operations until it had got too blunt, when I had given it to Rembrandt who was forever complaining that he could not get a piece of steel that was really fit for a good job at dry-point work. He held it out for me to see and asked: "You gave this to me, didn't you?"

"No," I replied. "I merely loaned it to you."

"Then it still belongs to you?"

"It most certainly does!"

"And you will let me borrow it a little longer?"

"With great pleasure."

319

For a few moments I saw him rummaging among the left-overs of old tubes and old brushes on a small table in the corner until he produced an old cork.

"I will just cheat the creditors out of the cork," he said, putting it on top of the steel needle, so as not to hurt the point, "and out of the copper plate. They won't notice the difference, and if they do, well, then, they can put me in jail for it. But I have got to have something to make me pull through the next few weeks." And he slipped the needle and the copper plate into his pocket.

I picked up his satchel and carried it downstairs. There was a knock at the door. I opened. Two men in black capes were standing on the stoop. I asked them their business.

"We are from the Bankruptcy Court and have come to make an inventory," they answered.

"Isn't that rather soon?" I asked them.

"Yes," they replied, "but some of the creditors are afraid that if we are not quick, part of these belongings might disappear."

To my intense horror, I noticed that Rembrandt was standing right behind me. It was impossible that he should not have heard that last remark. I saw him take the small copper plate out of his pocket and hold it out to the oldest of the two men.

"You were right," he said, "I was on the point of stealing this. You had better take it."

But the official shook his head.

"I know how you feel," he answered, with more consideration than I had expected. "I know exactly how you feel, sir. You are not the first man I have ever met under these unfortunate circumstances, and most likely you won't be the last. But cheer up and don't take it too much to heart. You are a famous man. A few years from now you will come back here riding in your own coach and four."

And he saluted the master most politely while he took a piece of paper and pencil out of his pocket and with a short "I am sure you will pardon me," began to jot down:

"The entrance hall—one picture by—who is it?—one picture by Adriaen Brouwer representing—"

But I had quietly taken Rembrandt's arm and had pushed him towards the door.

Rembrandt van Rijn

For a moment we stood silently on the stoop, and then turned towards the left, carrying the heavy satchel between us.

Rembrandt never entered his house again.

Two years later it was sold to a shoemaker who turned it into two small apartments. One of these he kept for himself and the other he rented to a butcher. For all I know, they are living there yet. But I am not certain, for I have not set foot in the Anthonie Breestraat for more than ten years. A street or a house in which one has been happy becomes something very sacred. And when that happiness has departed, there remains nothing but a melancholy memory. And one should not spend too much time among the dead. The living need us so much more.

THE BEHEADING OF JOHN THE BAPTIST (ETCHING)

321

ST. JEROME READING (ETCHING)

Chapter 31

REMBRANDT SHOWS SIGNS OF BEGINNING OLD AGE

CHRIST PRESENTED TO THE PEOPLE (ETCHING)

THE greater part of the year '57 I spent with the fleet in different parts of the North Sea and the Baltic. My son proved himself a somewhat erratic but conscientious and trustful correspondent.
His letters were not exactly samples of orthography and his style
resembled that of an architect writing out specifications for a bricklayer, but as a rule he managed to tell me that which he thought
would interest me and thus I was kept fairly well informed of what
was happening to my own family and to that of our friend.

Hendrickje was still living at the Houtgracht. In the beginning I had been afraid that there might be trouble between her and my own faithful Jantje. For servants as a rule do not take very kindly to those of their own class who are supposed to have done rather better in the world than they have themselves, and are very touchy about any "uppishness" on the part of the latter. But in the first place, Hendrickje was the simplest of all people and the disaster that had overtaken her had made most people willing to forget that she was Mrs. van Rijn only by act of common courtesy and not in virtue of a stamped and sealed document handed to her by the register of the matrimonial records.

Besides, Jantje was a good soul and deeply devoted to the small bundle of clothes and smiles called Cornelia, and the two women lived peacefully together beneath the same roof without ever causing the slightest amount of friction or jealousy. As for the two boys, they were so absolutely different that it was easy for them to remain on friendly terms. Titus stuck to his paint-box. And my own son stuck to his mills and his calculations and they met at meals and sometimes they took a walk together to the Diemermeer or to Ouderkerk (where Spinoza was still living with his friends, the Tulps, and where the boys were always certain of a free meal), but for the rest they left each other severely alone and caused very little trouble to their elders.

Rembrandt's position was a little more difficult. He had a good enough room in the Keyserskroon but he was lonely and he complained that he could not work. I offered to fix up my workroom for him as an atelier, but he complained that the light was wrong and that he could not use it and then he had once more met the little shyster lawyer who had been his adviser in the matter of the transfer of his house to Titus (that very questionable affair that had almost got him into jail), who apparently had told him with a great ado of words that he need not have been in such a hurry—that he had a perfect legal right to stay in his house until the day before the sale was actually going to take place and being nervous and dispirited, he had believed the fellow and had gone to see de Dekker and Francen to ask them why they had told him to do a thing he had never wanted to do, and he had been quite disagreeable about it.

To which they had answered him quite truthfully that they had

SELF-PORTRAIT (PAINTING)

SELF-PORTRAIT AT THE EASEL (PAINTING)

only taken him away so soon because they were afraid that further residence in the house would expose him to a great deal of unnecessary suffering and that furthermore, the sale of his goods might begin at almost any moment and then he would have been obliged to leave under even more harrowing circumstances.

But he refused to believe them—vaguely talked of a plot (what sort of a plot he did not explain) and locked himself in his room for days at a time—drinking a great deal more than was good for him and alternately spending entire days in his bed or working at his etchings with such uninterrupted violence that he was beginning to experience trouble with his eyesight. The latter piece of information did not in the least surprise me, for there is no greater strain on the eyes than scratching tiny lines onto a shining plate of copper by the flickering light of a candle.

Fortunately the next letter brought better news.

Rembrandt had left his hotel and would not return there until immediately before the sale of his furniture and his art treasures. He had at last accepted my offer to come and live in my study and was painting again. As soon as he had once more felt a brush in his hand, most of his worries had dropped away from him like the water that drops from the back of a duck. He no longer drank gin to forget his worries. He was extremely sober, as he had always been in the past, but he continued to complain that he was not feeling quite well and he was worried about the sale of his belongings. At least once a week he would send Titus or my son to the office of the Bankruptcy Court to ask when the sale would begin and invariably he got the answer: "Not yet. A few weeks more. The times are bad. We must wait until the war is a little further behind us and then we shall get better prices."

And he had to wait all this time in miserable uncertainty, for the only way in which he could hope to escape his bondage was by means of that sale. If it brought enough, he would be able to pay his creditors and would be discharged by the court. If it did not produce enough, he would continue to be a bankrupt and every portrait he painted and every etching he made would belong to his creditors.

Finally, in the fall of '57, the commissioner appointed Thomas Jacobszoon Haringh to start the sale as soon as convenient. Rembrandt once more moved to the Keyserskroon and waited. But the

THOMAS JACOBSZOON HARINGH (ETCHING)

first bids showed that the public had not yet recovered from the ravages of the recent conflict, and after a week Haringh went to the commissioners and suggested that the bulk of the articles be reserved until next year when there would be a chance of their selling at double and triple the amount they brought now.

The commissioners acceded to this request and the paintings and drawings and etchings which Rembrandt had collected with such great care and discrimination and at such tremendous outlay of money, went back to the store-house.

Meanwhile the creditors continued to hold unofficial meetings and devised innumerable little tricks that should put them on the preferred list. But of all this I know nothing except the few odds and ends of gossip that I picked up talking to my friends. As far as Rembrandt was concerned, that part of his life was over—was dead and buried—was forgotten as if it had never been. He knew what his collection was worth and felt certain that with the efficient handling of Haringh, who was a personal friend of his, it would produce much more than he owed. If the creditors therefore would stop bothering him, so that he could do his work in peace and make a few extra guilders for Hendrickje and the children, all the rest would come out all right, but they must wait—they must wait and not bother him, bother him morning, noon and night.

He finally grew so exasperated at the continued interruptions he was forced to suffer from the side of his tormentors, that he asked Jantje not to open the door unless she had first made certain that the person who called was a personal friend and did not belong to the dunning guild. And in that way, the spring of '58 went by and affairs in the North were hastening to their final conclusion and as for the moment I had done all I could possibly hope to do, I returned to Amsterdam and found my house occupied by a happy little family, Rembrandt painting and Hendrickje busy with Cornelia and doing as many of the chores as she was able to do (for she remained ailing most of the time), and my son working on a project for a sailing-carriage that should be quite unlike that of Stevin in that it also would be able to navigate against the wind, and Titus coloring pretty little pictures which unfortunately did not show a great deal of originality.

We let the boys sleep in the attic (a change which delighted them) and I took their room and the next day after dinner I had a long talk with Rembrandt and listened to his complaints. For that interminable year of enforced idleness and waiting had done him little good and when he first opened his heart to me, it seemed as if he were suffering from every disease ever known to Galen or Hippocrates. His head ached. A million little ants were crawling up and down his arms. His fingers tingled as if they had been frozen. When he sat still for ten minutes, his feet would fall asleep. He had pains in his back and in his chest and was sure he was going to die of the same disease that had taken Saskia to her grave. But what worried him most of all was the strange notion that there was something the matter with his bones, that they were, as he himself called it, "melting away" and that some day soon he would not have any bones at all—that he would collapse in the street and would be carried home dead.

Where and how and from whom he got the idea that such a disease existed, I do not know unless he had heard it from some itinerant quack in the market-place who might have tried to frighten his audience with the old stories about the "pulverized man" to sell them his "Elixir Ossificationis."

I soon realized that nothing was the matter with the poor patient except a too sedentary life—too much loneliness—the bad habit of eating indifferent food at irregular hours—and as a result, a tendency to meditate a little too consistently and too profoundly upon his own pains and woes. But I knew from practical experience that it would do me no good to tell him, "Cheer up, my friend, all this is imagination pure and simple. A few days of fresh air and sunshine and you will be well again." I hoped to be able to cure him but I could not begin to do this until the sale of his possessions had become an accomplished fact and he had been definitely discharged from all further obligations and in the second place until he had had some great new success—until some token of recognition on the part of the public at large had made him feel that after all he counted for something in the hearts of his neighbors and had not been forgotten by them as completely as he now thought.

In the meantime I could only mark time and pray that his profound melancholic moods would not drive him to suicide. I watched him very carefully. I accompanied him whenever he went out for a walk, or sent my son to go with him. In the beginning I also suggested that he join Jean-Louys when the latter went forth again upon one of his famous sailing expeditions but I soon had to give this up as Rembrandt detested life on board ship as much as he had always done and complained that he would rather sit in jail (but only on dry land) with the worst bore in the world than listen to the wittiest conversation of the most brilliant Frenchman alive, if he were obliged to go to sea to hear it.

Jean-Louys, on the other hand, declared that he had never quite understood why he had been born until that former galley-slave had initiated him into the secrets of navigation. And as for me, I divided my Sundays between walks to Watergraafsmeer and along the Amstel, and trips on the Zuyder Zee, and meanwhile I waited and Rembrandt waited and Hendrickje waited and we all waited until finally in the fall of the year '58, exactly two years after he had first been declared a bankrupt, the last chest and the last picture and the last etching press and the last half dozen chairs were auctioned off and were removed from the Keyserskroon by their new owners.

The famous collection of etchings of Dutch and French and Italian and German etchers, which he had been collecting with such great discrimination for at least twenty years (for he had bought the first ones when he was a mere boy), were offered to the public on the 24th of September of that same year. Then the book-keepers of the Bankruptcy Court got busy and a few weeks later we were able to compare figures.

According to Rembrandt himself (but he was a most unreliable guide in all matters pertaining to finance) he had spent between 30,000 and 35,000 guilders to buy all these treasures. According to the estimate of the officials of the Court (who as a rule are very conservative in such matters) the sale ought to have produced approximately 13,000 guilders, which would have been enough to satisfy at least the most clamorous of the creditors and give Rembrandt a chance to begin again without any further obligations. And according to the balance sheet that was produced after everything had been sacrificed, Rembrandt had realized a trifle less than 5,000 guilders, or about one-seventh of his original investment.

The house had fared a little better. Liven Symonse, the shoemaker who bought it, paid 11,000 guilders for it. And of these 11,000 guilders Titus' relatives (after a terrific legal battle) salvaged 7,000 guilders for their young nephew, who now had a regular guardian (a certain Jan Verwout, a very decent fellow, by profession and inclination a clerk) but who throughout all this remained pathetically loyal to the man who according to his mother's relatives was a mere spendthrift and good-for-nothing paint-slinger, but according to himself, the best and kindest father that any boy had ever had.

CHRIST TAKEN FROM THE CROSS (DRAWING)

Chapter 32

HENDRICKJE GOES INTO BUSINESS

BEGGAR SEATED ON A BANK (ETCHING)

THE situation, instead of having been improved by this painful sacrifice, had become considerably worse. The creditors were still hanging around outside my door and with the persistence of wolves they besieged my house day and night to see whether Rembrandt had perhaps painted another picture which they could then attach and claim as their own. I knew two of the members of the Bankruptcy Court and went to see them and I found that they understood and even sympathized with our position but it was absolutely impossible for them to suggest a way out.

Our nation, when it turned its back upon the ancient faith, had abolished the old saints, but their place had been taken by a new celestial spirit, and the name thereof was "Respect for Property." Little children no longer prayed to the holy men and women of a bygone age who had taught them "Thou shalt love" but reverently bowed their knee before the image of an austere and relentless God who spake, "Thou shalt possess."

Whether this change had been a change for the better or a change for the worse, I cannot here decide. I will merely say that it had taken place and that those who failed to take account of the existence of this deity were most severely punished.

Rembrandt, driven by his inner urge to create—a man mad with painting—who could see things that no human being before him had ever suspected, had, alas! been blind when he passed the temple of the new deity to which the faithful hastened at every hour of the day and at many hours of the night.

He had been punished.

He had been cast out. And he would never (of that, alas! I felt convinced with absolute certainty) be able to rehabilitate himself in the eyes of the respectable part of society.

The problem that had faced those of us who loved him in spite of his many failings (and perhaps a little on account of them) was this—how could we make the rest of his days tolerably happy? And then, when none of us seemed to know quite what to do, it was the faithful Hendrickje who showed us the way out of our dilemma.

She was not at all well. Adversity had struck her a terrible blow and she was failing fast. Rembrandt thought that he was a very sick man and on the point of dying and he was forever telling Hendrickje what she ought to do for Titus and for little Cornelia when he was gone, but I knew that he would survive her for a long time, while she, who never complained, had at the very most three or four more years to live.

I think that she realized this herself but she was a woman of incredible courage. There was not a task in the house she considered too much for her. She took care of little Cornelia. She cooked for Rembrandt and Titus, refusing to let my own Jantje do this for her. She repaired their clothes and knitted their stockings for them and she kept track of every cent that came into the house, though how she managed to hide these few poor pennies from the ever-present eyes of the hungry creditors is more than I can understand.

And then one evening she came forward with a plan. She asked whether she could speak to me alone for a moment and of course I said yes and as it was a pleasant night in June (we used to have two or three pleasant days every June, but the rest of the month it would usually pour) I took her out into the garden and there she told me what she wanted to do.

"That poor man," she said, "ought never to be trusted with another stiver. He is blind when it comes to money. His mind is on other things. He would give away his last shirt or exchange his only pair of breeches for a picture he saw if he should happen to want it at that particular moment. I never really was happy in that big house. It was too grand and too rich for me. I did not belong there. I was always afraid that I would break something, and in the end there was hardly room for one to sit down. Besides, I never knew what he would bring home next. It makes me feel uncomfortable to think how we are abusing your hospitality, but for the rest I have never been as happy as I am right now. Only I know that as soon as Rembrandt gets discharged by the Court, he will go right back to buying things. Not because he wants them—it is so hard to explain this. The things themselves mean nothing to him—it is not that. But they seem to fill a gap somewhere—they are bits of upholstery for his mind—and when it comes to his work, he is in some ways the strangest man I ever knew and in some ways the weakest.

"And so perhaps it is just as well that for a short while at least he should stay where he is at present. Only he must go back to his painting and etching or he will die. And what I have been thinking about is this: suppose that Titus and I started a little art store of our own and then hired Rembrandt to work for us—paid him just as a carpenter pays the assistants he hires or a bricklayer. One of my own brothers is a mason and hires two men to help him and one of those once had trouble with his wife, who tried to attach his wages, and then the judge said she could not do it and that is how I happened to think of it.

"Of course, Titus is still very young and I don't know anything about pictures, but you could help me or Francen or de Jonghe or some of his other friends, but I wish you would think of it and perhaps ask a lawyer and see whether we could not do something of that sort, and then we could once more have a place of our own, for we have put you to all this inconvenience quite long enough."

I took both her hands and assured her that she could stay until the end of her days and at the same time I was deeply touched not only by the kindness of her heart and her loyalty but also, I might as well confess it, by the clear common sense of her suggestion.

The next day being Sunday, I asked Rembrandt to take a walk with me to the Overtoom, where I had not been since that memorable day in the spring of '50 when I had seen the Prince of Orange there, trying to find out with his bamboo cane whether the water was rising.

We took some bread and cheese with us, for I knew that Rembrandt felt embarrassed every time I was obliged to go to some small extra expense on his account and he would not have liked it if we had gone to an inn.

We sat by the side of the canal and watched little white clouds that looked like sheep placidly grazing in an enormous blue pasture and I delivered myself of a short speech I had carefully prepared that morning. For I knew that Rembrandt had an almost physical aversion to any concrete discussion of his painful financial situation, but the thing simply had to be done if we were ever going to get him back on his feet. And upon this occasion too, as soon as he noticed what direction the conversation threatened to take, he took a small sketchbook out of his pocket and fished around for a piece of crayon. But I said, "Never mind, those sketches can wait until some other time. Suppose you listen for a moment now to what I have to say. I am not going to preach to you. I just want to see whether we can't find some way out which will allow you to go back to work."

At once he became suspicious.

"You mean to say that I have abused your hospitality long enough?" he asked, stiffening up.

"Rembrandt," I said, "you are a full-grown man with a son who will need a razor ere long. Now don't behave like a child. These years have been damnably hard on you and I don't blame you if your nerves are a bit frayed. As far as I am concerned, you can stay until you die, and you know it."

"Of course," he answered, "I am sorry, but I feel as if I were locked up. My head is full of ideas. They seem to come faster than ever. I need space. I need a room of my own in which I can putter around. You know that sometimes I find it difficult not to shriek when I have done a bit of work on a plate and want to try and find out what it looks like—just one proof would be sufficient—but all I can do is mess it up with a bit of black and then wait until two or three days later when some friend is perhaps kind enough to let me use his press for a few minutes. And I can't turn your house into a workshop. The smell of paint and the smell of acid would be all over the place. Your patients would stay away. They would think you were busy cooking some evil poison. I don't know how I can ever thank you for all you have done for us—"

"You can thank me," I interrupted him, "by listening for about ten minutes and keeping your mind on what I am going to say."

"Very well," he said, "I will be good." And he closed the sketch-book and put it back again into his pocket.

"Well, then," I said, "we know where you stand financially "

"I would hardly call that standing!"

"Never mind such details. And I am not going to talk economy to you. It would not do any good. If you were the sort of person who could keep his accounts straight, you probably would be a book-keeper at the West India House to-day instead of being—"

"Yes. Instead of being what?" he interrupted me.

"Instead of having painted a few pictures that the world will recognize—"

"That the world will recognize three hundred years after I am dead."

"Perhaps, and perhaps sooner. What your friends want to do is to get you back to a place of your own where you can work."

"But what would be the use of my working? As soon as I had finished a picture, Hertsbeeck or de Coster or Ornia or one of those noble patriots would appear with an order from the Court and would carry it away under his arm. The Court would credit me for a few guilders (they never pay me the full price) and twenty years from now I would still be in debt."

"That is just what we want to prevent, or rather Hendrickje, for she it was who thought of the idea. We will help you. But let us start from the beginning. I don't want to criticize you, but I don't think you were very happy in the choice of your lawyer."

"He seemed a nice fellow."

"Perhaps so, but that does not quite make him a good lawyer. How did you get him?"

"Oh, a man who stopped and looked at a picture I was drawing of the South Church and with whom I happened to get into conversation (he was born in Hazerswoude and had known one of my father's aunts—she was quite an old woman when she died)—he told me about him and gave me his address."

"An excellent recommendation! And when did this happen?"

"When I had that trouble with Geertje's brother."

Here was something that was news to me. I asked him what that trouble had been and when it had taken place.

"Well," Rembrandt said, "you remember that nurse I had when Saskia died?"

"I am afraid that I shall never be able to forget her."

"Yes, she was pretty bad. But I felt sorry for her. Then afterwards I had to send her to Gouda, to an asylum. And I promised to pay for her keep. Anything to be rid of her! I was very busy at that time. She had a brother Pieter and he took her down to Gouda. I gave him quite a sum of money. In those days my credit was good and I could raise as much as I wanted to. Well, two years ago, just before all this happened, I thought that I would try and get some of it back. The fellow refused to pay me. Perhaps I had no right to ask for it. I went to see that lawyer. He found out that the brother was in Amsterdam. He was a ship's carpenter and on the point of sailing to India. He was afraid that he would try and get away and we had him put in a debtors' prison. It was foolish of me. But I was in a terrible state just then. And I had come to hate that woman until I was glad to be nasty to her brother. Nasty is the word. I am not very proud of what I did. Then Francen got me a decent lawyer—Arnout Vingboom—you know him. He got the case straightened out."

"Then it is 'out' now—straight or crooked but 'out'?"

"Absolutely out."

"And there are no other troubles, no further lawsuits? No cases in court?"

"None. Except those in the Chamber of Horrors."

"Very well," I answered, and then I explained what Hendrickje had suggested. "It seems an excellent idea to me," I finished. "What do you think of it?"

He sat silent for a while and picked up a few pebbles that were lying in the grass and threw them into the water.

"Funny," he said at last. "And that is the woman whom they did not think fit to partake of Holy Communion."

"That is something else again," I suggested.

"Yes," Rembrandt said. "That is something else again. Of course I accept. Let us go home and tell her. And to-morrow I can begin working again."

Chapter 33

HENDRICKJE AND TITUS FORM A PARTNERSHIP
BUT ARE NOT VERY SUCCESSFUL

CHRIST AND HIS DISCIPLES IN A STORM (DRAWING)

BUT he did not begin to work that next morning nor the next, nor for several weeks afterwards. For that evening Francen came in and he had still another plan that seemed almost as good as Hendrickje's.

"I thought of this," he told us, "the moment I left you yesterday. But let us place ourselves in the position of Rembrandt's creditors. What do they want? They want their money. How they get it is all the same to them provided they get it and get it fairly soon. Of course Rembrandt can go back to painting portraits. That is really his business, but portraits are slow work and now that everybody is either bankrupt through this damned war that has just come to an end, or afraid to spend a stiver, through fear of the next one, the portrait business will hardly be profitable. I know that I myself have not sold a picture for almost two years. But I have sold a whole lot of etchings during that same period. Etchings are the thing for the present. Twenty years ago, it was tulips. To-day it is etchings. Not because most of the people who buy them like them particularly. They never even look at them. But they have heard of others who bought an etching for a few pennies and sold it the next day for hundreds of guilders and they hope that they will be equally lucky. There always has been a demand for Rembrandt's etchings. Even when people no longer liked his paintings (I don't mean to hurt his feelings, but he will know what is in my mind)—even when he painted pictures they could not quite follow—they could not quite understand—they paid good prices for his etchings. Now what I would like to know is this: what has become of the plates?"

"I don't know," Rembrandt answered. "They were sold. Mostly to local art-dealers."

"You could find out to which ones?"

"I think we could," Hendrickje said. "Titus kept a list of them."

"Well," Francen continued, "they won't be of much value to them. They can have others make prints off them, but that is never quite the same as when the artist does them himself. We ought to be able to get those plates back. We may have to pay something for them, but in the past these fellows have made a lot of money out of you, for whenever you wanted one of their antiques, they would ask you anything that came into their heads and you would pay it. Perhaps we can make an arrangement by which we promise to pay them a small royalty for every print. But we ought to get them. A few days ago I heard just by chance where we can get a good press for very little money. It belonged to some one who has given up etching and has taken a job as a servant."

"Not Piet de Hoogh?" Rembrandt asked.

"No, some one nobody ever heard of. He had bought himself a press when etchings became fashionable. Hoped to make a lot of money easily. Found it would take him at least ten years to learn to turn out something that could be sold to the public and was glad to be offered fifty guilders a year as butler with a family on the Heerengracht. Anyway, it means that we can lay our hands on a first-rate press for about sixty guilders. I will buy it and donate it as my con-

THE SHEPHERD AND HIS FAMILY (ETCHING)

THE BATHERS (ETCHING)

tribution to the new venture. To-morrow Rembrandt can go and look for a place to live that will have some sort of a room that can be fixed up as a studio. Hendrickje meanwhile can buy beds and sheets and a few pots and pans and Titus and I will make the rounds of the art-shops and see what we can do about the old plates."

"And I?" I asked. "What shall I do?"

"For the moment," Francen said, "you shall take it easy. You have done quite enough as it is. Unless you want to ask Vingboom when he can give us a little of his time, and then I will take those three innocent babes to see him and have a regular contract drawn up. This is beginning to sound like one of those plays of Joost Vondel in which Virtue appears at the end of each act to offer us her bright consolation. And now, if the doctor will send out for a mug of beer, we will drink to the health of the new firm, 'van Rijn, van Rijn and Stoffels.'"

I thought the occasion was worthy of something better than mere beer and went into the cellar myself to get one of my few remaining bottles of papish wine. And going down the narrow staircase I bumped my head, as I had done these last twenty years, and I swore and stopped to rub the sore spot, and standing there in the dark and thinking of what I had just seen and heard, it struck me that the situation would have been more fit for the pen of gruesome Aeschylus than that of our own amiable Vondel.

The greatest painter of his time being kept out of the poor-house by the combined efforts of a sick girl who had nothing in this world beyond her beauty and her kind heart and a boy of sixteen or seventeen, who loved his father and who would probably die as soon as Nature, in the pursuit of her own mysterious purposes, had driven him into the arms of a woman.

Then I got the bottle I had promised to bring up and we spent a happy hour, talking of the future.

It was the first time I had seen either Hendrickje or Rembrandt smile for more than two years.

Chapter 34

THE VAN RIJN FAMILY FINDS A NEW HOUSE

ABRAHAM FRANCEN (ETCHING)

THE first thing for us to do was to get the permission of Titus' guardian, for his affairs were by now so hopelessly interwoven with those of his father that the latter could not take a step without being taken to task both by the members of the Court of Bankruptcy and those of the Chamber of Orphans.

Verwout had soon discovered that he was too busy to devote the necessary time to the case and he had been succeeded by a certain Louis Crayers, whom I had never met before but who sent me a brief but courteous note saying that he would be glad to see me and my friends the next Friday at eleven in the morning. Abraham Francen and I, however, had agreed that nothing is ever accomplished in this world by committees and we decided to do everything by ourselves. Then when the arrangements had been completed, we could tell the others what had been done and ask them to give the new household such help as they thought fit.

At the appointed hour we were ushered into Crayers' office. We found him very busy so that he could not spare us a great deal of his time, but he was an easy man with whom to transact business, for he went right to the point and treated the whole affair as if it were merely a problem in mathematics, which indeed it was.

"Gentlemen," he said, "I hope that you will understand my position. I have given my word—and an oath before that court means an oath, let me assure you!—that I would protect this boy's interests to the best of my ability. Besides, I like the young man. I am sorry he is not a little stronger physically, but his mother was very delicate, so they tell me, and he seems to take after her more than after his father. All the same, I have rarely seen such a pleasant and affectionate relationship as exists between van Rijn Sr. and his son. As for the father, I never knew him very well but in my spare time I sometimes buy a few etchings. No, I am not just keeping up with the fashion. I was collecting etchings when most of the people who are buying them nowadays were making ten stivers a day digging ditches out there in the new part of the town. I am too busy a man to give much of my time to the arts, but I recognize the genius of the older van Rijn. A little too muddy for my taste in some of his pictures, but when he is at his best, I don't know any one who is better. But when it comes to business, may God have mercy upon me for the language I used when I first studied the documents in this case!

"I don't want to sound harsh, but in this instance it would have been infinitely better for the boy—of course, I am speaking strictly from a business point of view for I know how devoted he is to his father—but looking at the matter in a less romantic way, it would have been infinitely more advantageous for him if his father had died instead of his mother. But that is neither here nor there. The mother is gone and we have to deal with the husband.

"You want to know what I think about your plans. Well, I am heartily in favor of them, provided the rights of my pupil are absolutely protected. That last point I can't insist upon strongly enough, for I don't think that old van Rijn will ever mend his ways, financially

Rembrandt van Rijn

speaking—he is too old and even if he were twenty years younger, he would be just as bad. I just wish you had seen the mess I had to straighten out! It was absolute chaos.

"When the appraisers of the Bankruptcy Court went through that house, they collected three pailfuls of bills—old bills—new bills—paid bills—unpaid bills—protested bills. The house looked neat enough, so they told me, but in all the cupboards, behind the pictures and the mirrors, they found bills.

"But not only bills. What was infinitely worse, they discovered almost as many notes and drafts and checks, all made out to Rembrandt and which he had never taken the trouble to present and turn into cash. They even found a dozen envelopes and a few small bags containing money which he had put somewhere and then had forgotten all about—just plain carelessness. Of course I tried to collect some of this paper, but in many instances the people were dead, had been dead for years or had moved away and could not be traced. The amount we lost that way must have run into several thousand guilders.

"Under ordinary circumstances, I would call this 'negligence' and with any other man I would have thought of bringing the matter to the attention of the Court. But van Rijn is not an ordinary man. He lives in an imaginary world of his own and has no sense of the realities of life. For example, I asked him whether he still had any relatives from whom he might expect to inherit something. He said yes, there was a grandson of his aunt, a certain Piet van Medemblick, from whom he would probably get several thousand guilders when he died, for so at least he had been told by one of his brothers the last time he saw him.

"I looked into the matter and found that he had spoken the truth. He was to inherit some money from this distant—well, let us call it cousin. But I also discovered that this mysterious cousin, his father's sister's son's son, as he was called in the official documents, had taken service on board a ship that had sailed for the Indies at some unknown date early in this century and that the ship on which he traveled was reported to have sunk off the coast of Portugal three weeks after it had left Texel; that during the last 45 years, not a word had been heard from this Piet van Medemblick, but that according to the law as interpreted by the municipal courts of Leyden, the man could not be officially declared 'dead' until at least half a century after he had first disappeared; that therefore the heirs would get nothing until the year 1665 and that even then, with all the accumulated interest, van Rijn's share would probably not exceed 800 guilders. A rather vague prospect, as you will see for yourself, and yet he was firmly counting on 'the inheritance of my aunt's grandson' as if it were something tangible—a chest of pearls—sent to him by the Emperor of China.

"I shall support you, gentlemen, in all you do for your friend (whom I bear nothing but good will out of respect for his great ability) and at the same time I shall use every means at my disposal to protect the interests of young Titus. Therefore whatever you do, I shall insist upon a contract, but for the rest, you will find that I am entirely on your side."

We thanked Crayers for his patience and courtesy and asked whether he had any suggestions to make about the contract.

"No," he answered, "it had better be a regular partnership contract. I have a friend, Notary Listingh, who does that sort of work for me and who is a very reliable man. Of course if you have some one you would rather suggest—"

But we assured him that we had no preference and agreed that the first thing to do now was to find a place where our friends could live—some sort of place that could be used as a shop and where Rembrandt could work. As soon as that had been done, we would return to Crayers and ask him to make out the necessary papers. Then we made our adieux and began house-hunting.

But this proved to be no easy task. During the war, very little building had been done and as a result people were paying enormous prices for very inferior accommodations. They were living in old barns and in converted stables and in deserted cellars and attics and on the outskirts of the cities. A good many families were obliged to content themselves with such shelter as under normal conditions would not have been thought fit for pigs. At last we found something, but entirely through luck, the sort of luck that was (as is so often the case) somebody else's misfortune.

One day a young man came to me who told me that I had been recommended to him by a friend. He had got some dirt into a little open wound on his right hand and it had caused an infection and would I please oblige and open it for him, without hurting him too much and his name was Lingelbach—Joannes Lingelbach, and his father was a German from Frankfort-on-the-Main and he himself was a painter and he had worked in Italy and hoped to go to Paris, where he heard there was a much better chance for painters than in Holland, and ouch! that hurt—but not as much as he had expected—and so on from the moment he came into the house until the time he left with his hand neatly bandaged and his arm in a sling.

Three days later he came back to let me change the bandage and by this time I had house-hunting on the brain and before he left me I asked Lingelbach whether he knew of any houses for rent anywhere and he answered, "Why, yes, of course I do. My father is the owner of the Labyrinth on the Roozengracht—at the end of the Roozengracht. You may know him? Old David Lingelbach? He used to manage the Orange Tree on the Looiersgracht twenty years ago, the first man to build a labyrinth in Amsterdam. Well, he had to break away several houses to make room for his present place but right opposite us there are three houses left, and one of them is free, at least half of it. I happened to see it yesterday."

"Is the rent very high?" I asked.

"I am going to have supper with the old man to-night," he answered, "and I will drop in and ask and let you know to-morrow."

The next day he brought me the information I wanted.

"It is only the left half of the house that is for rent," he said. "It has one large room and I had almost taken it myself—it has a fine big window on the north and would have made a wonderful studio. The other four rooms are much smaller and there is a kitchen and the rent is 150 guilders a year, but you may be able to get it for a little less. The landlord is called van Leest. He lives on the premises. I talked to him. He seemed a very decent sort of person—not the usual type. You had better go and see him, for there are mighty few houses to be had in this town nowadays."

I took Rembrandt out to the Roozengracht late in the afternoon of that same day. Hendrickje said that she did not feel up to the walk and she remained at home, but on the corner of the Saint Anthonie Lock we met Titus and my son, who were coming home together, and they went with us.

We saw the house and we saw van Leest and we signed a lease then and there at a rental of 125 guilders a year.

Rembrandt van Rijn

A week later the van Rijn family moved into their new quarters.

All of the old friends had contributed something to their household. Francen gave them four beds, Dusart contributed the sheets and pillows, van den Eeckhout and Roghman looked after the kitchen utensils, Suythof took care of the tables and chairs and I presented him with the large brass chandelier that used to hang in my own room which he had used as his studio for almost two years, and to which he had become very much attached. We rented a cart and filled it with the pictures he was working on and as many of his copper plates as we had been able to get hold of and then we put Hendrickje on top of it, together with Cornelia (who by this time had grown big enough to be immensely pleased and greatly amused by this unexpected trip across town), and we drove them to their new home.

When we arrived, we found everything in terrible disorder, beds, tables, wash-basins and chairs all standing pell-mell in the front room and sheets and pillows and pots and pans filling the sleeping quarters in a most picturesque and disharmonious fashion. We had expected to meet Rembrandt on the door-step, ready to welcome us, but we could not find him anywhere.

Then Hendrickje, inspecting her new domain, opened the door to the large room in the back of the house. Rembrandt was sitting in the center, right on the floor, in the most uncomfortable position imaginable, painting away for dear life at a large canvas that stood leaning against a barrel containing the family china.

"Oh," he said, without looking up, "are you there? I hope you will pardon me, but the light was so good—I thought I had better begin."

"Yes, dear," said Hendrickje, "that is quite all right." And she came back to us and quietly started unpacking the small satchel containing Cornelia's clothes and toys.

Chapter 35

I GET REMBRANDT AN ORDER FOR A FINAL
PICTURE

SKETCH FOR THE BOARD OF THE CLOTH-MAKERS' GUILD AT AMSTERDAM
(DRAWING)

WHEN I returned to Amsterdam, I heard that Hendrickje had
been quite sick, that Titus was working hard, trying to convert the little front room into an art store, and that Rembrandt himself was busy with the sketches for that allegorical picture in the
Town Hall which was to find no favor in the eyes of Their Lordships and that was to find a final resting place in the rubbish corner
of the aldermanic attic.

347

But of course at that moment we could not know all this and the mere fact that he was busy once more made him so happy that even Hendrickje was caught in an occasional smile and Titus had started to dream once more of becoming a famous painter instead of spending his days as a peddler of pictures and bric-à-brac.

They were delighted to see me, wanted to know all about young Spinoza and whom I had met in Rijnsburg and what the Leyden professors had said (they had said nothing, so far), and they kept me for dinner and told me that the house was a great success but of course, the creditors still continued coming around, trying to find something that might possibly be considered to belong to Rembrandt himself ("The clothes on my back are all I have left," he interrupted us), but the Roozengracht was far removed from the center of the town and only those who really cared for them would take the trouble to walk that long distance, and by the way, my friend the Frenchman had come to visit them several times but he had looked very ill and had come in a coach, accompanied by his sailor, who had to support him when he climbed the stoop, but he had made them promise that they would not write to me and tell me that he was sick, and Francen had been in and he had just returned from Haarlem where he had seen Hals, old Frans Hals, I surely knew whom they meant, and Hals had laughed right merrily when Francen had told him that he was a good friend of Rembrandt's.

"Give him my regards," Frans had said, "and tell him that now I can call him brother. And also tell him that he was a lucky devil. For when he went bankrupt, some of the grandest people in town were proud to be among his creditors while I was sold out at the behest of a baker, a common, ordinary, everyday baker, whom I had tried to please by painting a picture of him while blowing his horn to tell the people that the fresh bread was ready. And when I went broke, all the sheriffs could find in my house were three mattresses, a table and a chest of drawers, and he, so I hear, had a house as full of things as the palace of the late King Solomon."

And Francen had brought other news. Hals was painting again, painting again although he had not done a stroke of work for almost twenty years (he could not sell anything anyway, so what was the use?), and he wanted Rembrandt to come and see him, for he had made a wonderful discovery, but he was eighty years old and would not be able to make use of it himself. "But tell Rembrandt," he had said, "that being poor is the best thing that can possibly happen to any painter. For if you are poor, you can't afford to buy all those expensive colors you use when you are young, when your father pays the bills; and then you have got to get results with only two or three pots of paint and it is then that you learn to suggest tints rather than put them down in the original red and yellow and green and blue—just suggest things—indicate them—and if you can do that and can do it really well, people will sometimes see what you mean just as well as they used to do before—when you could still afford to paint in all the colors of the rainbow." And so on and so forth, for the old man was getting to be a little vague and repeated and contradicted himself continually, but then, he had been in the poor-house for so long, no wonder he was no longer as bright as in the olden days.

And oh, yes, they had almost forgotten to tell me, but Crayers had sent word that the case of Titus against that man van Hertsbeeck, who had got part of the bankruptcy money that really belonged to Titus ("Good God!" I said to myself. "Still another case? Is there no end to these lawsuits?"), would probably come up for a decision before the end of the year and that he was sure van Hertsbeeck would have to pay Titus several thousand guilders and that would be wonderful, for they still had to manage very skimpily . . . and so the evening went by and when at last I went home (it was ten o'clock and I was almost thrown into the canal by some playful roisterers who had been evicted from old Lingelbach's labyrinth as it was long past closing time)—when finally I went home, I was happier than I had been for a long time. For just ere I left, Hendrickje, her cheeks flushed by fever and her eyes wide with excitement, had drawn me aside into a corner of the room and had whispered: "He works all day long, and everything is all right."

Indeed, for the moment at least, the Fates that had so doggedly followed this poor man's footsteps seemed to have wandered off in search of some fresh victim, for not only did the creditors gradually begin to leave him alone, but I was at last able to get him a commission that was exactly the sort of thing he liked to do best.

Except for my son, I had only one relative in the town of Amsterdam. How we happened to be cousins, I did not know. My grandmother had explained it to me any number of times, but I was not greatly interested in the man and invariably I failed to listen just at the moment when she said, "And so you see, his mother's sister's grandfather was the uncle of your father's uncle's nephew," or something of the sort. But we observed a certain outward cordiality towards each other, which rarely exceeded the bounds of mere politeness, and we made it a point to call upon each other every New Year's morning, when we would say, "Good day, Cousin, and I hope you have a very happy and prosperous New Year." But that was all, for we had nothing in common except the accidental tie of blood and a dead great-great-grandfather.

This particular van Loon was a few years younger than myself and a cloth manufacturer in a small way. But as he was not married and had more spare time than most of his colleagues, he had been several times elected to the board of managers of the cloth-workers' guild and this year again he was one of the Syndics, as he happened to tell me when I met him by accident on the corner of the Rokin where he had his store (he was also in the retail business) and where he lived with an old servant and three very fat and very lazy cats.

I congratulated him on his new dignity and asked him, more as a matter of having something to say than through curiosity, whether he and his colleagues had made any plans yet to have their picture made. He said no, they hadn't thought about it yet. And then, through a sudden impulse, I found myself putting both my hands on his shoulders and I heard myself blurting out: "I have got just the man for you. He is a splendid painter and he won't charge you such a terrible sum either. When will you pose for him?"

But the dried-up draper looked hastily around to see whether any one could possibly have observed my unseemly behavior (he was most correct, and respectable in all his personal dealings) and then asked me curtly, "Who may that be, Cousin?" and I answered, "A man by the name of Rembrandt, Cousin," and he again, "I have never in my life heard of him, Cousin," and I, "That does not matter, Cousin. I will take you around to see him and then you can judge for yourself, Cousin. Good night now, Cousin, and I will call for you to-morrow at ten in the morning."

God only knows how I was able to persuade this dry-as-dust woolcarder and his equally uninspired confrères that Rembrandt was the man for them, but it is a fact that I finally persuaded them to sign a contract for a picture and at a very fair price.

I was curious to see how Rembrandt would go to work about this picture. It was a long time since he had painted anything of the sort and in the meantime, as he himself put it to me more than once, he had been pulled through the mangle so repeatedly that nothing remained of his former self except his skin and his bones and his honest homely face. Twenty years before, it had been all the same to him what size canvas he needed—what sort of color he used, nor had he given a fig for the opinion of those who in the end would be asked to pay for the picture.

This time he had to take the smallness of his studio into consideration, he must be careful not to waste any of the bright lakes and the expensive ochers which Titus had bought for him on credit and as he needed money and needed it badly, he must be very considerate of the feelings of his customers and give every one of them an equal chance.

I am not the best possible judge of paintings, but it struck me that Rembrandt had never come quite so near his ideal as this time. I was reminded of the somewhat incoherent message which Francen had brought back from Haarlem and which Hendrickje had related to me on the evening I returned from Leyden, that strange artistic last will and testament which exhorted the younger man to try and "suggest color" and "to hint at things rather than expose them in concrete form and color."

Everything in this picture was a matter of suggestion and yet one actually felt the presence of those honest, commonplace drapers as if one had been present at one of their meetings—one sensed that they were secretly very proud of the high office which their fellow members had bestowed upon them and at the same moment one knew that in their heart of hearts they were convinced that this much envied dignity had come to them entirely in recognition of their outstanding probity and the unimpeachable integrity of their business morals.

It was the strongest picture I had ever seen, and of one thing I am sure, no one had ever achieved such a brilliant effect with the help of such incredibly sober means.

I was delighted, and the day after the picture had been finished, I hastened to the house on the Rokin where the sign of the Pelican

Rembrandt van Rijn

hung out to tell all people that this was the Drapery Shop of Gerard van Loon and Sons (the old man was all that remained of those "sons") and I found the honorable Syndic eating his midday meal consisting of a bowl of lentil soup and he looked at me with considerable surprise, for he was not accustomed to familiarities of this sort, and I said:

"Good morning, Cousin, have you seen your picture?"

And he answered, "Yes, Cousin, and none of us are particularly impressed by it, but we will pay the man all the same."

And I turned on my heel and he called after me, "Don't you want to stay, Cousin, and share my meal with me?"

And I answered, "No, thank you, Cousin, some other time I shall be delighted."

And I went home to talk with my son about a new sort of saw-mill which he wanted to construct—a saw-mill that should be able to take care of three trees at the same time. He had gone to see one of our neighbors, the only wood-dealer left on the Houtgracht, and the man had been delighted with the plan and had told him to go ahead and construct a working model and very likely (if it could be arranged with the carpenters' guild) he would let him build one for him in Zaandijk.

The boy (he was taller than I but my affection for him was so great that I could never think of him except in terms of a child—a sentiment which sometimes caused considerable difficulty between us)—the boy, who in his own way loved me very deeply, noticed at once that something was wrong.

"What has happened, Father?" he asked. "Uncle Rembrandt in trouble again?"

"No," I protested, but he knew that I lied.

"Too bad." He spoke quietly to himself. "Too bad. Uncle Rembrandt is a fine fellow and I like him tremendously, but he just has no sense. Who wants to go on painting pictures when the world needs mills?"

I suppose there was an answer to that question, but (for that moment, at least) I must confess I could not think of it.

Chapter 36

POOR HENDRICKJE GOES TO HER FINAL REST

THE GOLDWEIGHER'S FIELD (ETCHING)

I NOW come to the years between 1661 and 1668, when a great many things happened, but few, I am sorry to say, that contributed in any way to the happiness of either myself or my friends.

In the first place, there was the sickness of Hendrickje. She had never quite been well since about a year after Cornelia's birth, when she had caught a cold and, refusing to stay in bed long enough, had developed pulmonary trouble which soon made me fear that she too was a candidate for an attack of phthisis. It seemed unbelievable and too cruel for words. Saskia had died of this dreadful disease and now Hendrickje was going the same way.

Rembrandt, who was singularly blind to symptoms of this sort, noticed nothing. He sometimes commented upon his wife's lack of appetite and her general listlessness, mildly complained when she refused to accompany him upon one of his walks through the deserted fields that surrounded his home on all sides, but as a rule he closed the sentence with a cursory "Oh, well, she will be all right again soon enough. When spring comes, we will take her home for a change of air. That will put her back on her feet."

But when spring came she was much worse, and when summer came she was not any better, and one day in the fall she asked me to

353

send for the same notary that had helped her and Titus draw up the agreement about their little art store, but to be careful that he did not call when Rembrandt was at home, because she did not want him to know how badly she felt. She could still walk about a bit and she hoped to deceive him about her condition until the very last.

I knew that on the seventh of August Rembrandt was going to take Titus to see his friend Joris de Caullery, who was living in The Hague at that time—who had been ailing for several months, but who had now sufficiently recovered to pay a short visit to Amsterdam to attend to some private business affairs. On the seventh of that month, accordingly, I walked with Notary Listingh to the house on the Roozengracht and Hendrickje made her last will.

She had little enough to leave, poor dear, but all she possessed she bequeathed to her daughter Cornelia, or in case of her death, to her stepson Titus. Furthermore, she stipulated that Rembrandt should be the only guardian of her child and insisted upon including a paragraph which stated that if Titus should inherit her property, the revenue of her investments (such as they were) should be paid out to Rembrandt, who was to enjoy them until the day of his death. As she could not write, she merely made a cross at the end of the document. I was asked to sign too, but just then Christiaen Dusart happened to drop in with a small picture he had finished the week before and which he wanted to show to Rembrandt. The notary thought it better that Dusart should be one of the witnesses than I, because Rembrandt or Titus might otherwise think that I had been in some way responsible for the strange stipulations of this extraordinary testament which might well be shown to further generations as a lesson in loyalty and unselfish devotion. One of the occupants of the other half of the house in which the van Rijns lived was the second witness, and got a guilder for his trouble.

When everything had been done according to the law, Hendrickje was so exhausted that she had to go and lie down.

For a few weeks it seemed that she was growing a little stronger, but in October she happened to see from her window how a drunken vagabond tried to stab a woman who had resented his improper advances with his clasp-knife. The excitement proved to be very bad for her. She went to bed and never got up again.

She lived almost a year longer. She never complained, and until the end she kept as busy as she could. Her love for Rembrandt and for her two children (Titus regarded her entirely as his own mother and she apparently knew no difference between her own child and Saskia's) never waned but on the contrary grew stronger as she felt herself more and more slipping away from this world. And she was so strong in her determination that no one should suffer on her account that until the last moment neither Rembrandt nor Titus appreciated the seriousness of her condition.

One morning Rembrandt found her unconscious on the floor. Apparently she had tried to get up to open a window to get some fresh air. She had often had attacks of choking and then fresh air had been the only thing that would bring her any relief. Titus was sent off as fast as his legs could carry him to fetch me. When I reached the house on the Roozengracht, Hendrickje was dead.

That afternoon we discussed the forthcoming funeral. Rembrandt wanted to bury her in the Old Church together with Saskia. But since the death of his first wife, he had moved to the other part of the city and the law provided that all dead people must be buried "in the church nearest to their most recent place of abode." In case the surviving members of a family wished to make other plans, they were obliged to pay the undertaker an extra sum for "every church the procession should pass on their way to the holy edifice they had selected for the interment."

Such a procedure was out of the question; it was too costly.

Early the next morning (it was the 27th of October, 1662) Rembrandt sold the grave containing the remains of Saskia to a certain Pieter van Geenen, who paid him cash. With that money he was able the next day to buy a grave in the South Church. And there Hendrickje was buried.

God must have been delighted to welcome her to his Heaven. But she must have been terribly lonely without her man and her children, for truly, beyond those, she had had no existence.

Rembrandt van Rijn

ABRAHAM'S SACRIFICE (ETCHING)

SELF-PORTRAIT (PAINTING)

LAST SELF-PORTRAIT (PAINTING)

Chapter 37

A FORGOTTEN MAN IN A LONELY HOUSE GOES ON PAINTING PICTURES

CURLY-HEADED MAN WITH A
WRY MOUTH (ETCHING)

STRANGE though it may seem at first, Hendrickje's death did not seem to have made a very deep impression upon Rembrandt. This, however, was not due to any callousness of heart on his part, as I heard some people say—people, by the way, who had never met him and only knew from hearsay. But there seems to be a saturation point for mental suffering as well as for physical pain, and during the last ten years Rembrandt had been dealt such terrible and incessant blows by fate that there was nothing now that seemed able to make any impression upon him whatsoever.

After the very indifferent reception of the Syndics he knew that as far as his artistic career was concerned, there was to be no "come-back" for him. He was, in the common parlance of that day, "out of the running" and a "back number."

I tried to console him once by telling him of something I had found in one of the old Greek writers, how the Athenians were running a race in the Stadium and how the public, seeing a man a few feet behind the very last of all the others, began to chide him for his slowness until they discovered that the unfortunate victim of their displeasure was so far ahead of all the others that he merely seemed to be running in the rear, while as a matter of fact, he had already won the prize. But this neither amused nor interested him. He merely grunted a casual "Yes" and went back to his easel.

For he worked very hard those days—entirely too hard to please me when I looked at him with a professional eye. He rarely left the

357

house either during the day or during the night. He was glad to see his few remaining friends and was polite to them and occasionally he even tried to be cordial. But all the time his mind was elsewhere and when addressed, it took him some time before he realized that he had been spoken to and that one expected an answer. Then he would smile a feeble smile and would stammer "Yes" or "I hardly think so," and would at once sink back into those meditations with which he endeavored to drug his soul.

The English (who, whatever their faults, are possessed of a much richer literature than we ourselves) have a proverb which says that kites rise against and not with the wind. That may be true but if the wind turns into a hurricane and blows too strong, the string that holds the kite is apt to break and the unfortunate kite comes tumbling down and is smashed to pieces on the ground.

Rembrandt came of a strong breed of men. His father and grandfather and great-grandfather (not to speak of his maternal ancestors) had fought their way through the great rebellion and had lived to tell the tale. They had been the sort of people that would never bend, but even the hardest iron will break if it is exposed to too severe a blow. Sometimes when I saw Rembrandt late at night, his short squat figure (much too stout around the hips on account of his lack of exercise) scratching away at some copper plate by the light of a single candle (the whole family sat and worked or read by the light of one single candle—they could not afford more), I wondered how long it would be before the crash came.

I tried to convince him that he must take at least one short walk every day but he said, "No, I am too busy."

I tried to persuade him that he ought to go out oftener and visit his friends—that it would be good for his painting and his etching if he refreshed his mind once in a while by an evening of laughter and jest, but he merely shook his head and replied: "No, it can't be done. I am too busy."

Then I made a point of walking across the town whenever the sun was shining and the weather was fine and knocking at the door and saying, "Titus, go tell your father that I am here to take him for a stroll." And in less than a minute Titus would be back with the message: "Father is sorry but he is too busy right now. He wants to

MORDECAI BEFORE ESTHER AND AHASUERUS (PAINTING)

know whether you won't come in and sit in the studio while he finishes something he is doing."

And I would find him busy with his sketches for still another picture of Haman's downfall and disgrace, a subject which seemed to occupy his mind a great deal in those days and of which I have seen him start and finish at least three full-sized pictures.

He rarely spoke of his work in those days but everything he did was in a minor key. Gone were the days of the laughing cavalier and of Saskias and Hendrickjes, dressed up like the ladies-in-waiting of those merry foreign queens.

In his bare little house there was nothing left that could serve as a fitting background for such scenes of gayety. And as he had never read much, and considered the pursuit of mere literature a rather scandalous waste of time, his choice of subjects was necessarily limited and he had to fall back upon the memories of his childhood days and those were of course restricted to the Biblical incidents of which his mother had told him when he was a small boy.

But the Christ he painted was not the handsome young prophet of his Italian rivals, preaching the good tidings among the sun-baked boulders of some Palestine hill. No, it was invariably the man of sorrows—Christ being scourged—Christ bidding farewell to his followers—Christ standing in deep thought before the walls of the Temple! And the other problems that filled his mind until he had to rid himself of this obsession by recounting them in the form of pictures—all of those had to do with that feeling of doom, that sense of futility, and that defiant air of hopeless rebellion which had descended upon him the moment he had walked for the last time out of his house in the Anthonie Breestraat.

Often I have sat in his studio and have watched him for hours while he was busy with his painting. And every time again I have been reminded of a picture he had painted years before when he was still quite young, of Samson threatening his father-in-law who had cheated him—the strong man who, for reasons which he has not been able to fathom (of which, as a matter of fact, he is totally unconscious), has been struck what he considers an unfair blow, and who defies Fate—who thumbs his nose at Providence—shakes his fist at the Deity himself, and with boy-like bravado shouts: "All right! I will show you! I will show you!"

CHRIST AT THE COLUMN (PAINTING)

For he was showing them. He was showing them with a vengeance. In that shabby room in a mean house on the Roozengracht, such miracles of color were now being performed that the world for ages to come will sit before them in stupefied silence and will say: "Beyond that point, no man could go without lifting himself to the rank of the gods."

SAMSON THREATENING HIS FATHER-IN-LAW (PAINTING)

Provided that any of these pictures would survive long enough to allow mankind to catch up with their maker. And that to me seemed highly doubtful. For nothing Rembrandt finished during those days was ever sold. And where they are at present, only a year after his death, I could not possibly tell. A praying pilgrim he painted during that time I saw only a few months ago in a pawn-shop in Leyden and it was hanging between a cheap fiddle and an old pair of sailor's trousers. What has happened to the others, I do not know, but I have my fears. An intelligent art-dealer with an eye to his grandsons' fortune would have hired himself a store-house and would have filled it with the pictures of Rembrandt finished during the period he lived on the Roozengracht, and which he was unable to sell for half a guilder or even less.

But why expect such foresight among the vultures of the world of art?

SKETCH (DRAWING)

CHRIST (PAINTING)

Chapter 38

REMBRANDT HAS ONE MORE PUPIL

THE GOOD SAMARITAN (DRAWING)

BY THE end of '64 it became clear that Rembrandt would not be able to afford the rent of the Roozengracht house any longer and that he would have to look for cheaper quarters. Titus found a place just around the corner and the whole family once more pulled up stakes and went to live on the Lauriergracht. There they had only three rooms and in every one of them the light was bad. It was then that Titus thought of the possibilities of having his father do some book illustrations which would probably be more lucrative than painting pictures.

He went to a publisher but the publisher had probably heard of the failure of the etchings which Rembrandt had submitted for Menasseh's book on Nebuchadnezzar and would not listen to the plan.

"If only your father knew something about steel-engraving, then

365

I would have a job for him." And Titus in his eagerness to get his father an order (any order at all), had answered, "But my father is one of the best steel-engravers there are in town. Just give him a chance!"

The publisher had agreed. Would Mr. van Rijn please engrave a picture of Jan Antonides van der Linden after a portrait that Abraham van den Tempel had painted of him half a dozen years before? Rembrandt said that he would. But he was an etcher and not an engraver and the experiment ended as disastrously as that of the Nebuchadnezzar book he had done ten years before. And Rembrandt was once more at the mercy of his creditors.

Although I was no longer rich in those days, I would have been delighted to help him but he would not hear of it. "You have trouble enough of your own," he invariably answered when I talked of taking over some of the burdens of his household, "and I am still strong enough to take care of my children myself."

He was immensely pleased when one day a young man who said that his name was Aert de Gelder asked to be allowed to become his pupil. De Gelder, who then must have been about twenty years of age, hailed from the town of Dordrecht and was a pupil of that Samuel van Hoogstraten who shortly after the English war had moved to England where it was said that he had done very well and had become quite a rich man. As van Hoogstraten too had for a short while worked in Rembrandt's studio, the old man felt touchingly grateful and de Gelder proved to be not only an apt student but a kind and loyal friend, which Rembrandt had not been able to say of all of his pupils.

But unfortunately I was not able to see much of Rembrandt during this period. For we were on the brink of another war with England and I was obliged to spend the greater part of my time in The Hague, so as to be at the beck and call of My Lord the Pensionary, who was about to venture forth upon the most dangerous but, as it proved to be, the most glorious adventure of his entire career.

Chapter 39

AND STILL REMBRANDT CONTINUES TO PAINT

AND STILL REMBRANDT CONTINUES TO PAINT (DRAWING)

I RETURNED to Amsterdam in the latter half of August. His Lordship the Pensionary had sent me a very flattering letter in which he expressed his gratitude for my services and commented upon the fact that during the entire expedition we had lost only fifty men. But this was not so much due to my skill as a surgeon and to the organization of the medical corps (for which, to a certain degree, I had indeed been responsible), as to the fact that the English in their panic (their country had not been invaded for almost six centuries) had rendered only a very limited resistance.

I was mustered out at Texel and from there hired a boat to Enkhuizen, from whence I made the rest of the voyage on foot, finding it agreeable to take a little exercise after so many months of close confinement on board a war vessel. I hired a man to row me across the Y and walked home through the twilight, happy to be once more among my own people and filled with a deep sense of pride when I contemplated the magnificent stone houses and palaces that had been going up during the last four years and that had been built in spite of a very costly war.

My son was not at home. The excellent Jantje, who had kept everything spick and span during my absence, explained that he had probably gone courting. For the first time I realized with brutal clarity how old I had grown. It seemed a few days ago that I had looked at this ungainly bundle of pink flesh, saying to myself, "Good God! will that ever grow up into a human being?" And now, but for the grace of God, I might at almost any moment stand revealed as a grandfather. But before I had been able to develop these frightening meditations to their fullest possibilities, Jantje handed me a letter, adorned with a big seal, which I recognized as the arms of Amsterdam and which, so she told me, had been delivered only that morning.

I opened it.

Their Lordships the Burgomasters informed me that in view of the "outrageous rebelliousness" which had caused the destruction of my property, they had voted to grant me the first part of my indemnity. Thirty thousand guilders in cash awaited my pleasure at the Town Treasury any time I cared to call with two witnesses who would be able to identify me.

I was dreadfully tired from my long and unaccustomed walk, but without bothering to get my hat I rushed out of the door and ran as fast as my old heart would permit me to the house on the Lauriergracht. Rembrandt had retired to his workshop. Titus was in the front room with Cornelia, ordering a number of etchings which they were hanging on strips that had been stretched across the windows, that they might dry during the night. They were delighted to see me and at once took me to the studio where Rembrandt lay awake on a narrow cot.

"Look who is here," Titus shouted. But all Rembrandt answered was, "Please take away that candle. The light hurts my eyes." Then he recognized me and tried to get up. I bade him not exert himself and took possession of the only chair I could find. Titus and Cornelia sat down on the side of the cot. As soon as I had become a little more accustomed to the darkness of the low-ceilinged room, I examined my old friend a little closer. His eyes looked bloodshot and he seemed to have trouble breathing. He was in bad shape.

"Rembrandt," I said, "I have come with good news for you and for the children. I have got back part of my money. Now, what can I do for you?"

I realized that this had not been a very tactful way to approach the subject, but in my enthusiasm, I had blurted out the first thing that came to my mind. But there was no immediate reply. Finally, a very tired voice said, "Nothing. It is too late." And then I realized how terribly he had altered during the three months I had not seen him. And I began again, and this time a little more carefully, to explain that soon I would be amply provided with funds and that I wanted Rembrandt to share in my good fortune. But nothing seemed any longer able to make an impression upon him. We sat there, the four of us, during the greater part of the night and finally Rembrandt was able to formulate a wish.

"If it would not be asking too much of you," he told me, "I would like very much to go back to the house on the Roozengracht. It had such excellent light and this place is so dark that I am afraid I shall go blind if I have to work another six months in this dark cellar."

Then he excused himself. "If you don't mind, I would like to try and go to sleep now. I lie awake the greater part of every night and to-morrow I must be up early. I want to start work on my Prodigal Son. Titus thinks he has found some one who wants to buy it."

He reached out his hand which was covered with paint and a little shaky. "Please don't think I am not grateful," he said. "I am deeply grateful. But I am very tired and I have not seen any one for so long that I am not much good at conversation nowadays." And he pulled his blankets over his head and turned his face towards the wall.

I remained talking to Titus and Cornelia for a few minutes before I went home.

"No," Titus said, "you must not think that things are as bad as he imagines them to be. I have got my money at last, I mean that share in my father's house. Crayers had to go to the Supreme Court to get it but the judges found for us, and a few months ago van Hertsbeeck

Rembrandt van Rijn

was told to pay me on pain of being sentenced to jail if he should keep me waiting. You know, it was half of the money that was paid for father's house when the courts sold it to pay his debts. It is quite a sum—almost 5,000 guilders."

"Congratulations," and I shook the young man warmly by the hand. "And what do you mean to do with it?"

He looked at me a little sheepishly. "I think I will use it to get married," he answered.

"And who is the lucky girl?" I asked.

"Magdalena van Loo. She lives on the Singel with her mother. I will bring her around to see you to-morrow."

I turned to Cornelia, who was green with sleep. "And you, my darling," I said, "you too will soon say good-by to us to get married, won't you?"

She shook her head with that wisdom that seems to be part of those children who have spent their earliest years without the society of their own contemporaries and solemnly answered, "No, Uncle Jan, I am never going to leave you. I am always going to stay right here with father."

And the poor girl meant it.

SKETCH (DRAWING)

Chapter 40

TITUS MARRIES

THE ROPE DANCER (DRAWING)

I AM reaching the end of my story.

Why dwell upon the misery of those last years?

Yes, financially Rembrandt was a great deal better off than before. Titus had got hold of his five thousand guilders, which he administered carefully, almost penuriously, for he knew from sad personal experience what poverty meant and he now had a wife of his own to support.

As for the wife, the less said the better. She was of equal age with Titus—they both had celebrated their twenty-seventh birthdays just before they were married. And she too had inherited a few thousand guilders from her father and would get a few thousand more when her mother died.

But she was a person without any charm or any color. She felt convinced that she could have done a great deal better if she had only tried a little harder. She tolerated her father-in-law (who painted a magnificent likeness of her and Titus which she did not like as it made her look a little too old), and she was patronizingly pleasant to her half-sister-in-law, whom she called a bastard behind her back.

Was Titus in love with her?

I never was able to discover.

He seemed fond of her in a quiet sort of way, but I felt that he would have married almost any one who had taken the trouble to set

371

her cap at him. Like most men who are predestined to die young of pulmonary trouble, he had strong sexual desires. But being a very dutiful son and sincerely devoted to his father, he had suppressed all such longings as long as he was responsible for the welfare of his family.

Now that he was at last able to afford a wife of his own, the inevitable happened and what that inevitable was, most people will know even if they have not been trained for the medical profession.

During the whole of that year I was very busy with the plans for my new infirmary. I had no intention of giving up my search for a more effective method of bringing about a state of artificial unconsciousness when people had to submit to an operation. But the regular hospitals remained closed to me as before and I had to have a place of my own if I wanted to make any progress.

One evening, early in September of the year '68, Rebecca Willems, an old servant who took care of Rembrandt's household now that his son was married, came to me quite late with a note signed by Cornelia. She asked me to come at once to Titus' house on the Apple Market, as her brother had been suddenly taken ill and seemed in a bad way.

When I arrived, he was unconscious from loss of blood. He had suffered an internal hemorrhage and I knew that he was doomed. He rallied a little towards morning, but died during the afternoon.

Rembrandt was present. He sat in a corner of the room. Cornelia and Rebecca took him back to the Roozengracht. He was sick for two weeks afterwards and could not attend the funeral of his son.

When Cornelia, trying to cheer him up, told him that Magdalena expected a baby, he shook his head.

"Merely some one else for me to lose," was his only comment.

He had reached the end of his strength and courage, and he knew it.

Chapter 41

I READ A FINAL CHAPTER IN GENESIS

THE PRAYER (DRAWING)

BUT somehow or other, after a few months, he seemed to rally. At least, he tried to paint again. But when he had sat in front of his easel for forty or fifty minutes or so, he used to complain of pains in his back. He tried to do some etching while lying in bed, but his eyes had grown so weak that they no longer could stand the strain of that sort of work.

JACOB WRESTLING WITH THE ANGEL (PAINTING)

Rembrandt van Rijn

In the end he merely puttered around in his studio for a couple of hours every morning and then went back to his cot. He rarely undressed but slept in his old paint-covered smock, like a soldier who is desperate but who wants to die in harness.

In the month of March of the next year, his first grandchild was born. It was a girl and it was called Titia after her father. We thought that it would do him good if he attended the baptism, and he finally allowed himself to be persuaded. But he could hardly stand on his feet during the short ceremony and his hands shook so severely when he tried to write his name that Frans van Bijlert, the other witness, had to help him.

I used to drop in every other day to tell him the latest news and cheer him up by little bits of local gossip which often seem to divert the sick. He was politely grateful, but answered little in return.

Once or twice he asked after Saskia, as if she had still been alive, and occasionally he mentioned Hendrickje.

"She was a good girl," he used to say. "She was very good to me and to the boy. If it had not been for her, I don't know what we would have done."

I sometimes asked him whether he wanted me to read to him, but he said no, he had so much to think about.

And then one evening in October of the year '69, when I was sitting by his bedside (he had not been able to get up for about a fortnight), he surprised me by asking that I get him the family Bible. It was in Cornelia's room and when I called to her, she brought it and put it on the table.

"I wish you would read me that story about Jacob," he said. "Do you know where to find it—the story of Jacob wrestling with the Lord?"

I did not know where to find it. Cornelia remembered that it was somewhere in Genesis. I turned the leaves until I found the name Jacob and then searched up and down the pages until I came to the passage which he seemed to have in mind.

"Yes," he nodded, "that is it. Where Jacob wrestles with the Lord. Now read that to me. Just that and nothing else."

And I read:

" 'And Jacob was left alone; and there wrestled a man with him until the breaking of the day.

" 'And when he saw that he prevailed not against him, he touched the hollow of his thigh; and the hollow of Jacob's thigh was out of joint, as he wrestled with him.

" 'And he said, Let me go, for the day breaketh. And he said, I will not let thee go, except thou bless me.

" 'And he said unto him, What is thy name? And he said, Jacob.

" 'And he said, Thy name shall be called no more Jacob, but Israel; for as a Prince hast thou power with God and with men, and hast prevailed.' "

But when I had got that far, the sick man stirred and I stopped reading and looked at him and I saw him slowly lift his right hand and hold it close to his eyes and look at it as if it were something curious he had never observed before. And then his lips moved and very softly I heard him whisper:

"And Jacob was left alone. And there wrestled a man with him until the breaking of the day . . . there wrestled a man with him until the breaking of the day . . . but he did not give in and fought back—ah, yes, he fought back—for such is the will of the Lord—that we shall fight back . . . that we shall wrestle with him until the breaking of the day."

And then, with a sudden effort, he tried to raise himself from his pillow, but could not do it and he stared at me in a helpless sort of way as if asking for an answer that he knew would never come.

"And he said, Thy name shall be called no more Jacob but Rembrandt," and while his gnarled old fingers, still covered with the stains of ink and paint, fell back upon his breast, "for as a Prince hast thou had power with God and with men, and hast prevailed—and hast prevailed unto the last . . . alone . . . but hast prevailed unto the last."

But when Cornelia a moment later looked at me with questioning eyes and said, "Thank Heaven! for now he is asleep," I went up to her and took her by the arm and answered, "Thank Heaven, indeed, for now he is dead."

EPILOGUE

BY A DISTANT DESCENDANT

IF DOCTOR JAN had not been killed during the battle of Kijkduin and had lived a few years longer, he would have seen the name of Rembrandt van Rijn completely disappear from the face of the earth.

Within less than a fortnight after Rembrandt's death, the body of Magdalena van Loo, the widow of Titus, was gently lowered into a grave in the West Church, not far away from that of his own.

As for Cornelia, on the third of May of the year 1670 she married one Cornelis Suythof, a young painter who could not make a living at his art and who that same year sailed to Java on the good ship *Tulpenburg* and went to work for the East India Company.

Then on Saint Nicholas day of the year 1673, Cornelia gave birth to a son who was duly baptized and received the name of Rembrandt Suythof and who apparently died shortly afterwards. Five years later, another son was born to the couple, Hendric Suythof. What became of the parents, we do not know.

A few years more and they disappeared from view as completely as if they had never existed.

Titia, the daughter of Titus and Magdalena van Loo, lived a little longer, but only a very little. When she was seventeen years old, she married the youngest son of her guardian, a certain Frans van Bijlert, who was in the same business as his better-known colleague, Kilian van Rensselaer, although his shop was in a less fashionable part of the town, on the Kloveniers Burgwal. They had a raft of children, whose funeral notices are duly recorded in the mortuary books of the West Church which soon became a sort of general receptacle for those who had a drop of Rembrandt blood in their veins.

But ere she herself died, in the year 1725, Titia could still have read the following estimate of her grandfather's work in a book that was considered the standard of good taste for all those who had genteel aspirations during the first quarter of the eighteenth century:

"In his effort to attain a mellow manner, Rembrandt van Rijn has merely succeeded in achieving an effect of rottenness. The vulgar and prosaic

377

aspects of a subject were the only ones he was capable of noting and with his so-called red and yellow tones, he set the fatal example of shadows so hot that they seem actually aglow and of colors that appear to lie like liquid mud on the canvas."

The man responsible for this piece of poetic prose was a painter by the name of Gerard de Lairesse, born in the town of Liége in Belgium in the year of mercy 1641. He had studied the rudiments of his trade in his father's studio, and then learning "where the big money was" (that expression, alas, is as old as the Pyramids or older), he had moved to Amsterdam, where he had covered endless miles of patient canvas with allegorical representations of whatever subjects were suggested by his patrons.

For a moment there had been danger of his fall from grace, for, as he modestly confessed in his "History of Painting," he himself had been tempted to try Rembrandt van Rijn's style of painting but soon he had recognized his mistake and had abjured "these errors and had abandoned a manner that was entirely based upon a delusion."

There it stands for every one to read: "Rottenness of effect . . . the fatal example of shadows that were so hot as to appear to be aglow . . . vulgar and prosaic aspects of every subject . . . colors that appeared to lie like liquid mud on the canvas . . . a manner founded on a delusion."

A funeral in an unknown grave—a half-open coffin from which the bones had been removed and thrown on the rubbish-pile . . . an undischarged bankrupt until this very day . . . as it was in the beginning . . . is now and probably ever will be . . . world without end. Amen.

FOR THIS SPECIAL EDITION OF "R. V. R." THE ORIG-
INAL TEXT HAS BEEN REVISED BY THE AUTHOR. IT
IS COMPOSED IN JANSON TYPES AND PRINTED ON
AN ESPECIALLY MADE PAPER. J. B. NEUMANN SE-
LECTED THE ILLUSTRATIONS FROM REMBRANDT'S
DRAWINGS, ETCHINGS AND PAINTINGS AND PLACED
THEM TO ILLUSTRATE THE NARRATIVE. THE IL-
LUSTRATIONS WERE REPRODUCED, UNDER THE SU-
PERVISION OF RALPH M. DUENEWALD, BY VARIOUS
PROCESSES.